MOLYBDENUM

Steels

Irons

Alloys

R. S. ARCHER • J. Z. BRIGGS • C. M. LOEB, JR.

CLIMAX MOLYBDENUM COMPANY

A Division of American Metal Climax, Inc.

New York

CLIMAX MOLYBDENUM COMPANY

A Division of American Metal Climax, Inc.

1270 AVENUE OF THE AMERICAS, NEW YORK 20, N. Y.

OFFICES

CHICAGO 1, ILLINOIS
230 North Michigan Avenue

DAYTON 39, OHIO
3300 South Dixie Highway

DENVER 2, COLORADO
Midland Savings Building

DETROIT 2, MICHIGAN
Fisher Building

LOS ANGELES 17, CALIFORNIA
650 South Grand Avenue

PITTSBURGH 19, PENNSYLVANIA
Union Trust Building

BUSINESS & INDUSTRY DIVISION

Printed in U.S.A.

ACKNOWLEDGMENTS

We herewith thank those in the metallurgical industry who contributed information and made helpful suggestions. We are also grateful to the many of the Climax technical staff who helped make the book possible.

R. S. ARCHER
J. Z. BRIGGS
C. M. LOEB, JR.

First Printing 1948 — Second Printing 1953
Third Printing 1962 — Fourth Printing 1965
Fifth Printing 1968

TABLE OF CONTENTS

SECTION I

SECTION IV

SECTION VIII

SECTION IX

SECTION X

SECTION 1

TECHNICAL EFFECTS OF MOLYBDENUM

STEEL

Hardenability

One of the major effects of molybdenum is its marked contribution to the hardenability of steel. Hardenability may be defined briefly as that characteristic of steel which makes it possible to harden the steel by rapid cooling from above the critical temperature range. As compared with a steel of low hardenability, a steel of high hardenability of the same section can be hardened by less drastic cooling, such as oil quenching instead of water quenching, or air cooling instead of oil quenching. With identical cooling methods, the high hardenability steel can be hardened in thicker sections than the low hardenability steel.

The mechanical properties of steel are in general at their best when the steel is fully hardened before tempering (1, 2, 3, 4, 5, 6).* The resultant tempered martensite usually has the most favorable combination of elastic properties (proportional limit, proof stress and yield strength), tensile strength, elongation, reduction of area, impact and fatigue strength. The superiority of fully hardened steels is found not only in laboratory tests but also in service under conditions demanding the highest toughness at a given strength. This fact has been stated to be the first principle in the design of steel parts requiring optimum properties (7). The assurance of real toughness plus strength has in some cases permitted designers to reduce the factor of safety and thus make large weight savings (1). Gun barrels are a prime example of the longer life obtained with fully hardened steels (free from temper brittleness) (8).

Since small additions of molybdenum promote relatively uniform hardness and strength even throughout heavy sections, the best possible properties can be obtained at low cost in molybdenum steels. Figure 1 shows as an example the effect of 0.17% molybdenum in increasing the center hardness of oil quenched bars of alloy steel.

---

* For references, see bibliography at the end of each section.

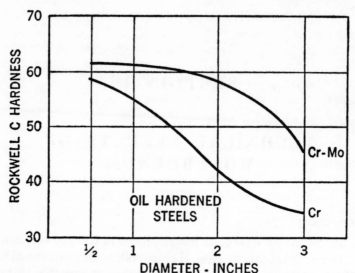

FIG 1 – Effect of Molybdenum on the Center Hardness of Oil Quenched Alloy Steel (9)

	%C	%Mn	%Si	%Cr	%Mo	
Cr...............	0.45	0.84	0.19	1.00	....	oil quenched from 1575 to 1625 F
Cr-Mo...........	0.45	0.80	0.16	0.94	0.17	oil quenched from 1575 to 1625 F

Toughness

Toughness may be defined broadly as the property of being difficult to break as opposed to brittleness, the property of breaking easily with little if any plastic deformation. Whether a given piece of steel exhibits toughness or brittleness depends on the specific conditions under which failure takes place. It is recognized that a steel which shows considerable ductility in a standard tensile test may fail in a brittle manner under some conditions encountered in service.

The notched bar impact tests were developed to appraise the tendency of materials to fail in a brittle manner under severe conditions. In these tests the energy absorbed in breaking a notched bar is measured. Various types of specimen have been employed, some of which have been adopted as "standard". Data from one type are not quantitatively convertible to any other type.

For a specific steel with a specific heat treatment, there are three principal factors that tend to cause brittle failures:

(1) increasingly unfavorable stress pattern (stress concentrations, multiaxial stresses)
(2) decreasing temperature and
(3) increasing rate of loading.

[2]

The general effects of these three factors are shown in Figure 2 where the term "transverse stresses" may be replaced by the more general term "unfavorable stress pattern". It is seen that the effects of the three factors are qualitatively similar. Quantitative relationships have been proposed (11, 12) between the effects of temperature and rate of loading. There is as yet no simple method of expressing quantitatively the influence of the stress pattern factor.* The severity of the notched bar impact test as a whole depends upon the combined effects of the three principal factors mentioned.

The transition region where the fracture is mixed ductile and brittle may be spread over a much wider horizontal range than indicated in Figure 2. In this region the energy of rupture is particularly sensitive to slight variations in the material or in the conditions of test. Hence, the scatter of values in "duplicate" tests in this transition region is greater than elsewhere.

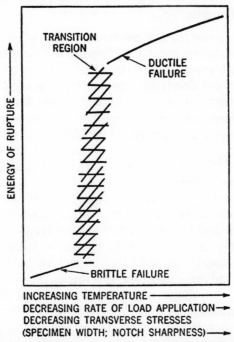

FIG 2 – Schematic Diagram Showing the Effect of Temperature of Test, Rate of Load Application and Transverse Stress on the Notched Bar Impact Values of a Non-Austenitic Steel (10)

The simplest method of increasing the severity of the notched bar impact test is by decreasing the temperature of test. It is very difficult to measure accurately the energy of rupture at high rates of loading such as those corresponding to ballistic velocities. Like-

---

* An interesting start has perhaps been made in the correlation of the transition temperature of notched bars and of circular disks under biaxial tension (13).

wise, it is impracticable to reproduce extremely sharp notches consistently. On the other hand, it is relatively easy to vary and control the temperature at which the specimen is broken, especially in the Charpy test where the specimen is not held in a grip as in the Izod test.

A curve of impact values vs testing temperature (for example, Figure 3) shows not only the effect of temperature on the energy of rupture under specific conditions but also, qualitatively, the effects of the rate of loading and the stress pattern. The lower the temperature of transition from ductile to brittle fractures, the greater is the resistance of the material to brittle failure resulting from any one or any combination of the three principal factors. The actual transition temperature is not characteristic of the material except for the specific conditions of the test. The tendency of the material to fail in a brittle manner is increased by any change that moves the transition region to higher temperatures.

Temper Brittleness

An important phase of the general problem of brittle failures in steel is the phenomenon known as "temper brittleness".* A common manifestation of temper brittleness is that specimens of certain steels that have been cooled slowly after tempering over about 1100 F exhibit substantially lower notched bar impact values than corresponding specimens that have been cooled rapidly after tempering at the same temperature. The tensile properties usually are practically the same in both cases. The ratio $\dfrac{\text{impact as quenched from temper}}{\text{impact as furnace cooled from temper}}$ has been frequently used as a measure of the susceptibility of steel to temper brittleness. Though this ratio may be useful under some circumstances, its numerical value depends upon the specific conditions of testing and is not a definite characteristic of the steel.

A more comprehensive view of the temper brittleness phenomenon is obtained by considering complete impact vs temperature curves for embrittled and unembrittled specimens, as in Figure 3. The curves in the bottom diagram are for a chromium steel susceptible to temper brittleness. The curve showing the lowest transition temperature (greatest toughness) is for specimens quenched after tempering. The middle curve with appreciably higher transition temperature is for specimens furnace cooled after tempering. It is evident that the "susceptibility ratio" varies with the temperature

---

* The phenomenon referred to here as "temper brittleness" is sometimes confused with the embrittlement that occurs in many hardened alloy steels when tempered in the blue heat range of approximately 425 to 750 F. The latter type of embrittlement was formerly associated with the decomposition of retained austenite, because it occurs in about the same range of temperature, but now is believed to be due to other causes (14). Embrittlement by heating in the blue heat range is encountered only in steels that have been previously hardened by quenching or in cold worked steels that are subject to strain aging. Temper brittleness, on the other hand, is developed in a range from approximately 850 to 1100 F and may occur in steels that have been previously hardened, normalized or annealed or that were in the as-rolled condition.

[4]

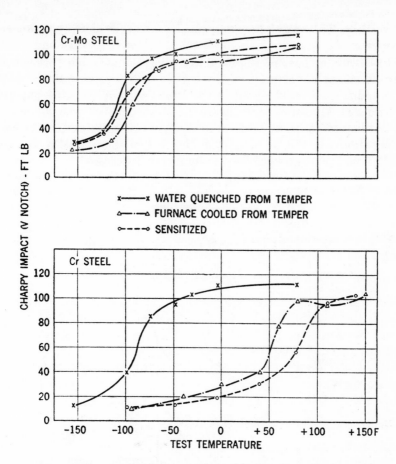

FIG 3 – Impact-Temperature Curves for a Chromium and a Chromium-Molybdenum Steel of Equal Hardenability

	Analyses							McQuaid-Ehn Grain Size
	%C	%Mn	%Si	%P	%S	%Cr	%Mo	
Cr.............	0.37	0.75	0.22	0.016	0.025	0.98	0.02	5 to 8
Cr-Mo.........	0.38	0.65	0.32	0.010	0.019	0.57	0.15	5 to 8

Tempering Treatment*		Rockwell C Hardness	
		Cr	Cr-Mo
Water Quenched	two hours at 1150 F, water quenched	23 to 24.5	23.5 to 25
Furnace Cooled..............	two hours at 1150 F, furnace cooled	25 to 26	23 to 26
Sensitized..................	two hours at 1150 F, water quenched; ten hours at 1025 F, furnace cooled	21.5 to 23	23 to 24

* specimens previously fully hardened by oil quenching from 1550 F

[5]

of testing. This point is illustrated in a more general manner in Figure 4.

In the upper part of Figure 3 are given comparable curves for a chromium-molybdenum steel having the same hardenability as the chromium steel represented in the lower part of the diagram. It is considered appropriate to compare these steels because, insofar as hardenability alone is concerned, they are suitable for the same applications. It will be noted that the molybdenum steel is substantially free from susceptibility to temper brittleness.

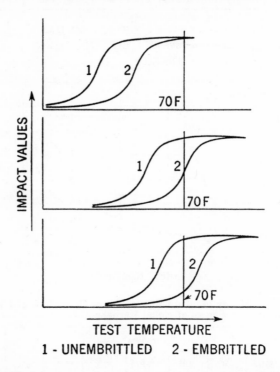

1 - UNEMBRITTLED   2 - EMBRITTLED

FIG 4 – Effect of the Position on the Temperature Scale of the Impact-Temperature Curves on the Possibility of Detecting Temper Brittleness by Room Temperature Impact Tests (15)

Temper brittleness actually develops in a temperature range from about 850 to 1100 F in those moderately alloyed engineering steels that are susceptible to this phenomenon. If the steel is tempered above 1100 F, embrittlement may occur during slow cooling through this range. Specimens that have been kept tough by quenching from above 1100 F may be embrittled by reheating to temperatures between 850 and 1100 F. Such reheating is often done commercially in the course of stress relieving after cold straightening. There is evidence that the development of brittleness after exposure at 850 to 1100 F is due to the precipitation of one or more unknown substances from solution (16). The time required for this precipitation, and therefore embrittlement, appears to be least at about 950 to 1000 F (16, 17). If the time within the range 850 to 1100 F is sufficient to cause precipitation, then the resultant embrittlement cannot be avoided by rapid cooling.

Many investigators have employed isothermal holding or "sensitizing" treatments for various periods of time at temperatures within the embrittling range. The rate of embrittlement at any given temperature may be so determined (Figure 5). Thus, the relative susceptibilities of various steels may be evaluated on a uniform basis without having to take into account possible variations in the original tempering temperature necessary to obtain the same hardness. The information obtained from such sensitizing treatments can be beneficially applied to practical problems.

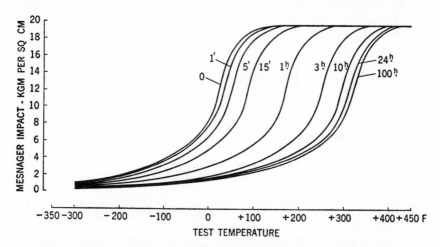

FIG 5 – Effect of Sensitizing Time at 975 F on the Impact-Temperature Curve of a Steel Containing 0.25% C, 0.30% Mn, 0.32% Si, 1.38% Cr. Steel oil quenched from 1605 F and tempered one hour at 1200 F prior to sensitizing at 975 F. Brinell hardness 241 after all sensitizing treatments (18)

Figure 3 compares the effect of sensitizing with that of furnace cooling from the temper on the impact-temperature curves of a chromium and a chromium-molybdenum steel. Figure 6 shows impact-temperature curves for a chromium-nickel and a chromium-molybdenum-nickel steel of substantially equivalent hardenability with and without sensitizing treatments. The presence of molybdenum has clearly imparted superior resistance to embrittlement.

Remedies for Temper Brittleness. When the tempering temperature is above 1100 F, it is possible in most cases to prevent the embrittlement of a susceptible steel by quenching after tempering.

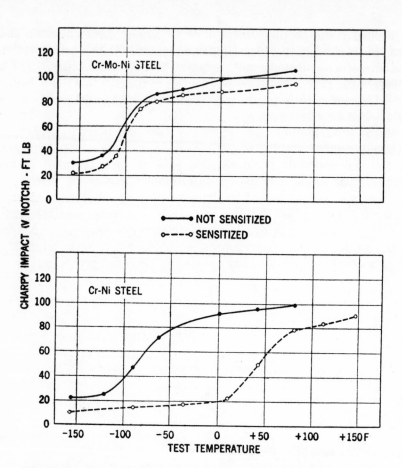

FIG 6 – Impact-Temperature Curves for a Chromium-Nickel and a Chromium-Molybdenum-Nickel Steel of Substantially Equal Hardenability

	Analyses							McQuaid-Ehn Grain Size
	%C	%Mn	%Si	%P	%Cr	%Mo	%Ni	
Cr-Ni.........	0.39	0.79	0.22	0.020	0.73	0.02	1.30	5 to 8
Cr-Mo-Ni.....	0.43	0.95	0.27	0.026	0.46	0.27	0.52	5 to 8

Sensitizing Treatment*		Rockwell C Hardness	
		Cr-Ni	Cr-Mo-Ni
Not Sensitized..............	none	27 to 28	26 to 27
Sensitized..................	ten hours at 1025 F, furnace cooled	27 to 28	25.5 to 26.5

* specimens previously fully hardened by oil quenching from 1550 F, then tempered two hours at 1140 F for the Cr-Ni steel and at 1210 F for the Cr-Mo-Ni steel, followed by oil quenching

[8]

(For heavy sections, however, the cooling rate even in quenching may not be sufficiently rapid to prevent embrittlement.) This operation is often inadvisable as it results in internal stresses and distortion which may be objectionable. If the final hardness requirement is such that precipitation during tempering cannot be avoided, some embrittlement will develop despite rapid cooling.

As the alloy content, and consequently hardenability, is raised, the susceptibility to temper brittleness will generally increase (7, 17, 19). Molybdenum is an exception to this general rule and, in fact, is used to eliminate or decrease temper brittleness (7, 19).

Resistance to Softening or Tempering

Molybdenum increases the resistance to softening on tempering as shown by the hardness or strength after cooling to room temperature. This action appears most prominently after tempering at about 1000 F. As an indication of the relative effect of various alloying elements commonly used in engineering steels, 0.06% molybdenum has been given as equivalent to 0.19% chromium, 0.40% manganese, 0.77% nickel or 0.22% silicon in retarding the softening of a 0.30% carbon steel at the higher tempering temperatures (20).

Figure 7 shows the effect of molybdenum in retarding softening on tempering of a 0.35% carbon steel. The resistance to softening of molybdenum steels persists in the presence of other alloying elements (Figure 8).

Figure 7 also indicates the secondary hardening caused by molybdenum when it is present in adequate amounts. This effect is likewise observed in more complex alloy and higher carbon steels. The development of secondary hardness on tempering is an important function of molybdenum in high speed steels and in some tool and die steels.

Elevated Temperature Properties

Molybdenum increases the strength and creep resistance of low and high alloy steels at elevated temperatures. Research on pure iron-molybdenum alloys has revealed that molybdenum produces a marked increase in the creep strength of ferrite (22) and also in the lowest temperature of recrystallization after strain hardening (23). These factors are as yet the best clues to an explanation of the remarkably improved elevated temperature properties of molybdenum steels as compared with molybdenum-free steels. In the case of low and medium carbon low alloy steels, an additional factor may be that molybdenum makes it possible to develop, by practical heat treatments, the intermediate structures which have better creep strength than pearlite or tempered martensite. Figures 9 and 10

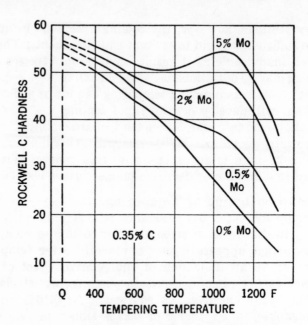

FIG 7 – Effect of Molybdenum on the Softening by Tempering of Quenched Steels with 0.35% C (steels were quenched from a temperature high enough to dissolve substantially all the carbides) (21)

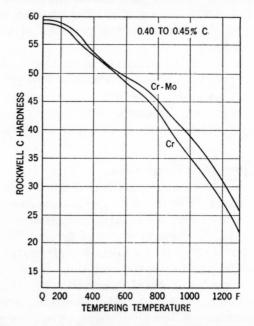

FIG 8 – Effect of 0.20% Molybdenum on the Softening by Tempering of Quenched Steels with 0.40 to 0.45% C and 1% Cr (steels were quenched from a temperature high enough to dissolve substantially all the carbides) (21)

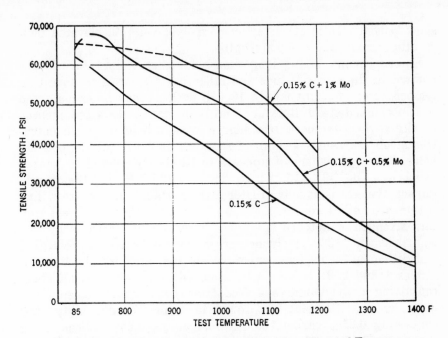

FIG 9 – Effect of Molybdenum on the Short Time Elevated Temperature Tensile Strength of 0.15% C Steel

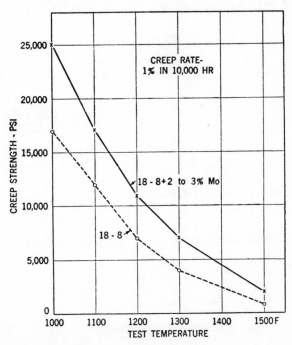

FIG 10 – Effect of Molybdenum on the Creep Strength of 18% Cr – 8% Ni Steel (AISI types 304 and 316) (24)

[11]

show typical results of the effect of molybdenum on elevated temperature tensile and creep strengths.

Embrittlement during long time holding at temperature is important in the case of studs and other parts exposed to operating temperatures of about 650 to 1000 F such as may be encountered in superheated steam lines or in oil refineries. After a few months service at these temperatures, highly stressed bolts of molybdenum-free steels may show an impact strength only 10% of the original value. This embrittlement appears to be closely related to temper brittleness (pp 4-9). It has been reported (25, 26) that the drop in impact strength is usually greater if the parts are under stress than if they are not. Moreover, there are indications that the stress rupture strength of notched specimens is markedly decreased by this embrittlement (26). Molybdenum is very effective in retarding embrittlement after long exposure, as indicated by the data in Tables 1 and 2. It is not to be assumed, however, that all steels containing molybdenum are free from such embrittlement. For example, embrittlement was found in a high hardenability steel containing 0.25% carbon, 0.50% manganese, 0.25% silicon, 0.7% chromium, 0.65% molybdenum and 3.25% nickel. After 210 hours at 930 F this steel showed a Charpy impact value of 3.3 kgm per sq cm as compared with 9.8 kgm per sq cm in the original condition (29).

TABLE 1

Effect of Molybdenum on Embrittlement due to Slow Cooling from the Tempering Temperature and to Long Time Holding at Temperature (27)

No.	%C	%Mn	%P	%Cr	%Mo	%Ni	Tempered* at F	Embrittlement Due to Slow Cooling from the Tempering temperature Susceptibility Ratio**	Embrittlement Due to Holding 50 to 2000 hr at 840 F Susceptibility Ratio***
1	0.38	0.49	0.012	1.2	....	...	1200	1.4	1.9
2	0.88	0.53	0.010	1.2	0.39	...	1200	1.1	1.1
3	0.40	0.45	0.010	1.3	....	1.6	1200	1.6	5.2
4	0.39	0.67	0.022	1.4	0.37	1.8	1200	1.2	1.2
5	0.42	1.08	0.027	0.1	....	5.1	1020	1.5	4.1
6	0.49	1.05	0.027	0.1	0.46	5.2	1020	1.0	2.2
7	0.37	0.80	0.132	1.2	....	1.8	1200	6.0	13.0
8	0.37	0.28	0.135	1.3	0.33	1.7	1200	1.6	2.6

* after oil quenching from 1740 F

** $\frac{\text{impact strength as oil quenched from tempering temperature}}{\text{impact strength as cooled at 3.6 F per min from tempering temperature}}$

*** $\frac{\text{impact strength as oil quenched from tempering temperature}}{\text{impact strength after long time holding at 840 F}}$

specimen 0.39 x 0.39 x 2.16 in. with a notch 0.12 in. deep and 0.08 in. in diameter

TABLE 2
Effect of Molybdenum on Embrittlement due to Slow Cooling from the Tempering Temperature and to Long Time Holding at Temperature (28)

No.	%C	%Mn	%Cr	%Mo	%Ni	Oil Quenched from F	Tempered at F
1	0.30	0.57	0.15	....	3.09	1525	1155
2	0.38	0.63	0.24	....	3.36	1525	1075
3	0.34	0.58	0.64	....	3.15	1525	1060
4	0.34	1.42	....	0.21	....	1525	1220
5	0.32	1.55	....	0.32	....	1525	1060
6	0.32	0.54	0.74	0.45	2.63	1525	1130
7	0.50	0.65	1.12	0.57	0.18	1560	1220

		Embrittlement Due to Slow Cooling from the Tempering Temperature			Embrittlement Due to Long Time Holding at Temperature		
		Izod Impact, ft lb				(3)	
No.	%Mo	(1) Quickly Cooled from the Tempering Temperature	(2) Slowly Cooled from the Tempering Temperature	Suscepti-bility Ratio (1)/(2)	Reheating Temperature and Time Giving Lowest Impact Strength	Lowest Izod Impact ft lb	Suscepti-bility Ratio (1)/(3)
1	....	82	61	1.36	750 F-1000 hr	11	7.45
2	....	57*	19	3.00	750 F-2000-3000 hr	7	8.14
3	....	61*	11	5.56	{ 750 F-3000 hr } { 840 F-500 hr }	5	12.20
4	0.21	88	89	0.99	750 F-3000 hr	75	1.17
5	0.32	56	53	1.06	840 F-1000 hr	38	1.47
6	0.45	63	47	1.35	840 F-3000 hr	35	1.80
7	0.57	55	55	1.00	{ 750 F-2000-3000 hr } { 840 F-1000 & 3000 hr }	51	1.08

* the fact that steels 2 and 3 exhibit rather high impact values when quickly cooled after tempering indicates either that the tempering temperatures were above the embrittling ranges for these particular steels or else that the time at these tempering temperatures was too short to develop much embrittlement

Low carbon contents (around 0.2%) also appear to promote embrittlement (26).

Molybdenum retards graphitization at temperatures around 900 F (30, 31). As compared with carbon steels, steels with as little as 0.5% molybdenum will have a slower rate of graphitization if all other factors are the same.*

Machinability

There is no single criterion by which machinability is always

* It should be noted, however, that other factors such as deoxidation practice may overshadow the effect of the molybdenum (see p 151).

judged. It is therefore impossible to give quantitative machinability ratings for steels except where wide differences exist as in comparing a free machining high sulphur screw stock with alloy steels. There is widespread opinion that, among the moderately alloyed steels, molybdenum-containing steels have superior machinability especially at high hardnesses (for example, 300 to 400 Brinell) (32). This opinion seems to be based largely upon general experience of a practical nature. There is a lack of published reports describing machining tests, or commercial machining operations, and defining the specific conditions under which this superiority of the molybdenum steels has been found.

Corrosion Resistance

Molybdenum improves the resistance to corrosion by pitting as well as the general corrosion resistance of the chromium and chromium-nickel corrosion resistant steels. The most popular of these steels usually contain about 16 to 20% chromium, 8 to 14% nickel and 1.75 to 5% molybdenum. Numerous examples of the superior corrosion resistance imparted by molybdenum may be cited but, as a specific case, Table 3 shows typical results of the contribution of molybdenum to the corrosion resistance in acetic acid.

TABLE 3
Effect of Molybdenum on the Corrosion Resistance in Acetic Acid of Chromium-Nickel Corrosion Resistant Steels

Composition	Weight Loss in 100 hr Test in 50% Acetic Acid g per sq m per hr	
	95 F	180 F
0.06% C, 18% Cr, 8% Ni..........................	over 0.10	0.80
0.06% C, 18% Cr, 9% Ni, 2.5% Mo.................	under 0.01	0.01

The addition of molybdenum likewise increases the resistance of austenitic chromium-nickel steels to contact or differential aeration corrosion such as may be caused by deposits settling on the steel. Molybdenum will also retard intergranular corrosion in austenitic chromium-nickel steels if the composition is balanced so that some delta ferrite is present.

Free Scaling

Molybdenum does not cause the formation of a tightly adherent scale on steel when heated in an oxidizing atmosphere for hot working. On the other hand, it actually promotes free scaling in many steels. This property is advantageous in die forging operation where the presence of abrasive scale materially increases die wear. In some forging operations, scale that does not free itself from the entire surface of the steel affects the accuracy and surface finish of the forging. Cleaning operations such as pickling and sand blasting are more difficult and costly if the steel has a tight scale. The detrimental effect of an adherent insulating scale on the hardening operation is widely recognized.

CAST STEEL

The specific effects of molybdenum in cast steels are in general similar to those in wrought steels. In the case of castings, however, certain special considerations are involved. The composition can be adjusted closely to the requirements of the particular casting to be made as the metal is often alloyed in much smaller batches than is generally the case with wrought steels. Because molybdenum (unlike boron, chromium, manganese, titanium and vanadium) is not lost by oxidation, the molybdenum content of the steel can be controlled very accurately. Since molybdenum is not a deoxidizer, it does not form non-metallic inclusions. The usual percentages of molybdenum can be added in the ladle if desired.

CAST IRON

As molybdenum is neither a graphitizer nor a strong carbide stabilizer, additions of molybdenum can be made to all classes of cast iron without changing the character of the charge, the normal melting practice, or the base composition. The benefits to be derived from the addition of molybdenum to cast iron are therefore available to all foundries. The better the quality of the iron, however, the more economical are the advantages gained from the addition of molybdenum.

Figure 11 shows the increase in tensile strength as a result of the addition of molybdenum to gray cast iron. This increase in strength is attributed to a direct solid solution effect in the ferrite and to the retardation of the transformation of the austenite. Molybdenum at the same time improves the toughness of cast iron.

One of the effects of molybdenum is to reduce the section sensitivity of gray iron. This makes it possible to obtain quite uniform properties with the same composition in different castings with widely varying mass and section as well as in a casting incorporating both light and heavy sections. Figure 12 illustrates the uniformity of hardness in a heavy section of a molybdenum cast iron. In the case of cast irons that are to be heat treated, molybdenum increases hardenability as it does in steel.

[15]

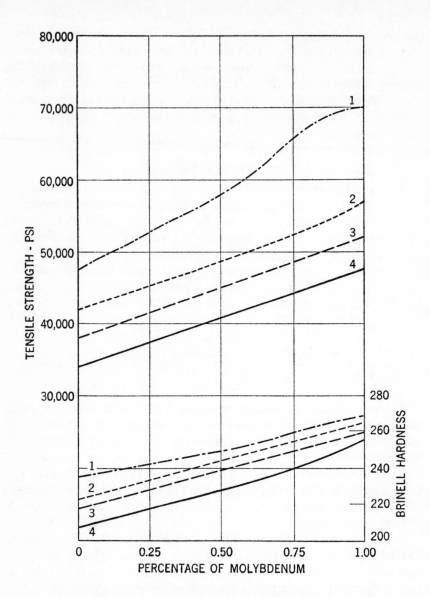

FIG 11 – Effect of Molybdenum on the Tensile Strength and Hardness of Gray Cast Iron (1.2 in. diameter section)

Curve	Composition	
	%TC	%Si
1..	2.75	2.50
2..	3.00	2.00
3..	3.25	1.75
4..	3.50	1.50

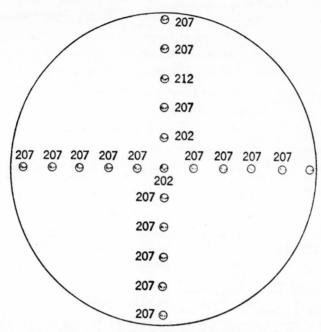

FIG 12 – Uniformity of Hardness Obtainable in a 6¼ in. Round of Molybdenum Gray Cast Iron. Analysis: 2.96% TC, 1.46% Si, 0.91% Mn, 0.128% P, 0.102% S, 0.23% Cr, 0.58% Mo, 0.61% Ni

Molybdenum improves the high temperature strength and toughness of cast iron. In combination with chromium, it gives irons with reduced tendencies towards growth and oxidation at elevated temperatures.

The large improvement in mechanical properties imparted by small amounts of molybdenum permits the addition to be made at the spout or in the ladle because the cooling effect on the molten iron is usually negligible.

The addition of molybdenum to chilled cast iron rolls improves markedly their resistance to chipping and spalling.

Section I — Bibliography

(1) S. A. Herres and A. F. Jones "A Method for Evaluating Toughness of Steel" Metal Progress, Vol 50 (1946)

(2) J. H. Hollomon, L. D. Jaffe, D. E. McCarthy and M. R. Norton "The Effects of Microstructure on the Mechanical Properties of Steel" Transactions, ASM, Vol 38 (1947)

(3) H. Allsop "The Significance of Variation in Jominy Hardenability with Respect to the Mechanical Properties of Some Hardened and Tempered B. S. En Steels" Section VA of Symposium on the Hardenability of Steel, Iron and Steel Institute Special Report No. 36, published by the Iron and Steel Institute, London, England (1946)

(4) "Hardenability and Mechanical Properties of a Series of B. S. En Steels" Section VIA of Symposium on the Hardenability of Steel, Iron and Steel Institute Special Report No. 36, published by the Iron and Steel Institute, London, England (1946)

(5) A. J. K. Honeyman "On the Relation between the As-Quenched Hardness and the Mechanical Properties of Quenched and Tempered Steel" Section VIC of Symposium on the Hardenability of Steel, Iron and Steel Institute Special Report No. 36, published by the Iron and Steel Institute, London, England (1946)

(6) W. E. Cooper and N. P. Allen "Observations on the Relationship between Hardenability and the Mechanical Properties of Quenched and Tempered Steels" Section VID of Symposium on the Hardenability of Steel, Iron and Steel Institute Special Report No. 36, published by the Iron and Steel Institute, London, England (1946)

(7) J. H. Hollomon and L. D. Jaffe, Ferrous Metallurgical Design, published by John Wiley and Sons, Inc. (1947)

(8) P. R. Kosting "Progressive Stress-Damage" Surface Stressing of Metals, published by the ASM (1947)

(9) P. Klain and C. H. Lorig "Hardness Characteristics of Some Medium Carbon S.A.E. Steels" Transactions, ASM, Vol 28 (1940)

(10) C. Zener and J. H. Hollomon "Plastic Flow and Rupture of Metals" Transactions, ASM, Vol 33 (1944)

(11) C. Zener and J. H. Hollomon "Effect of Strain Rate upon Plastic Flow of Steel" Journal of Applied Physics, Vol 15 (1944)

(12) C. W. MacGregor and J. C. Fisher "A Velocity-Modified Temperature for the Plastic Flow of Metals" Journal of Applied Mechanics, Vol 13 (1946)

(13) C. W. MacGregor, N. Grossman and P. R. Shepler "Correlated Brittle Fracture Studies of Notched Bars and Simple Structures" Welding Research Supplement to the Journal, AWS, Vol 26 (1947)

(14) M. A. Grossmann "Toughness and Fracture of Hardened Steels" Transactions, AIME, Vol 167 (1946)

(15) H. Jolivet and G. Vidal "The Value of the Impact Test in the Study of Temper Brittleness" Revue de Métallurgie, Vol 41 (1944)

(16) J. H. Hollomon "Temper Brittleness" Transactions, ASM, Vol 36 (1946)

(17) W. S. Pellini and B. R. Queneau "Development of Temper Brittleness in Alloy Steels" Transactions, ASM, Vol 39 (1947)

(18) G. Vidal "Temper Brittleness of Steels Containing Chromium, Molybdenum and Tungsten" Revue de Métallurgie, Vol 42 (1945)

(19) P. C. Rosenthal and G. K. Manning "Heat Treatment of Heavy Cast Steel Sections" Foundry, Vol 74 (1946); also Steel, Vol 119 (1946)

(20) W. Crafts and J. L. Lamont "Effect of Alloys in Steel on Resistance to Tempering" AIME TP 2036; Metals Technology, Vol 13 (1946)

(21) E. C. Bain, Functions of the Alloying Elements in Steel, published by the ASM (1939)

(22) C. R. Austin, C. R. St. John and R. W. Lindsay "Creep Properties of Some Binary Solid Solutions of Ferrite" Transactions, AIME, Vol 162 (1945)

(23) C. R. Austin, L. A. Luini and R. W. Lindsay "Annealing Studies on Cold-Rolled Iron and Iron Binary Alloys" Transactions, ASM, Vol 35 (1945)

(24) Steel Products Manual, Section 24, Stainless and Heat-resisting Steels, published by the AISI (1946)

(25) P. B. Michailow-Michejew "Temper Brittleness and Embrittlement of Alloy Steels" Archiv für das Eisenhüttenwesen, Vol 17 (1944)

(26) H. Thum and K. Richard "Embrittlement and Damage of Heat-resisting Steels under Creep Conditions" Archiv für das Eisenhüttenwesen, Vol 15 (1941)

(27) E. Maurer, O. H. Wilms and H. Kiessler "Effect of Phosphorus and Various Alloying Elements on Temper Brittleness and Embrittlement on Long Heating of Low Alloy Steels" Stahl und Eisen, Vol 62 (1942)

(28) J. A. Jones "Temper Brittleness in Alloy Steels" Metal Treatment, Vol 4 (1938)

(29) C. Schaub "Fracture Phenomena in Steels at Elevated Temperatures" Jernkontorets Annaler, Vol 130 (1946)

(30) H. J. Kerr and F. Eberle "Graphitization of Low-Carbon and Low-Carbon-Molybdenum Steels" Graphitization of Steel Piping, published by the ASME (1945)

(31) S. L. Hoyt, R. D. Williams and A. M. Hall "Summary Report on the Joint E.E.I.-A.E.I.C. Investigation of Graphitization of Piping" Welding Research Supplement to the Journal, AWS, Vol 25 (1946)

(32) A. L. Hartley "Steel Standardization" Iron Age, Vol 144 (1939)

SECTION II

FUNDAMENTAL EFFECTS OF HEAT
TREATMENT ON MICROSTRUCTURE

TRANSFORMATION OF AUSTENITE

The practical application of research on the transformation of austenite has done much in recent years to put the heat treatment of steel on a sound, scientific basis. This work has proved valuable in interpreting the structural changes that occur in annealing and hardening and also in clarifying the effect of factors such as composition and grain size.

The basic relationship between time, temperature and transformation of a specific steel is usually presented in the form of a transformation diagram (also called an S or TTT curve). A transformation diagram is essentially a graphic summary of the results of a series of laboratory tests on the transformation characteristics of a given steel.* To reduce the number of variables, these diagrams are generally based on transformation at constant temperatures (isothermal).

Idealized Transformation Diagram

The schematic diagram in Figure 13 shows an idealized picture of the transformation of a carbon steel that has been subjected to a high enough temperature to form a homogeneous austenite. This austenite is stable only above the critical range and becomes unstable at lower temperatures. The nature of the product then formed and the time required for its formation depend upon the transformation temperature. As shown in Figure 13, the transformation diagram can be divided roughly into four zones, depending upon the product of transformation — proeutectoid, pearlitic, bainitic and martensitic.

Both the hypo and hypereutectoid steels show a proeutectoid zone.

---

* For methods of determination of the isothermal portion of transformation diagrams, see (1, 2, 3, 4). For the quench-temper method of following the formation of martensite, see (5, 6, 7).

Here the product of transformation is free ferrite in the former and free cementite in the latter. The time required for the initial separation of the proeutectoid constituent decreases with decreasing transformation temperature, as indicated by the dotted line. Austenite of eutectoid carbon content, however, is still stable above the Ae1 temperature. Therefore, as soon as the separation of the proeutectoid constituent has changed the carbon content of the residual austenite to a eutectoid composition, transformation in this zone ceases.

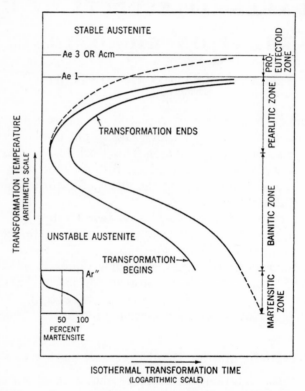

FIG 13 – Schematic Transformation Diagram of a Carbon Steel

The pearlitic zone is characterized by the formation of pearlite, although the separation of the proeutectoid constituent (if any) will continue in this zone. The separation of the proeutectoid constituent will start at the time indicated by the dotted line and continue until the first solid line is reached when the formation of pearlite starts. As shown by the solid lines, the times for the beginning and ending of the pearlite reaction become progressively less as the transformation temperature decreases. The minimum transformation times, or "nose" of the curve, are located at about

[20]

1000 to 1100 F for carbon steels. The nature of the pearlite changes with the transformation temperature. Pearlite formed just under the Ae1 temperature will consist of coarse lamellae. The lower the temperature of formation, the more closely spaced are the lamellae and the greater is the hardness.

In the bainitic zone, decreasing transformation temperatures generally require increasingly longer times for the transformation to start and finish. The structure of the bainite varies appreciably with the temperature of formation. The upper or high temperature bainite, formed just below the nose, has a feathery or acicular structure quite distinct from that of martensite; but it is frequently difficult to distinguish microscopically between lower bainite, formed slightly above the Ar″ temperature, and martensite. In general, the hardness of the bainite increases as the temperature of formation decreases. In some steels the hardness of the bainite formed just under the nose may be lower than that of the fine pearlite formed at somewhat higher temperatures.

The martensitic zone starts at a temperature designated Ms or Ar″. The Ar″ temperature is markedly affected by the composition of the austenite (8), but no significant influence is exerted by prior time at subcritical temperatures (provided no transformation has occurred)*, grain size, cooling rate, or the presence of undissolved carbides. For pure iron-carbon alloys, the Ar″ temperature will decrease from about 1000 F for very low carbon materials at a rate of about 63 F for each 0.10% increase in the carbon content.

The formation of martensite does not take place isothermally. Increased amounts of martensite are formed only by decreasing the temperature (10).** In some cases, if the steel is held within the martensite range, the untransformed austenite may transform isothermally to bainite, as indicated by a continuation of the isothermal portion of the curve below the Ar″ temperature. Also, a partial stabilization of the austenite may occur during such holding; the rest of the martensite formation curve is then shifted to lower temperatures.

The temperature at which the formation of martensite is finished is called Mf. Although the Ar″ temperature is unaffected by cooling rate, higher rates of cooling may raise the Mf temperature slightly† and therefore increase the rate of martensite formation below the Ar″ temperature (11, 12). When Mf lies below room temperature,

---

* In certain steels, the Ar″ temperature may be lowered by holding at temperatures in the bainitic zone even though no observable decomposition of the austenite has taken place (9).
** Where data on the formation of martensite are available, they are shown in this book as an insert in the transformation diagram. In these inserts, temperature is plotted against the percent martensite formed on cooling to that temperature. It will be noted that the scale is arithmetic, rather than semi-logarithmic as in the isothermal portion of the diagram.
† This would explain the often observed fact that more retained austenite is found after an oil quench than after a brine quench.

some austenite is retained after the steel has cooled to room temperature. This austenite can generally be transformed to martensite by further cooling, although this is not always the case (13, 14).

Variations From Idealized Transformation Diagram

Transformation diagrams similar to the schematic diagram of Figure 13 are characteristic mainly of carbon and nickel steels. With other alloying elements present, there tends to be a more or

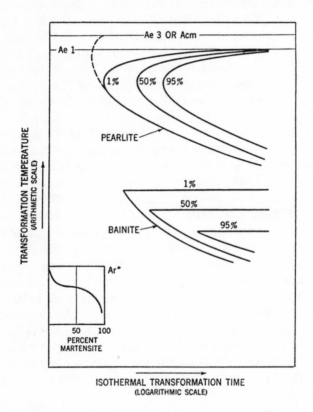

FIG 14 – Theoretical Transformation Diagram (adapted from 15)

less distinct discontinuity in the temperature range where the reaction changes from austenite → pearlite to austenite → bainite; although there may be a range in which both pearlite and bainite can form. In the limiting case the latter steels will approach the theoretical diagram of Figure 14. It will be seen from this figure that the curves for the start of the pearlite and of the bainite reactions are C shaped. In nickel steels, and presumably in carbon steels, the C curves for the start of the two reactions merge to such an extent that there is no measurable discontinuity at the nose of the transformation diagram. In steels containing other alloying elements, the variation in the position and form of the C curves may be sufficient to account for a complete separation of the reactions. The discontinuity in some transformation diagrams as well as the occurrence of bainite in some molybdenum steels transformed at temperatures as high as 1150 F is thus explained. It will also be observed from Figure 14 that there is a temperature range where the bainite reaction ends before all the austenite is decomposed. In some alloy steels, the degree of completion of the bainite reaction appears to be a function of the transformation temperature with the degree of completion increasing rapidly with decreasing temperature (16, 17).

Effect of Alloying Elements. The chemical composition of the austenite is the major factor in determining the shape and position of the curves. The composition of the austenite normally corresponds to that of the steel in steels of lower alloy and carbon contents. This does not necessarily hold true in steels of higher alloy and carbon contents, where appreciable amounts of the alloying elements and carbon may not be dissolved in the austenite prior to transformation. The effects of the common alloying elements on isothermal transformation diagrams may be briefly summarized as follows. Additions of carbon, manganese, nickel and probably of copper, silicon and phosphorus tend to shift the entire curve towards longer times. Chromium and molybdenum retard the transformation markedly at about 900 to 1100 F, somewhat less at higher temperatures and still less at lower temperatures.

The effect of molybdenum on isothermal transformation is shown in more detail by a comparison of the transformation diagrams for steels with varying molybdenum content but otherwise substantially the same chemical composition (compare Figure 15 for a hypoeutectoid carbon steel with Figure 16 for an analogous steel containing 0.29% molybdenum; Figure 17 for a eutectoid carbon steel with Figures 18 and 19 for analogous steels containing 0.32 and 0.52% molybdenum, respectively; and Figure 20 for a hypereutectoid carbon steel with Figure 21 for an analogous steel containing 0.33% molybdenum). Figure 22 shows perhaps more clearly the action of molybdenum in retarding the transformation of a eutectoid carbon steel.

The effect of carbon and alloying elements on the Ar″ temperature is not the same as it is on the isothermal portion of the transformation diagram. Since the Ar″ temperature is determined almost entirely by the chemical composition of the austenite, it can be

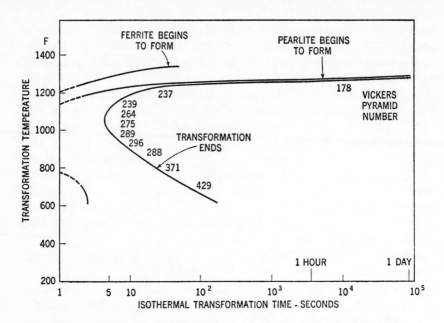

FIG 15 – Transformation Diagram of a Steel Containing 0.45% C, 0.67% Mn, 0.26% Si, 0.009% Mo. Austenitizing temperature: 1550F (18)

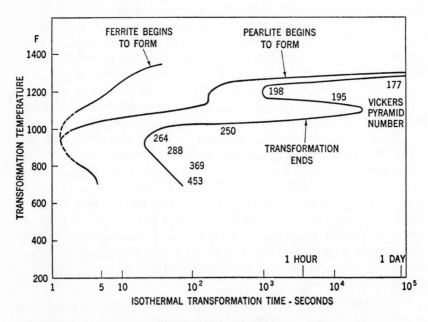

FIG 16 – Transformation Diagram of a Steel Containing 0.41% C, 0.69% Mn, 0.23% Si, 0.29% Mo. Austenitizing temperature: 1550 F (18)

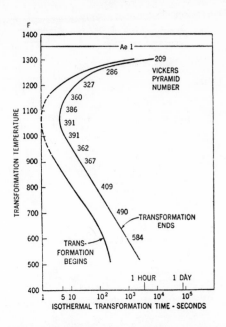

FIG 17 – Transformation Diagram of a Steel Containing 0.77% C, 0.71% Mn, 0.29% Si, 0.017% Mo. Austenitizing temperature: 1550 F. Austenite grain size: 8 (19)

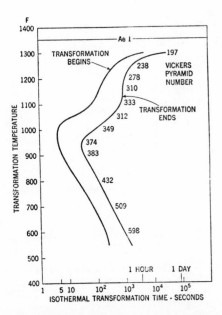

FIG 18 – Transformation Diagram of a Steel Containing 0.78% C, 0.73% Mn, 0.28% Si, 0.32% Mo. Austenitizing temperature: 1550 F. Austenite grain size: 8 (19)

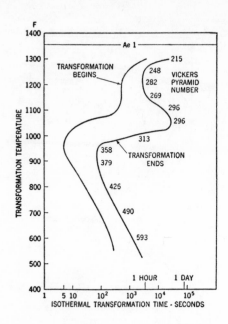

FIG 19 – Transformation Diagram of a Steel Containing 0.77% C, 0.72% Mn, 0.28% Si, 0.52% Mo. Austenitizing temperature: 1550 F. Austenite grain size: 8 (19)

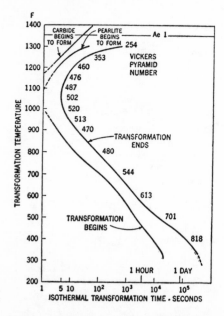

FIG 20 – Transformation Diagram of a Steel Containing 1.18% C, 0.76% Mn, 0.29% Si, 0.009% Mo. Austenitizing temperature: 1700 F. Austenite grain size: 8 (19)

[26]

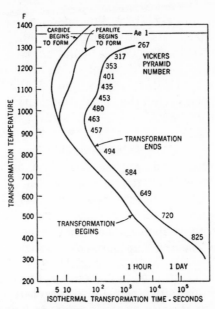

FIG 21 – Transformation Diagram of a Steel Containing 1.19% C, 0.77% Mn, 0.28% Si, 0.33% Mo. Austenitizing temperature: 1700 F. Austenite grain size: 8 (19)

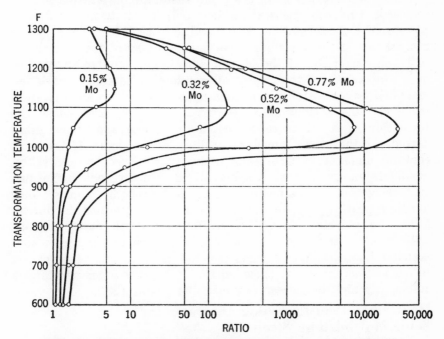

FIG 22 – Effect of Molybdenum in Retarding the Isothermal Transformation of Steels with 0.77 to 0.79% C, 0.70 to 0.76% Mn. Ratio of time for transformation of the molybdenum steels to the time for transformation of the eutectoid carbon steel (adapted from 19)

[27]

calculated approximately from the chemical composition of the steel if substantially all the carbon and alloying elements are dissolved in the austenite. This calculation is often used because any more accurate actual determination is rather exacting. Of various formulas which have been proposed, the following appears reasonably satisfactory for the usual engineering steels (20):

$$Ar'' \text{ in degrees } F = 1020 - 630(\%C) - 72(\%Mn) - 63(\%V) - 36(\%Cr) - 31(\%Ni) - 18(\%Cu) - 18(\%Mo) - 9(\%W) + 27(\%Co) + 54(\%Al)$$

Silicon appears to have no appreciable effect on the Ar'' temperature. There are insufficient data to permit calculation of the finish temperature of the martensite reaction (Mf). Moreover, its determination appears to be appreciably less reliable than that of the Ar'' if the metallographic quench-temper method is used.

Effect of Other Factors. The shape and position of the curve may be affected by various factors other than chemical composition, such as austenitic grain size, homogeneity, presence of undissolved carbides and non-metallic inclusions. Increasing austenitic grain size shifts the formation of pearlite towards longer times, but has no significant effect on the isothermal formation of bainite (21). Chemical inhomogeneity in the prior austenite, on either a macroscopic or a microscopic scale, affects both the initiation and completion of transformation. The resultant local variations in the composition of the austenite cause the beginning of transformation to be characteristic of the leanest alloy region and the ending to be characteristic of the richest alloy region. Undissolved carbides, and possibly non-metallic inclusions, appear to nucleate and therefore to hasten the formation of pearlite. They may also cause the formation of a structure composed of ferrite and spheroidized carbides rather than lamellar pearlite. For example, if the steel contains undissolved carbides or undissipated carbon concentration gradients as-austenitized, a spheroidized structure will be formed just below Ae1. If the prior austenite is thoroughly homogeneous, lamellar pearlite will form (22). Also, in fine grained, aluminum killed, hypoeutectoid steels, the pearlite may be only partly lamellar with most of the carbide present in the form of scattered, non-lamellar particles. Well-formed lamellar pearlite can be developed in such steels, however, provided the austenitizing temperature is sufficiently high to coarsen the austenite grains (23).

Isothermal Transformation Diagrams for Some Molybdenum Steels

Most of the available transformation diagrams have been determined on wrought steels. Figures 23 to 34 inclusive show transformation diagrams for 12 commonly used molybdenum steels.

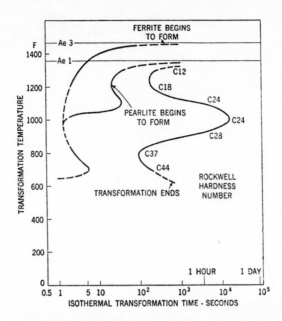

FIG 23 – Transformation Diagram of a Steel Containing 0.33% C, 0.53% Mn, 0.90% Cr, 0.18% Mo (4130). Austenitizing temperature: 1550 F. Austenite grain size: 9 to 10 (24)

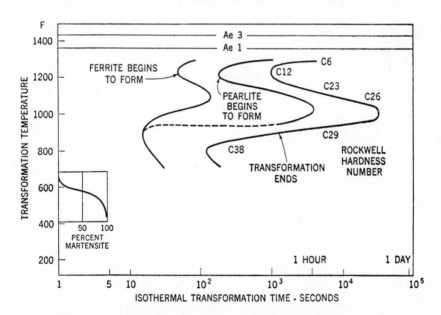

FIG 24 – Transformation Diagram of a Steel Containing 0.38% C, 0.82% Mn, 0.23% Si, 1.02% Cr, 0.20% Mo, 0.29% Ni (4140). Austenitizing temperature: 1550 F (2). Information on martensite formation obtained on a steel containing 0.37% C, 0.77% Mn, 0.15% Si, 0.98% Cr, 0.21% Mo. Austenitizing temperature: 1550 F (7)

[29]

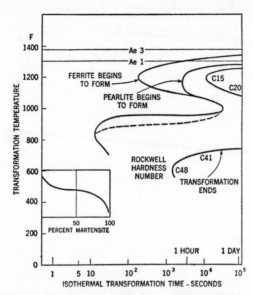

FIG 25 – Transformation Diagram of a Steel Containing 0.42% C, 0.78% Mn, 0.24% Si, 0.80% Cr, 0.33% Mo, 1.79% Ni (4340 slightly modified). Austenitizing temperature: 1550 F. Austenite grain size 7 to 8 (24). Information on martensite formation obtained on same steel with same austenitizing temperature (7)

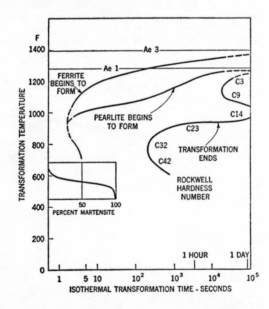

FIG 26 – Transformation Diagram of a Steel Containing 0.36% C, 0.63% Mn, 0.19% Si, 0.23% Mo, 1.84% Ni ("4635"). Austenitizing temperature: 1550 F. Austenite grain size: 7 to 8 (24). Information on martensite formation obtained on same steel with same austenitizing temperature (7)

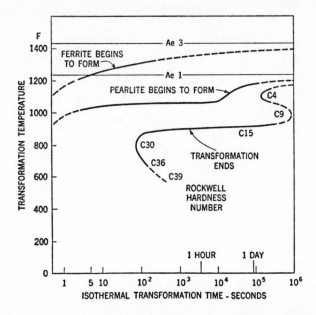

FIG 27 – Transformation Diagram of a Steel Containing 0.16% C, 0.52% Mn, 0.19% Mo, 3.36% Ni (4815). Austenitizing temperature: 1650 F. Austenite grain size: 8 to 9 (24)

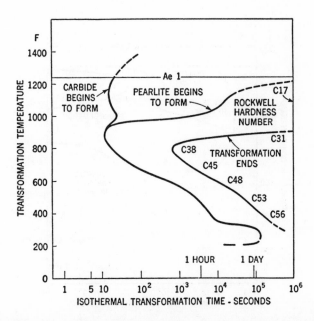

FIG 28 – Transformation Diagram of a Steel Containing 0.97% C, 0.52% Mn, 0.20% Mo, 3.36% Ni ("48100" – carburized case of 4815). Austenitizing temperature: 1800 F. Austenite grain size: 7 (24)

[31]

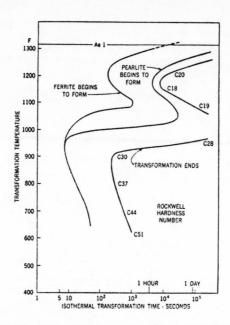

FIG 29 – Transformation Diagram of a Steel Containing 0.43% C, 1.65% Mn, 0.29% Si, 0.36% Mo. Austenitizing temperature: 1550 F. Austenite grain size: 8 (25)

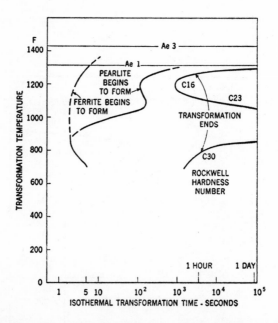

FIG 30 – Transformation Diagram of a Steel Containing 0.44% C, 0.90% Mn, 0.54% Cr, 0.22% Mo, 0.45% Ni (8645). Austenitizing temperature: 1550 F. Austenite grain size: 9 to 10 (24)

[32]

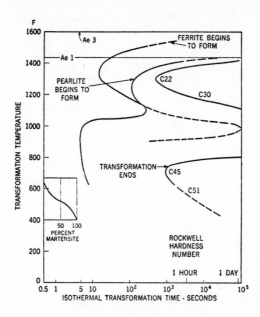

FIG 31 – Transformation Diagram of a Steel Containing 0.41% C, 0.57% Mn, 0.24% Si, 1.26% Al, 1.57% Cr, 0.36% Mo, 0.17% Ni (Nitralloy G Modified). Austenitizing temperature: 1700 F. Austenite grain size: 7 to 8 (adapted from 26)

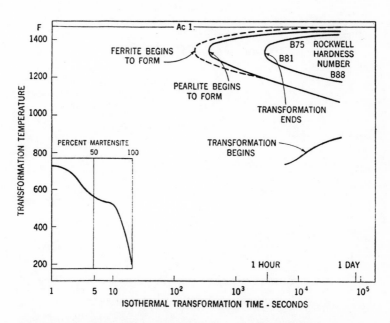

FIG 32 – Transformation Diagram of a Steel Containing 0.14% C, 0.41% Mn, 0.21% Si, 5.12% Cr, 0.51% Mo, 0.19% Ni (Type 502 with molybdenum). Austenitizing temperature: 1650 F (adapted from 27)

[33]

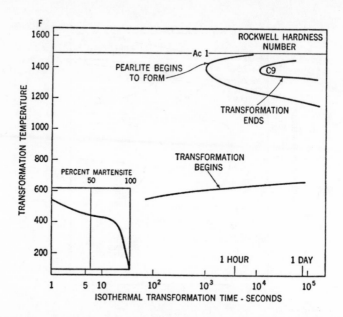

FIG 33 – Transformation Diagram of a Hot Work Steel Containing 0.32% C, 0.35% Mn, 0.95% Si, 4.86% Cr, 1.45% Mo, 1.29% W. Austenitizing temperature: 1850 F (adapted from 6)

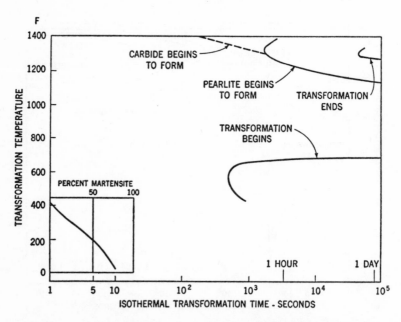

FIG 34 – Transformation Diagram of a High Speed Steel Containing 0.81% C, 0.24% Mn, 0.26% Si, 4.10% Cr, 4.69% Mo, 1.64% V, 5.95% W. Austenitizing temperature: 2235 F (adapted from 28)

[34]

Some work that has been done on cast steels has indicated that diagrams for wrought steels can be used as a guide in the heat treatment of steel castings, as the differences are minor in comparison with those resulting from normal variations in commercial heats (29).

Uses of Transformation Diagrams

*Annealing.** The old practice of slowly cooling steel in the furnace from above the critical to room temperature actually is very wasteful of time, because transformation to the desired structure occurs only during a small part of the total cooling time. Once the austenite has been fully transformed, further retarded cooling has no significant effect on either the structure or hardness. When full annealing is carried out, the upper part of the transformation diagram may be used to save annealing time and to help attain the desired structure. The austenitizing temperature is also an important factor in determining the final structure of the annealed steel. In general, the higher the austenitizing temperature, the greater is the tendency to form lamellar pearlite on subsequent transformation at temperatures above the nose. On the other hand, a low austenitizing temperature and a high transformation temperature will tend to promote the formation of a spheroidal structure (30).

The transformation diagrams also indicate which steels are prone to form banded structures on annealing and the temperature ranges where this is likely to occur. If the spread between the time for the initial formation of ferrite and for the initial formation of pearlite is large, then the subsequent structure is apt to be banded (30). With some steels it is possible to avoid this type of structure by selecting a transformation temperature where the curves are closer. With low carbon steels, there is often no temperature range where a suitable hardness can be obtained in a reasonable time without banding. In such cases, the usual expedient is to normalize or normalize and temper to the desired hardness. This latter procedure is common with low carbon carburizing steels.

With the information from the diagram, it is possible to select a temperature at which the desired type of structure is produced most quickly and to predict, at least approximately, how long the steel must be held in the temperature range of greatest efficiency. It should be remembered that a transformation diagram represents a single heat of steel; therefore, a factor of safety must be applied

---

* This section applies only to full annealing where the steel is heated above the critical temperature. Subcritical annealing does not involve the transformation of austenite; therefore, the transformation diagrams are of no assistance. They likewise cannot be used if the steel is prepared for machining by normalizing and tempering.

to allow for the heat-to-heat variation in the time required for the completion of transformation.* Very close control of structure can be obtained by approaching a truly isothermal anneal, for which special equipment may be required. When continuous cooling is employed, a retardation of the cooling in the temperature range where transformation is desired, together with accelerated cooling through other temperature ranges, will decrease the total annealing time. The temperature range of maximum efficiency is rather narrow so that close control of the temperature of the steel itself is required to obtain the desired structure in the shortest practical time.

Measure of Hardenability. Transformation diagrams may be used to give qualitative indications of hardenability. If a part is to be hardened to a completely martensitic structure, it must be cooled rapidly enough to avoid the formation of ferrite, pearlite and bainite. Since the diagrams give the time for the initial formation of the softer constituents, it is relatively simple to estimate roughly the cooling conditions necessary to prevent the transformation of austenite in these ranges. The less rapid the required cooling, the higher is the hardenability. As an indication of hardenability, however, the transformation diagram is neither as practical nor as precise as an actual hardenability test. In the first place, the accuracy of the determination of the minimum times for the initiation of transformation is limited. In the second place, the transformation diagrams are usually based on isothermal data and therefore cannot be directly applied to continuous cooling.† For example, isothermal transformation diagrams indicate that molybdenum has little effect on the time required for the formation of bainite although it greatly retards the formation of pearlite and ferrite (see Figure 22). This has led to the assumption that molybdenum has no effect on bainitic hardenability (37). There is evidence, however, that molybdenum does increase the time required for the initial formation of bainite on continuous cooling (38).

Special Quenching Methods. The transformation diagram is of great assistance in connection with various special quenching methods employed in practical heat treating operations. Two procedures that have long been used to minimize distortion and cracking

---

* In high carbon, high alloy engineering steels, the time for complete transformation may be so long in some heats that excessive time would be required for annealing treatments designed to insure complete transformation to pearlite in all heats. Failure to obtain complete transformation to pearlite during annealing is likely to result in the transformation of the remaining austenite at lower temperatures to structures that are too hard for machining (low temperature bainite or martensite). In such steels, therefore, it may be more practical to use an annealing cycle that will result in the transformation of most of the austenite to pearlite and then to follow the annealing treatment with a high temperature tempering operation, say at 1150 to 1200 F, to reduce the hardness of any hard constituents that may have been present.

† Continuous cooling transformation diagrams are available for 4130 (31), 4315 (32), two heats of 4330 (33, 34), 4340 (35) and 8630 (36).

are the interrupted or timed quench and the delayed quench. These empirical methods have been made more reliable by the use of transformation diagrams.

In the most modern application of the interrupted quench, commonly called martempering*, the steel is cooled from a temperature above the critical to just over the Ar″ temperature at a rate fast enough to avoid the formation of ferrite or pearlite. The cooling medium is generally a salt bath. The steel is permitted to remain in the bath until the temperature has become practically uniform throughout the piece, after which it is allowed to cool slowly (usually in air) to form martensite (39). Since cracking and distortion in conventional quenching result to a large degree from the thermal gradients existing in the piece while martensite is forming, they are minimized in martempering because the temperature of the steel is equalized just before the formation of martensite starts. Much of the advantage of this process can be realized even though the quenching bath is held slightly below the Ar″ temperature. The important point is that only a little martensite should be allowed to form until the temperature of the piece has become substantially uniform.

The delayed quench is based on the fact that transformation on cooling starts at a temperature considerably lower than that required for austenitizing. Therefore, the steel may be air cooled for a certain period (which varies with the type of steel) before quenching in a liquid bath, without loss of hardening. The temperature gradients caused by the quenching are then less severe since quenching is done from a lower temperature. Distortion, internal stresses and the tendency to crack are thus reduced. The transformation diagrams show that molybdenum steels are particularly suitable for the practice of delayed quenching, because of the effect of molybdenum in retarding the formation of proeutectoid ferrite and pearlite.

Measure of Susceptibility to Cracking and Flaking. A high Ar″ temperature is considered favorable to the prevention of cracks in quenching and welding and also to the prevention of flakes or thermal ruptures during cooling after hot working (20). The higher the temperature of martensite formation, the greater is the plasticity of the steel as a whole; thus, a steel with a high Ar″ temperature is more able to distribute the stresses caused by the martensite formation without cracking. There is also more opportunity during cooling for a certain amount of stress relief in the martensite itself. An additional factor is involved in the case of

---

* There has been a tendency of late to term this process "marquenching" as it precedes but does not replace the tempering operation.

welding cracks and flakes, which are caused at least in part by hydrogen (40, 41, 42, 43, 44, 45, 46, 47, 48). The solubility of hydrogen in austenite is much greater than in ferrite, so there is a pronounced increase in its rate of evolution when the austenite transforms (48). If the martensite is formed at a high temperature, it is believed that there is more opportunity for the hydrogen to escape without contributing to the formation of cracks or flakes.

It has been observed that the tendency to flaking in some types of alloy steel is almost as marked in low carbon as in high carbon heats. This may seem paradoxical since the Ar″ temperatures are considerably higher for the steels with low carbon content. Ferrite is rejected, however, during the rather slow cooling of blooms, billets and heavy forgings. Final transformation therefore takes place in austenite enriched in carbon by this rejection of proeutectoid ferrite. Regardless of the carbon content of the steel as a whole, the governing factor is the Ar″ temperature of an alloy steel of the type under consideration but of almost eutectoid carbon content. It is common practice in many steel plants to insist that slow cooling be continued to lower temperatures in the case of steels containing substantial amounts of alloying elements that markedly lower the Ar″ temperature.*

In the equation on page 28, it is apparent that carbon lowers the Ar″ temperature more than any other element. This is believed to be one of the reasons, although of course not the only one, why a low carbon content helps to avoid cracking in quenching and welding. It is also to be noted that molybdenum has very little effect on the Ar″ temperature, especially in view of the fact that only small amounts are required to produce large increases in hardenability. Therefore, from this standpoint, molybdenum steels are less susceptible to quenching and welding cracks and flakes than other steels of equivalent carbon content and hardenability.

EFFECT OF MOLYBDENUM ON MICROSTRUCTURE

Isothermally Transformed Steels

One effect of molybdenum on the microstructure of steel with about 0.40% carbon is in the volume and character of the proeutectoid ferrite. On transformation at about 950 to 1250 F, the ferrite in a carbon steel appears almost wholly at the grain boundaries. Upon the addition of as little as 0.15% molybdenum, the formation

---

* Isothermal annealing cycles have been used for flake prevention in susceptible steels. In using the data from isothermal transformation diagrams to establish such cycles, the following factors must be taken into consideration (49): 1) the long time required to cool heavy blooms and forgings to the transformation temperature and the possibility of transformation during this cooling; 2) the close temperature control necessary; 3) the additional time factor needed to allow for the occurrence of sluggish localized transformations due to segregation.

of pearlite in this range is delayed much more than that of ferrite so that there is a significant increase in the volume of ferrite produced. The ferrite thereupon precipitates both at and within the prior austenite grain boundaries. This effect increases with the molybdenum content up to at least 0.75%.

In the medium carbon steels the tendency for the ferrite to precipitate in an acicular manner in the range 900 to 1100 F is promoted by molybdenum. This acicular type ferrite occurs in parallel blades which become more closely spaced with the decrease in transformation temperature. The pearlite, which forms after the ferrite blades have grown in all directions, occurs in smaller and smaller patches as the temperature of transformation is lowered. At approximately 950 F the character of the ferrite formation is such that the microstructure of the higher molybdenum steels consists chiefly of carbide-containing blades widely dispersed in ferrite. The final structure obtained then in the range 900 to 1100 F is a Widmanstätten type. The spacing between the carbide-containing constituents of this structure decreases with the lowering of the transformation temperature.

In eutectoid and hypereutectoid steels, molybdenum markedly increases the interlamellar spacing of pearlite formed at 1200 F. The structure of a steel with 0.79% carbon and 0.77% molybdenum, transformed at 1200 F, is scarcely recognizable as pearlite. At temperatures below 1100 F the product of transformation is largely bainite in steels with 0.52 and 0.77% molybdenum and about 0.77% carbon. Steels with the same carbon content but with no molybdenum, or only 0.15% molybdenum, contain predominantly fine pearlite. After transformation at 1000 F a hypereutectoid steel with 0.77% molybdenum is composed mainly of acicular carbide in a matrix of ferrite.

For transformation temperatures below 900 F the structures of hypoeutectoid, eutectoid and hypereutectoid molybdenum steels are similar to those of the corresponding carbon steels.

Continuously Cooled Steels

Structure diagrams are convenient devices for showing the effect of molybdenum on the structures formed on cooling from temperatures above the critical. Specimens $\frac{3}{4}$ in. in diameter x $1\frac{1}{8}$ in. long were air cooled from 1800 F before final heat treatment. The microstructures were observed at a point half way between the surface and center of the specimens. Figures 35 to 38 inclusive reproduce structure diagrams for still air cooling and for water quenching from 1550 and 1650 F.

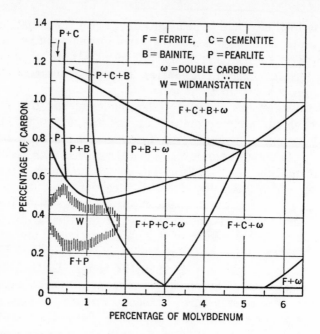

FIG 35 – Structures of Iron-Carbon-Molybdenum Alloys, Cooled in Still Air from 1550 F (50)

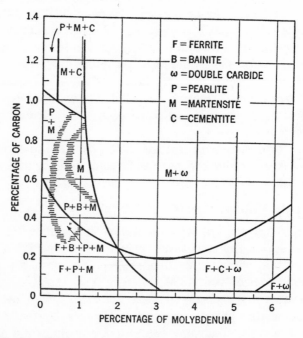

FIG 36 – Structures of Iron-Carbon-Molybdenum Alloys, Water Quenched from 1550 F (50)

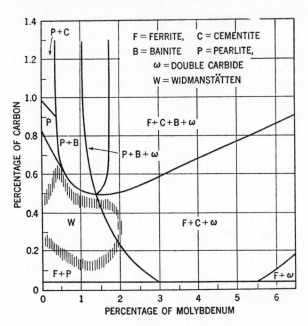

FIG 37 – Structures of Iron-Carbon-Molybdenum Alloys, Cooled in Still Air from 1650 F (50)

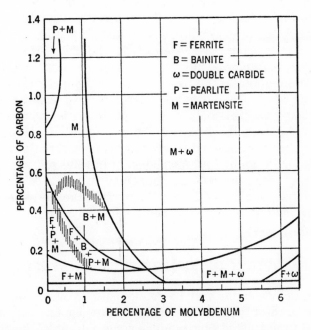

FIG 38 – Structures of Iron-Carbon-Molybdenum Alloys, Water Quenched from 1650 F (50)

ACICULAR CAST IRONS

High wear resistance, toughness and strength may be attained in alloy cast irons if the structure as-cast is acicular or bainitic. This means that the composition of the casting must be so adjusted that, for the cooling rate involved, the transformation of austenite to pearlite will be avoided. The added alloy content should not, however, be such that the transformation to bainite is also suppressed since brittle martensite would then form (51). Because molybdenum retards the formation of pearlite more than that of bainite, it is generally used in cast irons of this type.

EFFECT OF MOLYBDENUM IN FERRITE
AND LOW CARBON IRON ALLOYS

Molybdenum expands the lattice parameter of alpha iron (52). The solid solution hardening effect of relatively small amounts of molybdenum in annealed low carbon iron-molybdenum alloys is given in Table 4. The order of increasing effectiveness of various alloying elements in raising the hardness of fully annealed binary alloys has been given (53) as: chromium, cobalt, nickel, manganese, molybdenum, silicon. On the basis of tensile strength per weight percent, the order of increasing strengthening ability has been listed (54) as: chromium, cobalt, tungsten, vanadium, nickel, molybdenum, aluminum, manganese, titanium, silicon, beryllium. In terms of increasing fatigue strength, the order is: chromium, cobalt, nickel, manganese, silicon, molybdenum, titanium (55).

Molybdenum increases the recrystallization temperature of ferrite as shown by the softening temperatures of cold rolled specimens (56). Carbon-free iron-molybdenum alloys with more than 6% molybdenum contain the intermetallic compound Fe_3Mo_2 (epsilon phase) if equilibrium is attained at room temperature. It is possible, however, to retain up to 24% molybdenum in solid solution in alpha by quenching from the solidus temperature (57). Alloys with 6 to 30% molybdenum therefore can be precipitation hardened. Table 5 shows the extent of such hardening in alloys with 10 to 30% molybdenum.

PARTITION OF MOLYBDENUM IN STEEL

In steels molybdenum will be found both in the solid solution and in the carbide phase. The molybdenum content of the first precipitated proeutectoid ferrite is the same as that of the austenite from which it forms (58).

TABLE 4
Solid Solution Hardening Effect of Molybdenum

Analyses %C	Analyses %Mo	Condition	ASTM Grain Size	Tensile Strength psi	Yield Strength* psi	Elongation percent	Reduction of Area percent	Fatigue Strength psi	Diamond Pyramid Hardness DPH/10	Reference
0.02	0.004	1	<1	......	......	.....	.....	......	67	(53)
0.03	0.11	1	3	......	......	.....	.....	......	76.5	(53)
0.03	0.54	1	3½	......	......	.....	.....	......	92.5	(53)
0.04	1.50	1	5½	......	......	.....	.....	......	99.5	(53)
<0.01	nil	2	3 to 5	33,900	......	48	71	......	.....	(54)
....	1.69	2	6	42,750	22,000	52	90	......	.....	(54)
....	3.48	2	5 to 6	48,750	18,200	50	88	......	.....	(54)
0.015	nil	3	...	......	......	.....	.....	15,600a	.....	(55)
0.015	0.13	3	5	......	......	.....	.....	19,250	.....	(55)
0.015	0.40	3	5	......	......	.....	.....	23,200	.....	(55)

* 0.2% permanent deformation
(a) approximate

Conditions
1 1785 F (one hour), furnace cooled to room temperature
2 Annealed to give indicated grain size, then held 50 hr at 1320 F in wet hydrogen
3 1200 F (24 hr), furnace cooled to room temperature

TABLE 5
Precipitation Hardening of Iron Molybdenum Alloys with 10 to 30%
Molybdenum (57)

%Mo	Rockwell C Hardness	
	as-quenched from 2600 F	as-reheated 20 hr at 1160 F
10...................................	7	25
15...................................	10	35
20...................................	23	51
22...................................	26	59
25...................................	35	63
30...................................	40	65

In the carbide phase the molybdenum may be dissolved in the orthorhombic iron carbide (Fe_3C – cementite) or it may enter a face-centered cubic iron-molybdenum carbide ($(Fe,Mo)_{23}C_6$ – kappa) (58, 59, 60). Within certain composition limits, the kappa carbide is formed by isothermal transformation at temperatures in the pearlite region (Figure 39). Cementite probably forms exclusively after transformation at about 1000 F or lower. During the tempering of steels so transformed, however, there is a definite migration of molybdenum from the ferrite to the carbide. Long holding at 1200 and 1300 F may result in a high concentration of molybdenum in the cementite or kappa may be formed (Figure 40). Nevertheless, even after holding for 250 hours at 1300 F, the extent of the concentration of molybdenum in the carbide phase is much less than in steels isothermally transformed at the same temperature.

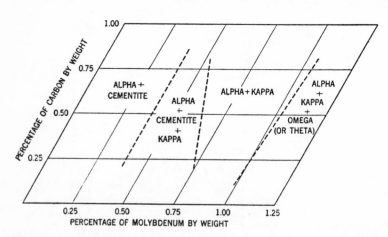

FIG 39 – The Approximate Phase Boundaries After Isothermal Transformation at 1300 F

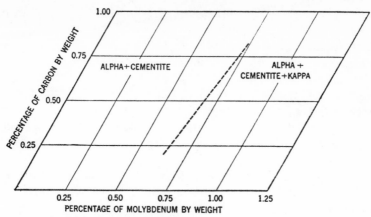

FIG 40 – The Approximate Phase Boundary After Tempering Martensite at 1300 F for 250 Hours

DIFFUSION OF MOLYBDENUM AND EFFECT OF MOLYBDENUM ON THE DIFFUSION OF CARBON

The coefficient of diffusion of molybdenum in both austenite and ferrite is extremely low as compared with that of carbon. The diffusion coefficient of molybdenum in ferrite is much greater than that in austenite. The presence of 0.4% carbon slightly increases the coefficient of diffusion of molybdenum in austenite at all temperatures (61).

A molybdenum content of 0.8% has little or no effect on the coefficient of diffusion of carbon in austenite at 2000 F. The molybdenum increases the diffusion coefficient slightly at higher temperatures and decreases it at lower temperatures (62).

IRON-CARBON-MOLYBDENUM SYSTEM

A brief résumé of the facts known at present about the phases existing at subcritical temperatures in the iron corner of the iron-carbon-molybdenum system follows:

A. Ferrite
 1. Body-centered cubic crystal; ferromagnetic
 2. Contains about 0.02% C at 1300 F.

B. The Cementite Carbide — (Fe,Mo)$_3$C
 1. Orthorhombic structure; ferromagnetic
 2. Apparently can contain a maximum of about 3% Mo by weight.
 3. Is formed by direct transformation of austenite or by tempering martensite within certain composition limits (see Figures 39 and 40).
 4. This type of carbide, formed either by direct transformation

or by tempering, graphitizes readily in about 50 hours in pure ternary alloys at 1300 F.

C. The Kappa Carbide — $(Fe,Mo)_{23}C_6$
1. Face-centered cubic structure; ferromagnetic
   a. Lattice dimension, a_0 – 10.52kX
2. Apparent minimum molybdenum content about 3.5% by weight. Maximum unknown but more than 10%.
3. Is formed by direct transformation of austenite or by tempering martensite within certain composition limits (see Figures 39 and 40).
4. Has never been directly graphitized. The results of a diffusion experiment indicated that graphite is the less soluble of the two phases and hence must be the more stable. In this experiment both sides of the couple were of the same composition; but one side had been quenched and tempered to form cementite and then graphitized, while the other side had been treated to form kappa by direct transformation. Apparently the nucleation of graphite in the presence of kappa is extremely difficult. Kappa is more stable than Fe_3C.

D. The Omega Carbide — $(Fe,Mo)_6C$
1. Face-centered cubic; nonmagnetic
   a. Lattice dimension, a_0 – 11.04kX
2. Maximum and minimum molybdenum contents not definitely known. Formula often given as Fe_3Mo_3C although it is known that the relative amounts of iron and molybdenum can vary considerably.
3. Is apparently formed, to a certain degree at least, directly from the melt. This carbide is, however, soluble to some extent in austenite. It has been stated that it is formed by the reaction $Mo_2C + melt \rightarrow Fe_3Mo_3C$ (63).
4. Is produced only by a slow cool from the melt (see Figure 39). No alloy was produced which contained only omega.

E. The Theta Carbide — Mo_2C
1. Hexagonal structure; nonmagnetic
   a. Lattice dimensions, pure Mo_2C, a_0 – 3.023kX, c_0 – 4.746kX
2. Minimum molybdenum content unknown, maximum is represented by Mo_2C. It appears that this carbide can dissolve at least 25% Fe by weight.
3. Is apparently formed from the melt. It is not definitely known whether or not it is even partially soluble in austenite.
4. Has been produced in the pure ternary alloys studied by chill casting the melt into copper molds (see Figure 39). No alloy containing theta exclusively was found in the range 0 to 10% Mo, 0.10 to 1.00% C.

Section II – Bibliography

(1) E. S. Davenport "Isothermal Transformation in Steels" Transactions, ASM, Vol 27 (1939)

(2) R. M. Parke and A. J. Herzig "Hardenability of Molybdenum S.A.E. Steels" Metals and Alloys, Vol 11 (1940)

(3) P. Payson, W. L. Hodapp and J. Leeder "The Spheroidizing of Steel by Isothermal Transformation" Transactions, ASM, Vol 28 (1940)

(4) J. L. Ham, R. M. Parke and A. J. Herzig "Kinetics and Reaction Products of the Isothermal Transformation of a 6 Per Cent Tungsten – 6 Per Cent Molybdenum High Speed Steel" Transactions, ASM, Vol 29 (1941)

(5) A. B. Greninger and A. R. Troiano "Kinetics of the Austenite to Martensite Transformation in Steel" Transactions, ASM, Vol 28 (1940)

(6) P. Payson and J. L. Klein "The Hardening of Tool Steels" Transactions, ASM, Vol 31 (1943)

(7) R. A. Grange and H. M. Stewart "The Temperature Range of Martensite Formation" Transactions, AIME, Vol 167 (1946)

(8) V. Zyuzin, V. Sadovski and S. Baranchuk "Influence of Alloy Elements on the Position of the Martensite Point, Quantity of Retained Austenite and Stability of the Austenite during Tempering" Metallurg, Vol 14 (1939)

(9) A. R. Troiano and A. B. Greninger "The Martensite Transformation" Metal Progress, Vol 50 (1946)

(10) H. Carpenter and J. M. Robertson, Metals, Vol II, published by Oxford University Press, London, England (1939)

(11) J. H. Hollomon and L. D. Jaffe, Ferrous Metallurgical Design, published by John Wiley and Sons, Inc. (1947)

(12) R. T. Howard, Jr. and M. Cohen "Austenite Transformation above and within the Martensite Range" AIME TP 2283; Metals Technology, Vol 14 (1947)

(13) S. G. Fletcher and M. Cohen "The Dimensional Stability of Steel. Part I – Subatmospheric Transformation of Retained Austenite" Transactions, ASM, Vol 34 (1945)

(14) S. G. Fletcher, B. L. Averbach and M. Cohen "The Dimensional Stability of Steel. Part II – Further Experiments on Subatmospheric Transformations" Transactions, ASM, Vol 40 (1948)

(15) C. Zener "Equilibrium Relations in Medium-alloy Steels" Transactions, AIME, Vol 167 (1946)

(16) E. P. Klier and T. Lyman "The Bainite Reaction in Hypoeutectoid Steels" Transactions, AIME, Vol 158 (1944)

(17) T. Lyman and A. R. Troiano "Isothermal Transformation of Austenite in One Per Cent Carbon, High-chromium Steels" Transactions, AIME, Vol 162 (1945)

(18) J. R. Blanchard, R. M. Parke and A. J. Herzig "The Effect of Molybdenum on the Isothermal Subcritical Transformation of Austenite in Low and Medium Carbon Steels" Transactions, ASM, Vol 29 (1941)

(19) J. R. Blanchard, R. M. Parke and A. J. Herzig "The Effect of Molybdenum on the Isothermal Subcritical Transformation of Austenite in Eutectoid and Hypereutectoid Steels" Transactions, ASM, Vol 31 (1943)

(20) L. D. Jaffe and J. H. Hollomon "Hardenability and Quench Cracking" Transactions, AIME, Vol 167 (1946)

(21) E. S. Davenport, R. A. Grange and R. J. Hafsten "Influence of Austenite Grain Size upon Isothermal Transformation Behavior of S.A.E. 4140 Steel" Transactions, AIME, Vol 145 (1941)

(22) R. F. Mehl "The Structure and Rate of Formation of Pearlite" Transactions, ASM, Vol 29 (1941)

(23) R. A. Grange "Factors Influencing the Pearlitic Microstructure of Annealed Hypoeutectoid Steel" Transactions, ASM, Vol 38 (1947)

(24) Atlas of Isothermal Transformation Diagrams, published by the United States Steel Corporation, Pittsburgh, Pennsylvania (1943)

(25) R. M. Parke, J. R. Blanchard and A. J. Herzig "New Data for Evaluating Manganese-Molybdenum Steels" Metal Progress, Vol 40 (1941)

(26) R. A. Grange. W. S. Holt and E. T. Tkac "Transformation of Austenite in an Aluminum-chromium-molybdenum Steel" AIME TP 2109; Metals Technology, Vol 13 (1946)

(27) L. F. Bowne, Jr. "The Use of Direct Transformation Data in Determining Preheat and Postheat Requirements for Arc Welding Deep Hardening Steels and Weld Deposits" Welding Research Supplement to the Journal, AWS, Vol 25 (1946)

(28) P. Gordon, M. Cohen and R. S. Rose "The Kinetics of Austenite Decomposition in High Speed Steel" Transactions, ASM, Vol 31 (1943)

(29) C. T. Eddy, R. J. Marcotte and R. J. Smith "Time-temperature Transformation Curves for Use in the Heat-treatment of Cast Steel" Transactions, AIME, Vol 162 (1945)

(30) P. Payson "The Annealing of Steel" Iron Age, Vol 151 and 152 (1943)

(31) C. A. Liedholm, S. E. Lopez and W. C. Coons "Transformation of S.A.E. X-4130 During Continuous Cooling" Metal Progress, Vol 46 (1944)

(32) C. A. Liedholm, S. E. Lopez and D. J. Blickwede "Transformation of S.A.E. 4315 During Continuous Cooling" Metal Progress, Vol 48 (1945)

(33) C. A. Liedholm "Transformation of SAE 4330 During Continuous Cooling" Metal Progress, Vol 45 (1944)

(34) C. A. Liedholm "Experimental Studies of Continuous Cooling Transformations" Transactions, ASM, Vol 38 (1947)

(35) R. A. Grange and J. M. Kiefer "Transformation of Austenite on Continuous Cooling and its Relation to Transformation at Constant Temperature" Transactions, ASM, Vol 29 (1941)

(36) C. A. Liedholm, A. I. Rush and D. J. Blickwede "Transformation of NE 8630 During Continuous Cooling" Metal Progress, Vol 46 (1944)

(37) J. H. Hollomon and L. D. Jaffe "The Hardenability Concept" Transactions, AIME, Vol 167 (1946)

(38) L. D. Jaffe "Anisothermal Formation of Bainite and Proeutectoid Constituents in Steels" AIME TP 2290 ; Metals Technology, Vol 14 (1947)

(39) B. F. Shepherd "Martempering" Iron Age, Vol 151 (1943)

(40) C. A. Zapffe and C. E. Sims "Hydrogen Embrittlement, Internal Stress and Defects in Steel" Transactions, AIME, Vol 145 (1941)

(41) J. H. Andrew, A. K. Bose, G. A. Geach, H. Lee and A. G. Quarrell "The Formation of Hair-Line Cracks – Parts I and II" Journal of the Iron and Steel Institute, Vol CXLVI, No. II (1942)

(42) S. A. Herres "Arc Welding of Alloy Steels" Transactions, ASM, Vol 33 (1944)

(43) G. L. Hopkin "A Suggested Cause and a General Theory for the Cracking of Alloy Steels on Welding" Transactions of the Institute of Welding, Vol 7 (1944)

(44) E. C. Rollason "The Influence of Hydrogen on Weldability of High Tensile Alloy Steels" Transactions of the Institute of Welding, Vol 7 (1944)

(45) S. L. Hoyt, C. E. Sims and H. M. Banta "Metallurgical Factors of Underbead Cracking" Transactions, AIME, Vol 162 (1945)

(46) M. W. Mallett and P. J. Rieppel "Arc Atmospheres and Underbead Cracking" Welding Research Supplement to the Journal, AWS, Vol 25 (1946)

(47) S. A. Herres "Practical Importance of Hydrogen in Metal-Arc Welding of Steel" Transactions, ASM, Vol 39 (1947)

(48) J. H. Andrew, H. Lee, H. K. Lloyd and N. Stephenson "Hydrogen and Transformation Characteristics in Steel" Journal of the Iron and Steel Institute, Vol 156 (1947)

(49) S. W. Poole "Flaking in Alloy Steels" Iron Age, Vol 160 (1947)

(50) J. R. Blanchard, R. M. Parke and A. J. Herzig "Constitution Diagrams for Iron-Carbon-Molybdenum Alloys" Transactions, ASM, Vol 27 (1939)

(51) R. A. Flinn, M. Cohen and J. Chipman "The Acicular Structure in Nickel-Molybdenum Cast Irons" Transactions, ASM, Vol 30 (1942)

(52) F. E. Bowman, R. M. Parke and A. J. Herzig "The Alpha Iron Lattice Parameter as Affected by Molybdenum, and an Introduction to the Problem of the Partition of Molybdenum in Steel" Transactions, ASM, Vol 31 (1943)

(53) C. R. Austin "Effect of Elements in Solid Solution on Hardness and Response to Heat Treatment of Iron Binary Alloys" Transactions, ASM, Vol 31 (1943)

(54) C. E. Lacy and M. Gensamer "The Tensile Properties of Alloyed Ferrites" Transactions, ASM, Vol 32 (1944)

(55) E. Epremian and E. F. Nippes "The Fatigue Strength of Binary Ferrites" Transactions, ASM, Vol 40 (1948)

(56) C. R. Austin, L. A. Luini and R. W. Lindsay "Annealing Studies on Cold Rolled Iron and Iron Binary Alloys" Transactions, ASM, Vol 35 (1945)

(57) W. P. Sykes "The Iron-Molybdenum System" Transactions, ASST, Vol 10 (1926)

(58) F. E. Bowman "Partition of Molybdenum in Hypoeutectoid Iron-Carbon-Molybdenum Alloys" Transactions, ASM, Vol 36 (1946)

(59) F. E. Bowman and R. M. Parke "The Partition of Molybdenum in Iron-Carbon-Molybdenum Alloys at 1300 Degrees Fahr. and the Nature of the Carbides Formed" Transactions, ASM, Vol 33 (1944)

(60) F. E. Bowman "The Partition of Molybdenum in Steel and Its Relation to Hardenability" Transactions, ASM, Vol 35 (1945)

(61) J. L. Ham "The Rate of Diffusion of Molybdenum in Austenite and in Ferrite" Transactions, ASM, Vol 35 (1945)

(62) J. L. Ham, R. M. Parke and A. J. Herzig "The Effect of Molybdenum on the Rate of Diffusion of Carbon in Austenite" Transactions, ASM, Vol 31 (1943)

(63) T. Takei "On the Equilibrium Diagram of the Iron-Molybdenum-Carbon System" Kinzoku no Kenkyu, Vol 9 (1932)

SECTION III

ADDITION OF MOLYBDENUM

The addition of molybdenum to iron and steel is a simple and straightforward operation. Molybdenum is not lost by oxidation during melting because, under normal conditions, iron is preferentially oxidized. Additions of molybdenum can be made in the form of the oxide, which is easily reduced, or in the form of ferromolybdenum. Furthermore, substantially complete recovery is obtained from the molybdenum contained in scrap, a fact of considerable economic significance.

The control of hardenability is facilitated by the fact that molybdenum does not oxidize from the bath as do the other effective hardening elements — carbon, chromium and manganese. The contribution of molybdenum to hardenability is thus reliable and not subject to unpredictable losses as the result of variations in oxidizing conditions during melting or casting.

FORMS OF MOLYBDENUM

For complete understanding of the various forms in which molybdenum is added to iron and steel, the recovery of molybdenum from its ore and the conversion of the concentrate to the products used by the metallurgical industry are briefly described here.

Over 99% of the world's production of molybdenum is derived from the mineral molybdenite (MoS_2). In the operations at the Climax mine, one ton of rock yields about 6 lb of molybdenum. After the rock is crushed and ground, the molybdenite is recovered by flotation. The product of this operation, molybdenite concentrates, retains about 5% of the siliceous gangue as well as some water and oil from the flotation.

The first operation on the concentrates is the conversion, by roasting, of the molybdenum sulphide to technical molybdic oxide (MoO_3). There is no further removal of gangue in this process. Technical molybdic oxide is supplied in the form of molybdic oxide, molybdic oxide briquettes and "calcium molybdate". The briquettes are produced by briquetting technical molybdic oxide in a hydraulic press with pitch as a binder. Although about 12% carbon is present in the briquettes, they do not cause a carbon pick-up in the steel since there is sufficient oxygen in the molybdic oxide to oxidize all the carbon content. The "calcium molybdate" is a mechanical mixture of the technical molybdic oxide and high grade powdered limestone. The selection of the type of oxide product to be used is largely a matter of individual preference.

Technical molybdic oxide is also the raw material for the production of ferromolybdenum. Produced by either thermite or electric furnace processes, ferromolybdenum contains between 55 and 75% molybdenum. The thermite product has the lower carbon content (0.10% max).

Molybdenum silicide, a thermally produced alloy containing approximately 60% molybdenum, 30% silicon and the balance mainly iron, was developed chiefly as a means of simultaneously adding molybdenum and inoculating gray cast iron (see pp 274, 277). The advantage of molybdenum silicide over a mixture of ferromolybdenum and ferrosilicon is that it contains less iron; hence, the weight of cold material needed and the chilling effect on the molten metal for a specific addition are less.

ADDITION OF MOLYBDENUM TO STEEL

The form of molybdenum used in making cast and wrought steels depends largely on the steel making process, on local conditions and on the percentage of molybdenum to be added. Ferromolybdenum is adaptable to any of the processes. Molybdic oxide is often used because it is cheaper. From the standpoint of close control and uniformity of composition, it is preferable to add molybdenum in the furnace. In steel foundries, however, it is often desired to add molybdenum to only a portion of a heat; in such cases, it is feasible to add up to 0.5% molybdenum, in the form of ferromolybdenum, to the ladle.

Basic and Acid Open Hearth Processes

Molybdic oxide is widely used in the basic and acid open hearth processes. Molybdenum costs less in this form than in the form of ferromolybdenum, so oxide is generally used for molybdenum additions up to about 1.0%. For additions above this amount, some operators prefer to use ferromolybdenum. The molybdenum may be introduced in the charge or it may be added after the charge is melted down. When alloy steel scrap is charged, it is desirable to make careful preliminary analyses on samples taken after the bath is completely melted for the closest control of the alloy content.

By careful determination of the molybdenum content of the bath before final additions of molybdenum are made, very close control of the molybdenum content of the steel can be achieved. The final addition of molybdenum to the bath should be made well before tapping to insure complete solution and mixing. Whenever late additions of molybdenum are required to adjust the composition, ferromolybdenum is used; it should then be introduced at least 15 minutes before tapping.

Basic Electric Arc Process

The practice is similar to that in the open hearth except that it is more common to make steels of higher molybdenum content in the electric furnace. Molybdic oxide may be added either with the charge or after melting to account for a molybdenum content up to at least 3.0%. The addition of molybdenum in this form is generally completed in the two-slag process before the carbide slag is made. In any case, it should be added at least 30 minutes before tapping. In high molybdenum steels, ferromolybdenum usually makes up the principal amount in excess of about 3.0%. Ferromolybdenum is also used for late additions as discussed above.

Acid Electric Arc Process

Molybdic oxide and ferromolybdenum have both been used in the acid electric arc process. Molybdic oxide can be added either with the charge or after the melt down, while ferromolybdenum is preferably added to the molten bath. Additions should be made well before tapping and ferromolybdenum should be used for late additions, as indicated for the basic and acid open hearth processes.

Induction Process

In the production of induction furnace steel, ferromolybdenum is the preferred form for all percentages of molybdenum.

Basic and Acid Bessemer Processes

Additions of ferromolybdenum to the converter may be made either before or after the blow. Lump size ferromolybdenum is added in a damp bag to blow away the slag. Ferromolybdenum can also be added in the ladle.

Additions of Molybdenum Sulphide

There has been a considerable production of certain molybdenum steels with sulphur additions up to about 0.08% to improve machinability.* In the production of such steels it is possible to add the sulphur, together with the corresponding amount of

* For example, 4024 with 0.035 to 0.050% sulphur, and 8641 with 0.040 to 0.060% sulphur.

molybdenum, in the ladle in the form of molybdenite concentrates. As the ratio of molybdenum to sulphur in the molybdenite is approximately three to two, an addition of 0.04% sulphur in this form would thus mean a simultaneous addition of 0.06% molybdenum. The cost of molybdenum in the form of molybdenite concentrates is lower than in other forms. Therefore, to the extent that molybdenite concentrates can be used as a direct addition to steel, there is a moderate saving in the cost of the molybdenum and the sulphur is obtained free.

Ladle Additions

Ferromolybdenum, crushed to a suitable size in relation to the quantity and temperature of the molten metal, is used in making ladle additions up to about 0.5% molybdenum. Care should be taken to avoid the addition of the molybdenum until the steel has covered the bottom of the ladle. It is advisable to add all the molybdenum before the ladle is three-quarters full so that the last of the steel will cause a churning action to facilitate solution and mixing.

ADDITION OF MOLYBDENUM TO CAST IRON

Ferromolybdenum is the most common means of adding molybdenum to cast iron. Lump ferromolybdenum can be added in the cupola, but very little is so added because of the ease of making relatively large ladle additions. Ferromolybdenum is therefore usually added at the cupola spout or in the ladle. In the latter case, the same precautions should be observed as are described above in connection with ladle additions to steel.

Molybdic oxide briquettes are used for direct addition to the cupola or furnace charge to produce up to 2% molybdenum in the iron. In electric or air furnaces. the briquettes can be added either to the cold charge or later when the bath is molten. If the addition is to be made to a cupola, the briquettes should be placed on top of the coke charge in the center.

When it is desired to add molybdenum and inoculate the iron simultaneously, molybdenum silicide is added either in the ladle or at the cupola spout.

CALCULATION OF MOLYBDENUM ADDITIONS

There is no loss of molybdenum due to oxidation. The factors used by steel works and foundries in determining the amount of the additions vary somewhat because different methods of calculation of the charge are used. However, factors ranging from about 90 to 98% are commonly employed.

WELD ROD COATINGS

Powdered ferromolybdenum is used in weld rod coatings to add molybdenum to the deposited metal.*

---

* For example, it is general practice to use weld rods that deposit metal containing up to 1.0% molybdenum for applications where strength higher than that obtainable from unalloyed weld rods is required.

SECTION IV

WROUGHT ALLOY
ENGINEERING STEELS

This section is devoted to alloy steels of the kind used for applications such as highly stressed gears, shafts and bolts in the construction of machines of many types, including automobiles, tractors, aircraft and machine tools. Most of these steels fall into three general groups according to carbon content and use:

(1) Low Carbon — 0.10 to 0.25% carbon, used chiefly for carburizing

(2) Medium Carbon — 0.25 to 0.50% carbon, used mainly in the quenched and tempered condition at hardnesses of about 250 to 400 Brinell

(3) High Carbon — 0.50 to 0.70% carbon, used largely for springs, torsion bars and wear resisting parts, which are quenched and tempered to approximately 375 to 500 Brinell.

The wide use of molybdenum in these steels is based largely on its economical contribution to hardenability. This economy is not based solely on the small amount of molybdenum required to produce large increases in hardenability. Because molybdenum is not lost by oxidation in melting or pouring, its contribution to hardenability is reliable and can be closely controlled. Also, it is possible to derive the full benefit from the molybdenum content of scrap, an important factor in view of the increasing use of alloy scrap. Since all of the molybdenum in scrap is recovered, greater uniformity of hardenability in the steel being made is maintained by specifying a definite molybdenum content. At the same time, other important advantages are gained, including decreased susceptibility to temper brittleness (pp 4-9) and the reputed superior machinability of molybdenum steels (pp 13, 14). The fact that molybdenum is now specified in a large proportion of the tonnage alloy steels* is the best evidence that its use is both effective and economical.

---

* For example, molybdenum is an essential constituent in 63.5% of the AISI alloy steels (1) and in 73% of the "H" steels (2).

MEDIUM CARBON ALLOY ENGINEERING STEELS

Three main subjects will be covered here: 1) the properties of tempered martensite, which represent the optimum mechanical properties that can be obtained in these steels; 2) the harmful effects of the non-martensitic constituents in steel which is incompletely hardened before tempering; and 3) hardenability, that property which determines the hardness pattern throughout a piece of steel which has been heated and quenched in a stated manner.

In the selection of steel for a given part the first requirement is the provision of sufficient hardenability to attain the required hardness. Various methods of measuring hardenability and their use are discussed under Hardenability (pp 71-93). The next question is whether satisfactory ductility and toughness will be obtained at the desired hardness. The results of tensile and impact tests have generally been depended upon to give an answer to this question. Mechanical or "physical" property charts based on small specimens fully hardened before tempering were formerly much used for this purpose. The properties shown in these charts actually applied only to sections of the same steel of such size that they could be fully hardened in quenching. The properties of the various grades of medium carbon alloy steels have been shown to be substantially equivalent, within certain limitations which will be stated, when these steels have been fully hardened before tempering. Hence, a single set of charts will be given showing normal expectancy bands for the various properties of all steels of this type. These bands will be discussed under Properties of Tempered Martensite. For the prediction of the properties attainable in actual parts which are to be fully hardened before tempering, this one set of charts is more convenient than and just as accurate as the former charts for the individual types of steel.

Many steel parts are incompletely hardened before tempering. In such instances properties predicted from either the old or new charts for fully hardened steels are misleading since they are substantially better than can be obtained at the same hardness in steel incompletely hardened before tempering. The detrimental effects of incomplete hardening will be treated under the heading Effect of Non-Martensitic Constituents (pp 66-71).

Properties of Tempered Martensite

First consideration will be given to the properties of tempered martensite as they are insensitive to chemical composition within broad limits.* Furthermore, the properties of quenched and tem-

---

* Steels containing tin are an exception. Tin in amounts over about 0.1% has a deleterious effect on the ductility, and especially impact properties, of heat treated alloy steels. Steels containing molybdenum, however, are less affected by the presence of tin than are steels without molybdenum (3).

pered steel can be defined most concisely when the steel is fully martensitic or hardened through before tempering.

The maximum hardness obtainable in a steel by quenching, that is, the hardness of untempered martensite, is determined almost entirely by its carbon content (Figure 41). The relationship between as-quenched hardness, percent martensite and carbon content is shown in Figure 42.* The curves of Figure 42 can be used for the estimation of the percent martensite present in any as-quenched section, although the relationship is less exact than that for carbon content and hardness of untempered martensite. Lower hardness values than those shown in Figure 41 will be obtained if some of the carbon is not in solution at the time of quenching. Hence, in order to obtain maximum hardening, the steel must be heated at a high enough temperature for a sufficiently long time to obtain complete solution of the carbides. In alloy steels in general as compared with carbon steels, it is often necessary to use higher temperatures or longer times to obtain complete carbide solution. In steels containing substantial amounts of carbide forming elements such as chromium, molybdenum and vanadium, this is especially true when the carbide size prior to hardening is fairly large.

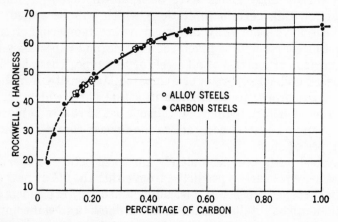

FIG 41 – Maximum Hardness Obtainable in Carbon and Alloy Steels. The values for the higher carbon contents may be a few points low due to the presence of retained austenite (4)

The hardness of martensite is progressively decreased by tempering at increasing temperatures (Figure 43). Hardness also decreases with increasing time at a constant tempering temperature.** Although longer tempering times decrease the hardness, the relationships between hardness, tensile and impact properties are unaffected by vari-

* Higher hardness values than those in Figure 42 have been given (6) for 50 and 80% martensite.
** A method is available for estimating the interrelationship of hardness, tempering temperature and tempering time for any specific steel (8).

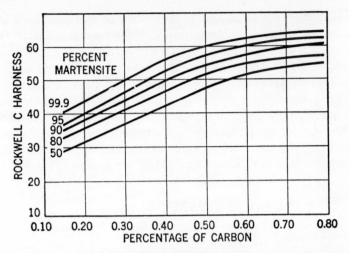

FIG 42 – Average Relationships between Carbon Content, Hardness As-Quenched and Percentage of Martensite (5)

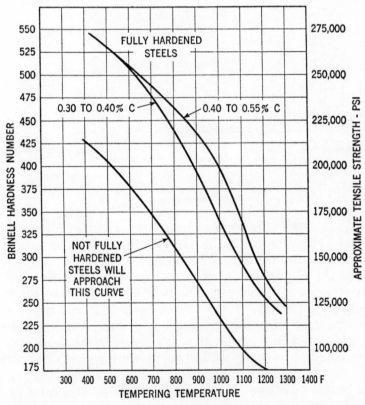

FIG 43 – Relationship between Hardness and Tempering Temperature (7)

ations in tempering time and temperature provided temper brittleness is not a factor (9). More highly alloyed steels sometimes show secondary hardening which may be evinced by a decreased rate of softening or by an actual rise in hardness as the tempering temperature increases (for example, see Figure 7, p 10). To attain a given hardness, molybdenum steels generally require somewhat higher tempering temperatures than other common alloy steels, especially when the tempering temperature is around 1000 F. As a guide for various molybdenum steels, Table 6 gives the approximate tempering temperatures for minimum tensile strengths from 100,000 to 200,000 psi.

TABLE 6

Approximate Tempering Temperatures for Various Specified
Minimum Tensile Strengths (10)

Type	Quenched		Approximate Tempering Temperature (F) for a Minimum Tensile Strength in 1000 psi of				
	from F	in	100	125	150	180	200
8620	1525 to 1575	oil	....	1000	....	....	...
4130	1575 to 1625	oil*	**	1050	900	700	575
8630	1525 to 1575	oil	....	1125	975	775	675
8735	1525 to 1575	oil	....	1175	1025	875	775
4037	1525 to 1575	water; oil	1225	1110	975	....	...
4140	1525 to 1575	oil	1350	1110	1025	825	675
4340	1475 to 1550	oil	....	1200	1050	950	850
8740	1500 to 1550	oil	....	1200	1075	925	850
4150	1500 to 1550	oil	....	1275	1175	1050	950

* bars and forgings may be water quenched from 1550 to 1600 F
** air cooling from 1600 to 1700 F will produce a tensile strength of about 90,000 psi
Notes: These values are based on holding the steel at the tempering temperature for approximately one hour per inch of thickness
"The temperature to be used . . . depends upon the exact chemical composition, hardness, and grain structure obtained by hardening, and the method of tempering. The tempering temperatures specified are only approximate, and the exact temperature should be determined by hardness or tension tests for individual pieces."

For ductile steels, the tensile strength is proportional to the Brinell hardness (Figure 44). On the average, the tensile strength in psi is about 500 times the Brinell hardness number.

For the usual tempering temperatures, the ratio of yield point to tensile strength in fully hardened steels is a function of the tensile strength (Figure 45). However, the ratio is generally lower for lower tempering temperatures (for example, see Figure 46). Hence, if high hardness and tensile strength are required, a higher ratio may be obtained by using steel of relatively high carbon content so that higher tempering temperatures can be employed.

The elastic ratio may be lowered markedly by cold working (for instance, straightening) after heat treatment. The effect is more noticeable the more sensitive the criterion used to determine the

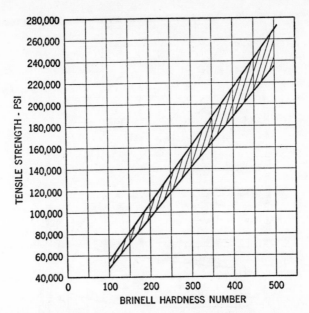

FIG 44 – Relationship between Hardness and Tensile Strength of Ductile Non-Austenitic Steels (7)

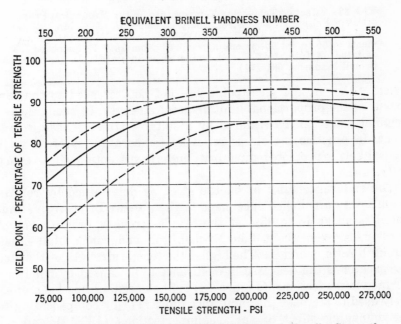

FIG 45 – Relationship between Yield Point and Tensile Strength. The solid curve shows the location of most points and can be considered as the normal expectancy. The dotted lines define the variation of remaining points. The low ratio of yield point to tensile strength represented by the lower side of the zone is indicative of incomplete response to hardening (7)

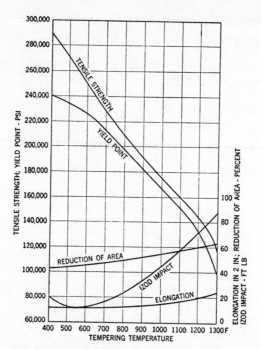

FIG 46 – Effect of Tempering Temperature on the Mechanical Properties of Fully Hardened Steel. Analysis: 0.39% C, 1.00% Mn, 0.25% Si, 0.012% P, 0.017% S, 0.52% Cr, 0.28% Mo, 0.53% Ni (8740). Treatment: 0.565 in. rd specimens normalized from 1600 F, quenched in agitated oil from 1525 F and tempered as indicated. As-quenched Brinell hardness: 601 (11)

"yield"; that is, the yield point will not be decreased to the same extent as the proportional limit or proof strength. In such cases the original value can be restored by a suitable stress relieving treatment. In practice the stress relieving temperature is often in the range likely to promote temper brittleness in susceptible steels (see pp 6, 7).

The endurance limit of ductile steel, as determined by rotating beam tests on polished specimens in the absence of corrosive influences, is about 45 to 65% of the tensile strength (Figure 47). At hardnesses over about 350 Brinell, the endurance limit–tensile strength ratio is erratic. The higher the tensile strength of the steel, the greater is the decrease in endurance limit caused by notches or surface imperfections (Figure 48).* Shot peening has been effectively used to increase the endurance limit (17) by compensating for the damaging effect of surface imperfections (18, 19) and cold straightening (20).

---

* The reduction in endurance limit of a specific part due to the effect of a notch, or of size, can be estimated from the notch dimensions and the ratio of the yield point to the tensile strength (14, 15). Charts are also available for predicting the endurance limit of steel parts, having ground, machined or hot rolled surfaces, from the hardness and stress concentration factor (16).

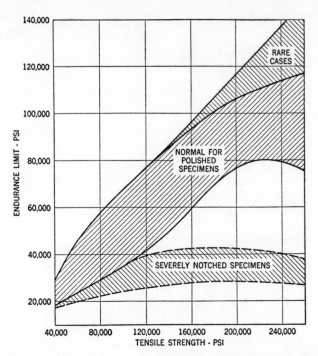

FIG 47 – Relationship between Endurance Limit and Tensile Strength (12)

The endurance limit, or stress for an "infinite" life, is significant in the case of parts, such as Diesel crankshafts, where at least 100,000,000 cycles of maximum load stress are involved (21). Many types of parts, however, are subjected to repeated stressing for only a limited number of cycles. For example, the lifetime requirement at maximum stress is about 100,000 cycles for rear axle automobile gears and automobile chassis springs (22) and only about 20,000 cycles for gun barrels (23). The endurance limit is therefore not directly applicable to such parts. Rather, the important value is the finite fatigue strength or the highest stress that will not produce failure in the number of cycles expected in operation. In such service, involving repeated stressing above the endurance limit, toughness is a major factor particularly for harder steels (21, 23). If all other conditions are equal, steels with low notched bar impact values will withstand less stress for a given finite life or will have a shorter life for a given stress than will steels with high impact properties. Consequently, temper brittleness impairs the finite fatigue strength (24) as well as the toughness.*

The ductility and toughness of hardened steel increase with increasing tempering temperature except for tempering temperatures

---

* In some cases the endurance limit itself may be lowered by severe temper brittleness (25).

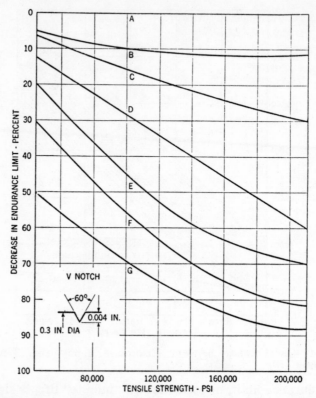

FIG 48 – Effect of Surface Condition and Notches on the Relationship between Decrease in Endurance Limit and Tensile Strength (13)
Curve A – Polished
Curve B – Ground
Curve C – Roughened
Curve D – Circumferential V notch
Curve E – Rolling skin (decarburized)
Curve F – Corroded in tap water
Curve G – Corroded in salt water

in the blue heat range, that is from about 425 to 750 F. The embrittling effect of tempering in this range is usually not shown by the elongation but may be shown by the reduction of area and is generally revealed in notched bar impact tests (Figure 46). The development of brittleness in this range has been associated with the decomposition of retained austenite but is now believed to be due to other causes (26). After such tempering at 425 to 750 F, impact values are inclined to be erratic and are usually somewhat lower than those obtained after tempering at higher or lower temperatures. The tempering temperature within this range which gives the lowest impact results probably varies with the tempering time, type of steel and even with the individual heat. In practice, the tempering of alloy steels in this range is almost always avoided.

The elongation and reduction of area of tempered martensite are functions of the tensile strength (Figures 49 and 50; Table 7).* The scatter of the elongation and particularly of the reduction of area values is greater when the tensile strength exceeds about 200,000 psi. One of the early papers on the similarity in tensile properties of fully hardened and tempered steels stated "Above a tensile strength of about 200,000 psi ... the reduction of area becomes an independently variable property depending on the individual steel. It is our belief that this variation is the result of retention of a variable amount of austenite on quenching, and the structural features which accompany the decomposition of such retained austenite at low tempering temperatures." (29)

TABLE 7
Relationship between Tensile Strength and Ductility (10)

Minimum Tensile Strength 1000 psi	Minimum Elongation, percent*				Minimum Reduction of Area, percent
	bars, forgings	sheet over 0.060 in. thick	sheet 0.032 to 0.060 in. thick	sheet under 0.032 in. thick	
100	21	12	9	6	58
125	17	10	7	5	55
150	14	9	6	4	53
180	12	7	5	3	50
200	10	6	4	3	46

* in 2 in. on a type 4 test specimen for bars and forgings; type 5 test specimen for sheet (28)

Notched bar impact tests are sensitive and may be affected considerably by factors that have comparatively little effect on tensile properties. Nevertheless, it appears that the notched bar impact strength of common alloy steels can be represented approximately as a simple function of the tensile strength in the usual range of strengths (Figure 51).** This relationship applies only if the steel is well made, fully hardened, and not embrittled during tempering. Under these conditions, variations in carbon content from about 0.20 to 0.50%, alloy content and tempering temperature seem to have little effect on the impact value. As in the case of elongation and reduction of area, this relationship is not dependable when the tensile strength exceeds 200,000 psi. When the steel composition and tempering temperatures are selected to avoid any form of embrittlement on tempering, the impact values at various strength levels shown in Figure 52 are attainable. The Charpy V notch impact test at – 40 F

---

* This applies to longitudinal specimens, that is, tensile specimens with their axes parallel to the direction of hot working. In transverse or tangential tests, the amount and type of hot working as well as the amount and distribution of non-metallic inclusions are important factors.
** The formula
   Izod Impact in ft lb = 2.8 (51.7 — Rockwell C Hardness)
has been given for fully martensitic, fine grained, alloy steels at hardnesses below Rockwell C 45. The accuracy is stated to be about ± 15 ft lb (30).

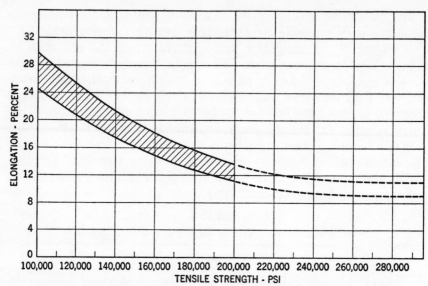

FIG 49 – Relationship between Elongation (percent in 2 in. on a 0.505 in. diameter specimen) and Tensile Strength. At tensile strengths up to 200,000 psi, 80% of the results on fully hardened steels with 0.30 to 0.50% carbon will fall within the shaded band. At higher tensile strengths the scatter will be greater (adapted from 27)

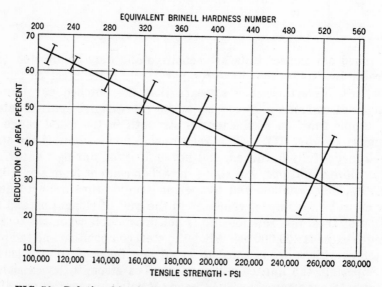

FIG 50 – Relationship between Reduction of Area and Tensile Strength of Fully Hardened and Tempered Alloy Steels. The diagonal line indicates the normal expectancy curve that can be used in estimating the normal reduction of area from the tensile strength or hardness. The cross lines indicate variations from the mean which may be caused by quality differences and by the magnitude of parasitic stresses induced by quenching (7)

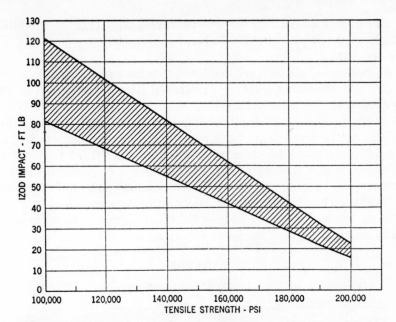

FIG 51 – Approximate Relationship between Izod Impact (longitudinal specimens) and Tensile Strength of Fully Hardened Alloy Steels not Subjected to Temper Brittleness (adapted from 27)

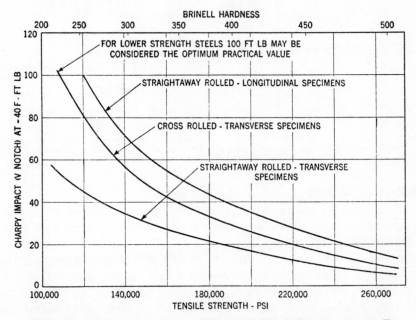

FIG 52 – Relationship between Charpy V Notch Impact at – 40 F and Tensile Strength of Fully Hardened Alloy Steels not Subjected to Temper Brittleness or Other Embrittlement During Tempering (31)

[65]

is considered sufficiently severe to reveal any lack of toughness which might lead to brittle failures under ordinary conditions of service (31).

As mentioned above it is considered that the properties of a particular grade of steel of the type considered here are represented just as accurately by these summary charts as by the various charts of properties often given for individual steels. Variations in quality may cause the properties of any particular sample of steel to lie near the upper or lower boundaries of the band. Different heats of the same grade of steel may show as much spread as heats of different grades (32). For convenience, similar information on the relationship between hardness and tensile properties is summarized in tabular form in Table 8. For more precise data it is necessary to make actual tests, particularly for hardnesses over about 400 Brinell.

TABLE 8

Approximate Relationship between Hardness and Tensile Properties*
of Fully Hardened Steels (33)

Rockwell C Hardness	Brinell Hardness	Tensile Strength 1000 psi	Yield Point 1000 psi	Elongation percent**	Reduction of Area percent
14	197	93 to 103	69 to 78	22 to 28	60 to 68
16	207	98 to 108	73 to 84	21.5 to 27.5	59 to 67
18	217	103 to 114	76 to 90	21 to 27.5	58 to 66
20	223	106 to 117	79 to 93	20.5 to 26.3	57.5 to 65.5
22	235	112 to 124	85 to 99	20 to 25.5	56.5 to 64.5
24	248	118 to 131	92 to 107	19.5 to 24.5	55 to 63
26	262	124 to 138	99 to 114	18.5 to 24	54 to 61.5
28	277	131 to 146	107 to 122	18 to 22.5	52 to 60
30	293	138 to 154	116 to 131	17 to 22	51 to 59
32	311	146 to 164	125 to 141	16 to 20.5	49 to 57
34	321	151 to 170	131 to 146	15.5 to 20	48 to 56
36	341	160 to 180	141 to 157	14.5 to 18.5	46 to 54
38	363	171 to 193	153 to 170	13.5 to 17	43.5 to 51.5
40	379	178 to 201	163 to 179	12.5 to 16	42 to 50
42	401	188 to 222	176 to 185	11 to 15	40 to 49

* this table will be more accurate for steels with 0.30% carbon or higher; steels with less than 0.30% carbon usually have yield point values lower than those shown
** in 2 in. on a 0.505 in. diameter specimen

Effect of Non-Martensitic Constituents

It is essential to consider the complex subject of the effect of non-martensitic constituents since many parts are not completely martensitic before tempering. Because of the diversity in the nature and distribution of these constituents, it is not possible to present the properties of incompletely hardened steels in the form of simple normal expectancy bands as has been done for tempered martensite. Moreover, when parts are not fully hardened, even slight variations in composition and heat treatment may result in appreciable differences in the quantity of non-martensitic constituents present. Two basic facts are, however, clear. First, the mechanical properties of incompletely hardened steel are inferior to those of fully hardened and tempered steel. Second, the degree of impairment depends upon the hardness of the heat treated steel. While small amounts of non-martensitic constituents may not significantly affect the room temperature tensile or impact properties of steel tempered to low hardnesses, even the presence of as little as 1 or 2% of a non-martensitic constituent may cause a marked loss in toughness at high hardnesses (26).

When the hardenability of steel is insufficient to produce full hardening under the quenching conditions employed, one or more non-martensitic structures will be present. The effect of ferrite appears to depend upon the hardness of the steel. At high hardnesses, for example in steels tempered at about 400 F, ferrite lowers the impact strength more than either pearlite or bainite. At lower hardnesses, however, the impairment caused by ferrite is less than that of either pearlite or upper bainite (34). Pearlite lowers the structure-sensitive properties more than bainite. Actually, tempered bainite formed just above the Ar" temperature may have room temperature properties similar to those of tempered martensite. Therefore, in general, the properties tend to be better, the more closely the carbide-containing constituents approach martensite in structure. As molybdenum is especially effective in retarding the formation of pearlite, bainite rather than the more harmful pearlite is likely to be found in incompletely hardened molybdenum steels.

The hardness-tensile strength relationship (Figure 44, p 59) is not structure-sensitive and will remain constant regardless of the structure of the steel.

Other properties cf incompletely hardened steels are quite structure-sensitive. They will depend to a considerable extent upon the nature, quantity and distribution of the non-martensitic constituents. Even though the total quantity of non-martensitic constituents can be estimated from transformation diagrams (see p 36) or determined more nearly from hardenability data, there are many possible variations in their distribution, with uncertain effects upon the final properties.

Among the structure-sensitive properties are the yield point, ductility and toughness. For equivalent tensile strengths, all will tend to be lowered by the presence of any of the non-martensitic constituents. The extent to which the yield point can be so lowered is indicated by Figure 45 (p 59). The elongation and reduction of area will also be decreased but the greatest effect of incomplete hardening is noticed in the notched bar impact toughness (Figure 53) (6, 24, 36). The effects of free ferrite, pearlite and high temperature bainite are usually shown by room temperature impact tests but the effect

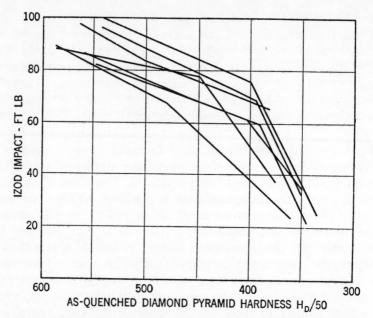

FIG 53 – Effect on Impact Strength of Incomplete Hardening as Indicated by the As-Quenched Hardness of Seven Heats of Manganese-Molybdenum Steel, Oil Quenched from 1560 F and Tempered at 1020 to 1185 F to a Tensile Strength of 134,400 to 143,400 psi (35)

Analysis Ranges of Heats Investigated									McQuaid-Ehn Grain Size
%C	%Mn	%Si	%P	%S	%Cr	%Cu	%Mo	%Ni	
$\dfrac{0.35}{0.38}$	$\dfrac{1.45}{1.57}$	$\dfrac{0.21}{0.29}$	$\dfrac{0.024}{0.037}$	$\dfrac{0.032}{0.047}$	$\dfrac{0.05}{0.14}$	$\dfrac{0.08}{0.11}$	$\dfrac{0.45}{0.50}$	$\dfrac{0.14}{0.29}$	$\dfrac{6}{8}$

of low temperature bainite, formed just over the Ar″ temperature, may be revealed only when the severity of the test is increased as by lowering the test temperature (see pp 2-4).

Work on various alloy steels, mainly chromium-molybdenum-nickel*, has indicated that the Izod impact** of incompletely hardened alloy steels can be estimated from Figure 54, with an accuracy of about ±20 ft lb, if the degree of incomplete hardening is known. The criterion used here for the evaluation of incomplete hardening is the difference between the "maximum Jominy hardness", as estimated from the carbon content† (Figure 55), and the as-quenched

---

* Types 1340, 3310, 3316, 4320, 4330, 4340, 8620, 8630, 8640, 8720, 8730, 8740, 9310, 9317, 9440, 9917 and three non-standard, high alloy chromium-molybdenum-nickel steels. It is probable that the non-martensitic constituent in most of these steels with low degrees of incomplete hardening was bainite rather than pearlite.
** Longitudinal specimens.
† This "maximum Jominy hardness" is the maximum hardness obtained on the Jominy test specimen. The high side of the band is almost the same as the values in Figure 41 but the average is somewhat lower.

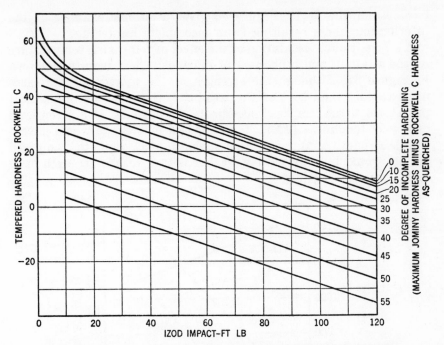

FIG 54 – Tempered Hardness – Izod Impact Relationship of Fine Grained Alloy Steels for Various Degrees of Hardening on Quenching (for estimation of Maximum Jominy Hardness from carbon content, see Figure 55) (30)

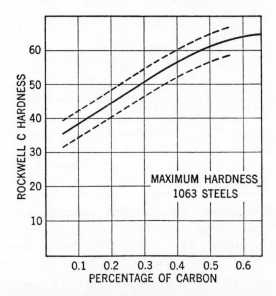

FIG 55 – Relationship between Maximum Hardness Obtained on Jominy Test Specimens ("Maximum Jominy Hardness") and Carbon Content. Based on 1063 Steels (37)

hardness of the part.* Figure 56 gives a specific example of the inferior toughness resulting from incomplete hardening.

A schematic representation of the effect of tempering temperature on the strength and toughness of martensite and bainite is shown in Figure 57. Although the strength of the martensite decreases more rapidly than that of the bainite**, the superior mechanical properties of the tempered martensite are obvious. At a given level of impact toughness (A-A), the tempered martensite would have a tensile strength of B and a proof strength of C, while the tempered bainite would be considerably weaker with a tensile strength of D and a proof strength of E.

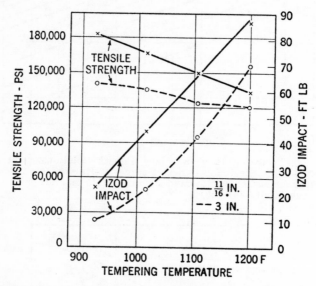

FIG 56 – Effect of Tempering Temperature on the Strength and Toughness of Completely and Incompletely Hardened Steel. Analysis: 0.33% C, 1.7% Mn, 0.30% Mo (38)

Diameter of Section in.	Tensile Strength as Oil Quenched Without Tempering psi
11/16	280,000
3	156,800

Although the endurance limit–tensile strength ratio is often considered to be unaffected by structure, there is some evidence (24, 39) that the endurance limit at any given tensile strength is lower if non-martensitic constituents were present before tempering.

---

* This relationship is based on aluminum treated steels with a McQuaid-Ehn grain size of about eight. The loss of impact strength may be more pronounced in incompletely hardened, coarse grained steels. It is stated that partially hardened, coarse grained steels may have Izod impacts more than 30 ft lb less than comparable values for fine grained steels (30).
** The effect of incomplete hardening on the tempering temperature – hardness curve has already been indicated in Figure 43, p 57.

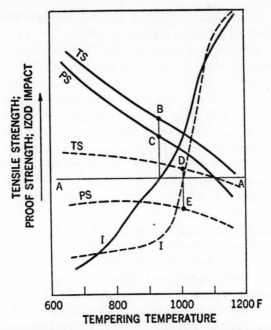

FIG 57 – Effect of Tempering Temperature on the Strength and Izod Impact of Steels Quenched to Martensite (full lines) and Isothermally Transformed to Bainite (dotted lines) (39)

The effect of incomplete hardening seems to be more pronounced on the resistance to repeated stressing above the endurance limit, which leads to failure in a finite time (such as 100,000 cycles). When either the yield strength or the toughness at any specific tensile strength is lowered by incomplete hardening, the life for a given stress or the stress for a given life is less than would be obtained with unembrittled, tempered martensite (21, 23).

It is clear, therefore, that the optimum properties are generally found in steel that has been hardened to a fully martensitic structure prior to tempering. The decision regarding the degree of hardening needed in any specific part requires careful consideration of the various factors involved in fabrication and service. Foremost, perhaps, is the question whether the service conditions demand the best possible combination of strength and toughness throughout the part.

Hardenability

In the selection of a steel for a particular article, the most important consideration is whether the mechanical properties required can be obtained, after suitable commercial heat treatment, in the size and shape of the article in question. The possibility of attaining this goal depends on various factors, some of which are inherent in the steel (composition and grain size of the austenite,

[71]

amount, nature and distribution of undissolved particles) and some of which are external (size, surface condition and heat abstracting power of the quenching medium). The inherent factors determine the critical cooling rate of the steel and are fixed by composition, deoxidation practice, prior structure and austenitizing conditions. The external factors determine the cooling rate of the part.

"Hardenability" and "mass effect" are two of the terms used to denote the relationship between cooling rates and hardness, mechanical properties or microstructure. Hardenability has previously been defined (p 1) as that characteristic of steel which makes it possible to harden the steel by rapid cooling from above the critical temperature range. It clearly emphasizes the inherent properties of the steel. "The term 'Mass Effect' is commonly employed by metallurgists to signify the effect of size and shape during the heat treatment, but though convenient, it is not strictly correct and may be misleading unless it is understood that it is the *Rate of Cooling* of a piece of steel which determines the properties resulting from a hardening or quenching process." (38) It appears to be advantageous to use cooling rates instead of bar sizes since service parts often do not correspond in shape to a standard bar. If the cooling is rapid enough (faster than the critical cooling rate) to produce martensite, further increases in the cooling rate will have little if any effect upon the properties* or structure of these medium carbon, low alloy steels. If the cooling is slower, however, so that non-martensitic constituents can form, changes in cooling rate will cause changes in the type and amount of such constituents which will be reflected in the mechanical properties (see pp 66-71).

The cooling rates obtainable in quenching obviously decrease as the section size increases. The maximum cooling rate is limited by the rate at which heat can be removed from the surface of the article being quenched. The highest cooling rate theoretically possible would be attained if the surface temperature could be instantaneously lowered to the temperature of the quenching medium and maintained at this temperature.** Under such ideal quenching conditions, the flow of heat is determined by the thermal diffusivity of the steel and the dimensions of the piece. Since an "ideal" quench has none of the uncertainties of an actual quench, this concept has been used in one means of expressing hardenability (40). In this method the hardenability is expressed as the diameter (D_I) of a bar that will just harden to 50% martensite at the center in an ideal quench. Although 50% martensite does not give the best properties

---

* Except stresses. Higher rates of cooling might lead to undesirable stresses and even to cracking. Frequently residual compressive stresses are favorable and can be induced by carefully controlled quenching methods.
** This rate has been referred to as the "ideal" cooling rate. The term ideal does not imply that such a cooling rate, if obtainable, would be desirable for any practical application.

after tempering (see pp 66, 67), this criterion has considerable justification as it may be readily measured by a fracture or etch test and may be determined empirically from the point of steepest slope of a hardness–depth curve. The D_I for 50% martensite may be converted to D_I values for other percentages of martensite (Figure 58). The D_I can also be converted to the diameter of the bar that will actually harden to 50% martensite in a given quench (Figure 59) provided the severity of the quench is known. Such factors for some common quenches are indicated in Table 9. One way of making Table 9 more intelligible is to present the data in terms of the sizes of bars which when quenched (using the same steel) attain the same center hardness (Table 10). For example, the same center hardness would be found in a one inch diameter bar quenched in still oil (H = 0.25) as in a two inch diameter bar of the same steel quenched in agitated water (H = 1.5). Thus, this latter table may be used (regardless of Jominy distances) to estimate the interrelationship among bar diameters and severities of quench.

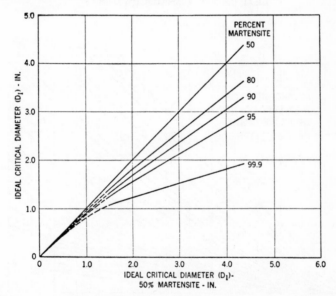

FIG 58 – Average Relationship between Hardenability Based on Higher Percentages of Martensite and 50% Martensite Hardenability (5)

This ideal rate of cooling may be approached closely in practice if ample volumes of water or brine are kept in intimate contact with the surface of the steel by thorough agitation or pressure. Such drastic quenching has certain disadvantages which result from the severe temperature gradients set up during cooling. Water and brine quenching in particular lead to internal stresses which may

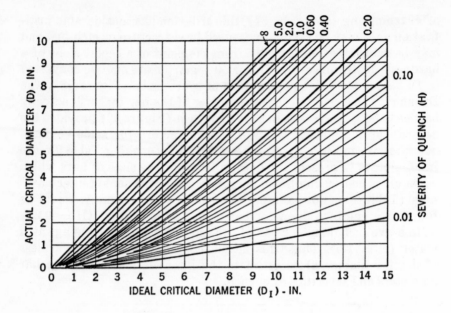

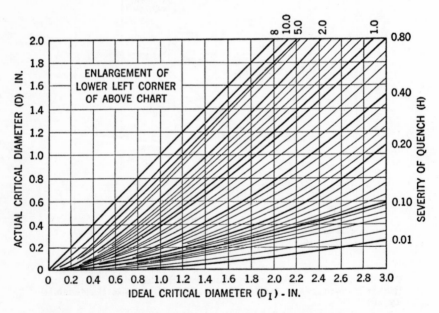

FIG 59 – Relationship between Ideal Critical Diameter (D_I), Actual
Critical Diameter (D) and Severity of Quench (H). D_I represents
the diameter in inches of the section that would harden to 50%
martensite at the center under ideal quenching conditions and D
represents the diameter in inches of the section that does harden to
50% martensite at the center in a quench with a severity of H. (See
Table 9 for typical H values for common quenches) (40)

[74]

TABLE 9
Quench Severity Factors* (41, 42)

	Air	Oil	Water	Brine
No circulation of liquid or agitation of piece...	0.02	0.25 to 0.30	0.9 to 1.0	2
Mild circulation (or agitation)...............	....	0.30 to 0.35	1.0 to 1.1	2.0 to 2.2
Moderate circulation.........................	....	0.35 to 0.40	1.2 to 1.3	....
Good circulation............................	....	0.4 to 0.5	1.4 to 1.5	....
Strong circulation..........................	....	0.5 to 0.8	1.6 to 2	....
Violent circulation..........................	....	0.8 to 1.1	4	5

* commonly called "H" factors; defined as "a heat transfer equivalent consisting of the ratio of heat transfer factor to thermal conductivity, with which heat can be dissipated from the bar to the particular quenching medium; in reciprocal inches" (40)

TABLE 10
Relationship between Jominy Distance and Equivalent Bar Diameters for Various Quenching Media (42)

Distance from Quenched End of Jominy Specimen		Equivalent Bar Diameter* in inches when Quenched in					
sixteenths of an inch	inches	Still Oil H=0.25	Circulated Oil H=0.45	Still Water H=1.0	Circulated Water H=1.5	Still Brine H=2.0	Infinite or Idealized Quench H=∞
1		0.1	0.15	0.3	0.35	0.4	0.7
2	1/8	0.2	0.3	0.5	0.65	0.75	1.15
3		0.35	0.55	0.85	1.0	1.25	1.6
4	1/4	0.5	0.80	1.15	1.3	1.5	1.9
5		0.6	0.95	1.4	1.6	1.75	2.2
6	3/8	0.8	1.2	1.6	1.8	2.0	2.4
7		1.0	1.4	1.8	2.0	2.3	2.7
8	1/2	1.1	1.5	2.1	2.3	2.5	2.9
9		1.3	1.7	2.3	2.5	2.7	3.2
10	5/8	1.4	1.9	2.5	2.7	2.9	3.4
11		1.6	2.1	2.8	3.0	3.2	3.6
12	3/4	1.7	2.2	3.0	3.2	3.4	3.8
13		1.9	2.4	3.2	3.4	3.5	4.0
14	7/8	2.0	2.5	3.3	3.5	3.7	4.2
15		2.1	2.7	3.5	3.7	3.9	4.4
16	1	2.3	2.8	3.7	3.9	4.1	4.6
17		2.4	3.0	3.9	4.1	4.2	4.7
18	1 1/8	2.5	3.1	4.0	4.2	4.4	4.9
19		2.6	3.3	4.1	4.4	4.5	5.0
20	1 1/4	2.7	3.4	4.3	4.5	4.7	5.1
21		2.8	3.5	4.4	4.7	4.8	5.3
22	1 3/8	2.9	3.6	4.5	4.8	4.9	5.4
23		3.0	3.7	4.7	5.0	5.1	5.5
24	1 1/2	3.1	3.8	4.8	5.1	5.2	5.6
25		3.2	4.0	4.9	5.2	5.3	5.8
26	1 5/8	3.3	4.0	5.0	5.3	5.4	5.9
27		3.4	4.1	5.1	5.4	5.5	6.0
28	1 3/4	3.5	4.2	5.2	5.5	5.6	6.1
29		3.6	4.3	5.3	5.6	5.6	6.2
30	1 7/8	3.6	4.4	5.4	5.7	5.7	6.2
31		3.7	4.5	5.5	5.8	5.8	6.3
32	2	3.8	4.5	5.5	5.8	5.9	6.4

* the hardness at the center of a bar of the "equivalent bar diameter", quenched as indicated, is expected to be the same as the hardness at the corresponding distance from the quenched end of a Jominy specimen of the same steel

result in distortion and sometimes in cracking. The common remedy for such difficulties is less rapid cooling, as in oil, molten salt or air. With any given quenching medium, the rate of cooling may be altered greatly by circulation of the medium (see Table 9). For some shapes, controlled quenching in water may be satisfactory or even preferred (see pp 36, 37 for descriptions of the interrupted and delayed quench). Very large parts are generally air cooled rather than liquid quenched. ASTM specification A 237-46, for instance, recommends that no solid forging over ten inches in diameter and no forging over ten inches in wall thickness be liquid quenched.

Many methods have been used to measure the mass effect in individual steels as well as to investigate the comparative contributions to hardenability of the various alloying elements. One of the oldest means of evaluation and, to the engineer at least, one of the most satisfying, is the actual determination of the mechanical properties of specimens from diverse positions in suitably heat treated large bars or parts made of the steel in question. These test results are commonly presented in the form of mass charts indicating the effect of section size on the tensile properties of a specific steel with a specific heat treatment. Figures 60 and 61 show typical mass charts for four steels of varying hardenability, as tempered at 1000 and 1200 F. This method has been used in many countries for large parts designed for critical applications.

The effect of section size on properties is also recognized in the British En specifications. "The En specifications were drawn up on the basic principle—successfully used by the nation for many years— of specifying the mechanical properties to be obtained from the individual steels after stated forms of treatment. . . The specifications also emphasized a factor which, in earlier years, had frequently been ignored, namely that of mass. . . Each specification gives the limiting sizes ('ruling sections') up to which the particular steel, when hardened and tempered within specified temperature limits, can be given certain standard ranges of physical properties." (44) The standard mechanical properties of these En specifications are indicated in Table 11*, and Figure 62 shows graphically the relationship between maximum ruling section and tensile strength for some of the 0.40% carbon En steels. Since the ruling sections are rounds, tables are available (Appendix D) for converting other simple sections to equivalent rounds. In actual engineering parts it is often necessary to consider varying sections. In such cases, approximate equivalent rounds may be obtained from these tables; but more precise values will have to be determined experimentally.

Much of the hardenability data is determined by quenching specimens in water or oil and measuring the hardness either at the center

---

* It should be observed that the properties in Table 11 are not necessarily limited to fully hardened steels. "This work has confirmed the already well-known fact that heat-treated bars in the larger sizes which satisfactorily pass mechanical-test requirements are not fully hardened by oil-quenching, although the as-quenched hardness is adequate. The largest bar diameter of many of the B.S. En steels which can be fully hardened on oil-quenching is surprisingly small and considerably less than the diameters in which the steels are recommended for service." (46)

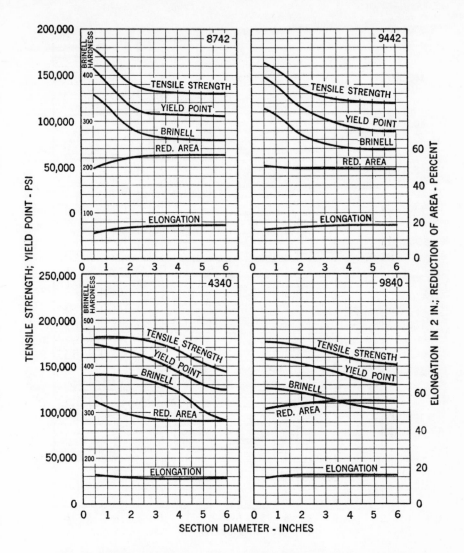

FIG 60 – Effect of Section Size on the Tensile Properties of Four Alloy Steels with about 0.40% Carbon, Oil Quenched and Tempered at 1000 F. In sizes over one inch, the properties represent those at the section midway between the surface and the axis on samples cut longitudinally (43)

Section Range in.	Austenitizing Temperatures, F		
	4340 and 8742	9442	9840
½ to 2	1500 to 1550	1525 to 1575	1525 to 1575
2 to 4	1525 to 1575	1550 to 1600	1550 to 1575
over 4	1550 to 1600	1575 to 1625	1575 to 1625

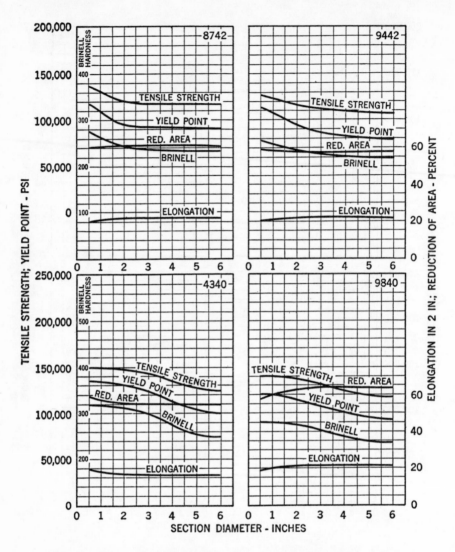

FIG 61 – Effect of Section Size on the Tensile Properties of Four Alloy Steels with about 0.40% Carbon, Oil Quenched and Tempered at 1200 F. In sizes over one inch, the properties represent those at the section midway between the surface and the axis on samples cut longitudinally (43)

Section Range in.	Austenitizing Temperatures, F		
	4340 and 8742	9442	9840
½ to 2	1500 to 1550	1525 to 1575	1525 to 1575
2 to 4	1525 to 1575	1550 to 1600	1550 to 1575
over 4	1550 to 1600	1575 to 1625	1575 to 1625

TABLE 11

En Specified Mechanical Properties for Hardened and Tempered Alloy Steels
with 0.50% Carbon Maximum (45)

Minimum Tensile Strength 1000 psi	Minimum Yield Point* 1000 psi	Minimum Elongation percent**	Minimum Izod Impact ft lb	Brinell Hardness*
78.4	53.8	24	45	152 to 207
89.6	67.2 a	22 b	40 c	179 to 229
100.8	76.2 d	22 b	40 e	201 to 255
112.0	85.1 f	20	40 g	223 to 277
123.2	98.6 h	18 j	40 k	248 to 302
134.4	107.5	17	35	269 to 321
145.6	116.5	16***	35	293 to 341
156.8	129.9	15***	30	311 to 375
168.0	141.1	14***	25	341 to 388
179.2	152.3	14***	25	363 to 415
224.0	190.4	10 m	10 m,n	444 min

* yield point and Brinell values are representative but not to be used for acceptance purposes
** in 2 in. on a 0.564 in. diameter specimen. The test specimens are machined concentrically from bars up to 1¼ in. in diameter. From 1¼ in. up to and including 2½ in., the longitudinal axes of the test specimens are not less than ⅛ in. from the surface of the bars. For sizes over 2½ in. in diameter, the test specimens are taken midway between the center and surface of the bars
*** reduce by two for ruling sections of four inches or over
Notes: Izod values are not applicable to En 41 (Al–Cr–Mo) for sections of 2½ in. or over
Complete composition limits of the En alloy engineering steels in Appendix B
(a) 58.2 for En 15 A, B (C–Mn); 62.7 for En 14 A, B (C–Mn), En 15 (C–Mn)
(b) 20 for En 14 A, B (C–Mn), En 15 (C–Mn) (for 100,800 psi minimum tensile strength), En 15 A, B (C–Mn), En 41 (Al–Cr–Mo)
(c) 25 for En 15 A, B (C–Mn), En 12 (C–Ni) (over four to six inches ruling section), En 15 (C–Mn (over four to six inches ruling section); 30 for En 14 A (C–Mn); 35 for En 12 (C–Ni) (up to four inches ruling section), En 14 B (C–Mn), En 15 (C–Mn) (up to four inches ruling section)
(d) 67.2 for En 14 A, B (C–Mn); 71.7 for En 15 A, B (C–Mn), En 18 (C–Cr), En 21 (C–Ni), En 41 (Al–Cr–Mo)
(e) 25 for En 14 A (C–Mn), En 15 A, B (C–Mn); 30 for En 14 B (C–Mn), En 15 (C–Mn)
(f) 80.6 for En 15 A, B (C–Mn)
(g) 25 for En 15 A, B (C–Mn); 30 for En 15 (C–Mn)
(h) 94.0 for En 15 B (C–Mn), En 41 (Al–Cr–Mo)
(j) 17 for En 41 (Al–Cr–Mo)
(k) 25 for En 15 B (C–Mn); 35 for En 41 (Al–Cr–Mo)
(m) 8 for En 24 (Cr–Mo–Ni)
(n) 15 for En 30 B (Cr–Mo–Ni)

and surface or across the section. A graphic representation of the results is often convenient (Figure 63). The practical value of this type of test is sometimes further increased by tempering the quenched specimens (Figure 64).

The Jominy end-quench test has been generally adopted as a hardenability test for engineering steels* because of its simplicity and general utility. The possibility of determining the effect of a wide range of cooling rates** with a single test specimen has led to the rapid accumulation of a large amount of Jominy hardenability data. Figure 65 shows typical Jominy curves for a number of steels with about 0.40% carbon but widely varying hardenability.

It is feasible to determine the hardenability of each heat so the extent of the heat-to-heat hardenability variation in steel of the same nominal composition can be evaluated. In fact, certain steels ("H" steels) with slightly broader chemical limits than the standard AISI-SAE steels† are supplied to specified minimum and maximum

* The test has also been applied to a certain extent to low alloy tool steels.
** The standard test is applicable to the cooling rates found in quenching sections up to about six inches round. A modified test has been proposed (48) to extend the Jominy hardenability curve to cooling rates corresponding to sections 12 inches in diameter.
† See Appendix A for composition limits.

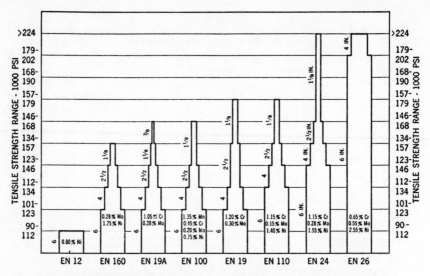

FIG 62 – Maximum Ruling Section – Tensile Strength Relationship for Some of the 0.40% Carbon En Steels. The test specimens are machined concentrically from bars up to 1⅛ in. in diameter. From 1⅛ in. up to and including 2½ in., the longitudinal axes of the test specimens are not less than 9/16 in. from the surface of the bars. For sizes over 2½ in. in diameter, the test specimens are taken midway between the center and surface of the bars. For composition limits see Appendix B (45)

Jominy hardenabilities (so-called hardenability bands) (2). Hardenability bands for four chromium-molybdenum steels are reproduced in Figure 66.

This test has also made it easy to investigate variables such as prior structure and time at austenitizing temperature (Figure 67) and composition (Figure 68). D_I values (see p 72) may be determined from Jominy curves (Figure 69). The field of usefulness of the end-quench hardenability test is sometimes extended by tempering (Figure 70). If either the cooling rate or the as-quenched hardness of a part is known, its tempered hardness can be predicted from the hardness at the corresponding position of the tempered Jominy specimen.

Hardness traverse curves, which many find more comprehensible, may be calculated from Jominy curves (Figure 71). While various other conversions have been suggested, hardness traverse curves calculated by Figure 71 have been found to correlate closely with actual hardness traverses except where the hardness – depth curve is changing rapidly. This correlation obviously applies only when the Jominy test bar truly represents the full cross section of the bars for which the estimates are being made. Figure 72 gives an example of the use of such conversions to present the hardenability of an entire series of steels in terms of the surface, half radius and

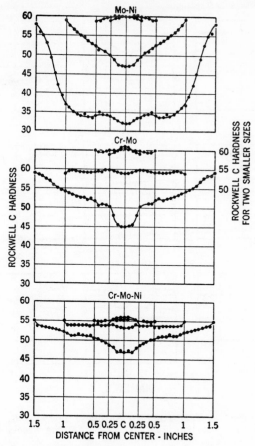

FIG 63 – Hardness Traverse Curves of Oil Quenched 0.40% Carbon
Molybdenum-Containing Steels (47)

	Bar Analyses								McQuaid-Ehn Grain Size
	%C	%Mn	%Si	%P	%S	%Cr	%Mo	%Ni	
Mo–Ni.....	0.46	0.65	0.21	0.014	0.017	....	0.23	1.72	5 to 8
Cr–Mo.....	0.45	0.80	0.16	0.020	0.027	0.94	0.17	....	6 to 8
Cr–Mo–Ni..	0.38	0.64	0.27	0.014	0.017	0.72	0.34	1.72	7 to 8

	Austenitizing Temperatures, F	
	Two Smaller Sizes	Two Larger Sizes
Mo–Ni..	1500	1550
Cr–Mo..	1575	1625
Cr–Mo–Ni..	1500	1550

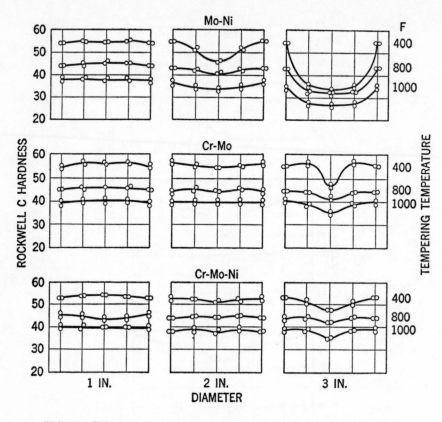

FIG 64 – Effect of Tempering on Hardness Traverse Curves of Oil Quenched 0.40% Carbon Molybdenum-Containing Steels (47)

	Bar Analyses								Austenitizing Temperatures, F	
	%C	%Mn	%Si	%P	%S	%Cr	%Mo	%Ni	one inch	two and three inch
Mo–Ni...............	0.46	0.65	0.21	0.014	0.017	....	0.23	1.72	1500	1550
Cr–Mo...............	0.45	0.80	0.16	0.020	0.027	0.94	0.17	....	1575	1625
Cr–Mo–Ni...........	0.38	0.64	0.27	0.014	0.017	0.72	0.34	1.72	1500	1550

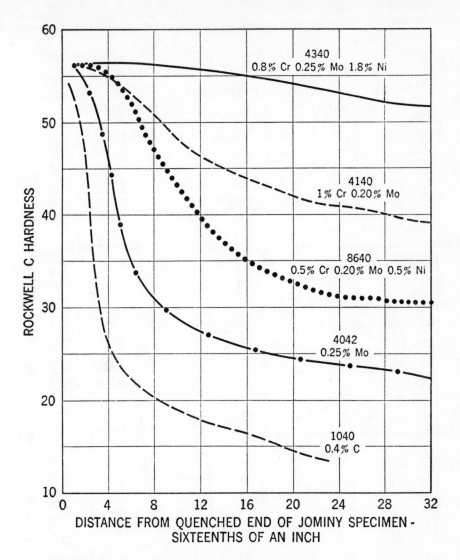

FIG 65 – Jominy End-Quench Hardenability Curves for Various 0.40% Carbon Steels

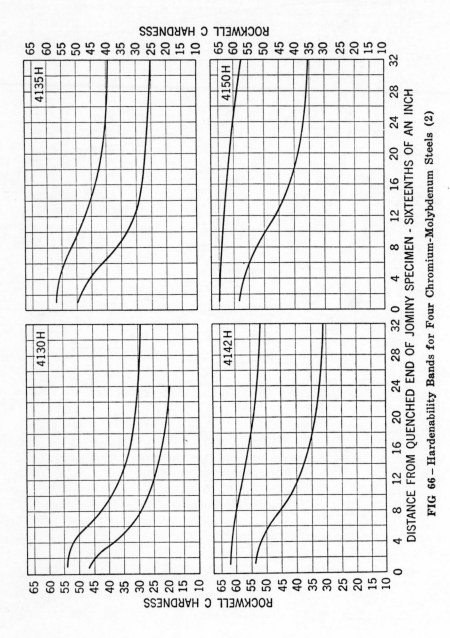

FIG 66 – Hardenability Bands for Four Chromium-Molybdenum Steels (2)

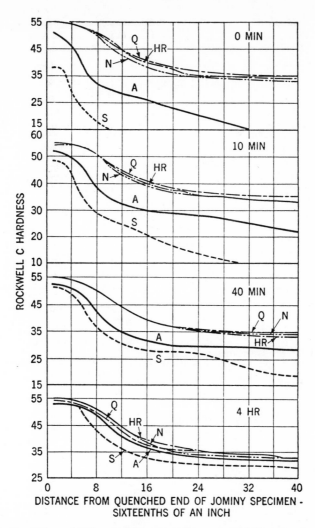

FIG 67 – Effect of Prior Structure and Time at 1525 F on the Jominy End-Quench Hardenability of a Chromium Molybdenum Steel. **Bar** analysis: 0.37% C, 0.74% Mn, 0.29% Si, 0.017% P, 0.023% S, 1.05% Cr, 0.21% Mo, 0.23% Ni (4137) (49)

Curve	Prior Structure	
	Condition	Brinell Hardness
S	spheroidized...	152
A	annealed (lamellar + spheroidized carbides)	170
HR	hot rolled...	331
N	normalized from 1650 F...................................	277
Q	oil quenched from 1550 F...................................	477*

* converted from Rockwell C

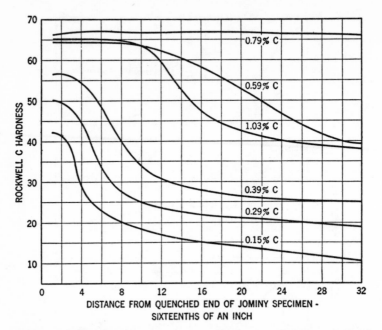

FIG 68 – Effect of Carbon Content on the Jominy End-Quench Hardenability of Molybdenum-Nickel Steels. Base composition: 0.5% Mn, 0.2% Si, 0.2% Cr, 0.25% Mo, 1.7% Ni (4600). Prior condition: air cooled from 1650 F. Austenitizing conditions for end-quench test: 40 min at 1550 F (50)

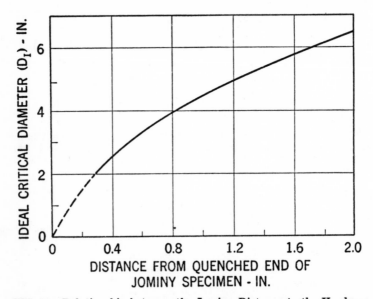

FIG 69 – Relationship between the Jominy Distance to the Hardness Corresponding to the Desired Percentage of Martensite (see Figure 42) and the Diameter of Bar Having the Same Center Hardness with an Ideal Quench (D_I) (51)

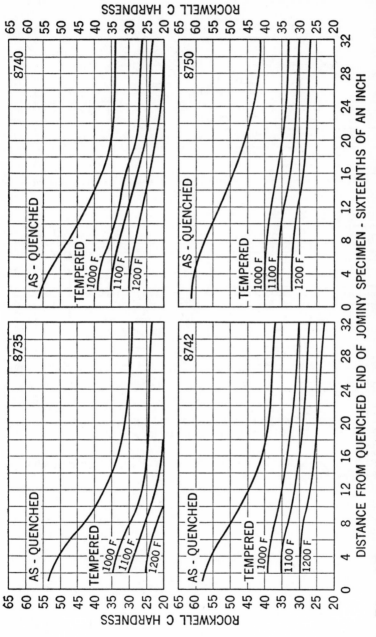

FIG 70 — Effect of Tempering on the Jominy End-Quench Hardenability Curves of Four Chromium-Molybdenum-Nickel Steels (A 8735, A 8740, A 8742, A 8750), End-Quenched from 1550 F. McQuaid-Ehn grain size: 5 to 8 (33)

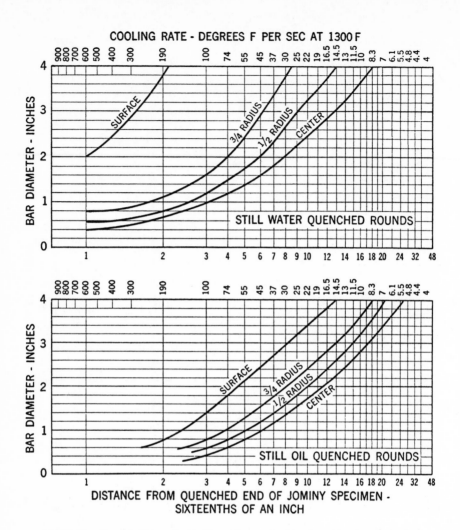

FIG 71 – Correlation of Cooling Rates in Jominy Specimen and Quenched Round Bars (7)

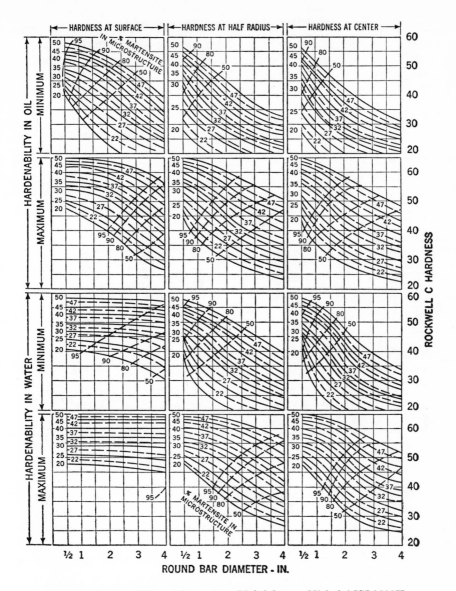

FIG 72--Hardenability of Chromium-Molybdenum-Nickel AISI 8600H Steels, as Converted from Jominy Hardenability Bands. Mean carbon content shown on each curve (52)

center hardness of various size bars. The relationship between Jominy hardenability and the center hardness of quenched bars has also been found reliable enough to serve as the basis of a specification (Table 12).

TABLE 12

Minimum Hardenability to be Specified to Secure Hardness Indicated at Center of Oil Quenched Rounds of 0.40% Carbon Alloy Steels (53)

Type*	Approximate Alloy Content				Distance from Quenched End of Jominy End-Quenched Specimen—sixteenths of an inch	Minimum Rockwell C Hardness to be Specified at						
						6	9	12	14	17	21	26
	Mn %	Cr %	Mo %	Ni %	for the Same Hardness at Center of Oil Quenched Round with Diameter in inches of	1.0	1.5	2.0	2.5	3.0	3.5	4.0
4042 H	0.8	...	0.25	....	....	24	20	..	..	..	..	..
1340 H	1.8	...	....	....⎫								
5140 H	0.8	0.8	....	....⎭	....	37	28	24	23	22	20	..
2340 H	0.8	...	....	3.5⎫								
3140 H	0.8	0.6	....	1.2⎬								
9440 H	1.1	0.4	0.12	0.4⎭	....	40	33	29	27	25	22	21
4640 H	0.7	...	0.25	1.8⎫								
8640 H	0.9	0.5	0.20	0.6⎭	....	43	35	31	29	27	25	24
8740 H	0.9	0.5	0.25	0.6	....	45	37	33	31	29	27	26
4140 H	0.9	1.0	0.20	....	....	47	41	37	35	33	31	30
9840 H	0.8	0.8	0.25	1.0	....	52	50	46	44	42	40	38
4340 H	0.7	0.8	0.25	1.8	....	52	52	50	49	47	45	43

*complete composition limits in Appendix A; it will be noted, however, that all of these compositions are not included in the AISI "H" steel list

Note: The center hardness values in the above table are based on round bars heated to the proper austenitizing temperature, quenched in moderately agitated oil with no tempering

Other correlations have to be used for parts that are not simple rounds. The cooling rates in the Jominy specimen have been correlated experimentally with those in water quenched plates (Appendix D). Also, tables are available for the conversion of rectangular and plate sections to "equivalent rounds" having the same cooling rate when oil quenched and air cooled (Appendix D). With this information, the approximate Jominy distances can be determined from Figure 71. Even these conversions, however, are not applicable to parts that are irregular in shape. In such cases, the hardness traverse curve may be derived from the Jominy curve by means of the substitution of equal hardness for equal cooling rates (32, 54).* Although this method may not be scientifically precise, it has proved useful from a practical engineering standpoint.

* The part in question and a Jominy specimen of the same heat are hardened and the hardness distribution determined. It is then assumed that a specific point in the part has the same cooling rate as the position on the Jominy specimen where the same hardness is found. In this way a correlation can be established for the part in question.

The calculation of hardenability from composition is often expedient, particularly in the formulation of new steels or the comparison of known and unknown grades. No simple method could possibly take into account all the complex factors involved. The Grossmann method (41) has gained wide acceptance as it gives reasonably accurate results ($\pm 20\%$) over a wide range of compositions when used with due consideration of its limitations.* In this method, the steel is considered to have a base hardenability due to its carbon content and grain size (Figure 73). This base hardenability is multiplied by a factor for each alloying element, including manganese and silicon.** There have been various adjustments in the original factors, so the AISI has established standard factors for the common alloying elements (Figure 74).*** The final product of the multiplication is the hardenability, expressed as the ideal critical diameter, D_I, in inches (Table 13). The D_I can be converted to the actual diameter that will harden to 50% martensite at the center in a given quench (Figure 59, p 74) or to D_I values for other percentages of martensite† (Figure 58, p 73) or to the Jominy distance to the critical hardness (Figure 69, p 86). A method is available for extending the calculation to cover the entire Jominy hardenability curve (55, 64).

TABLE 13

Calculation of Ideal Critical Diameter (D_I) from Composition and Grain Size

Element	Percent	Factor	
Carbon..	0.39*	0.195	from Figure 73
Manganese.....................................	0.95	4.17	from Figure 74
Silicon..	0.25	1.18	from Figure 74
Chromium......................................	0.50	2.08	from Figure 74
Molybdenum..................................	0.20	1.60	from Figure 74
Nickel...	0.54	1.20	from Figure 74

* 8 grain size
0.195 x 4.17 x 1.18 x 2.08 x 1.60 x 1.20 = 3.84 in. (D_I)

It should be noted that the first small addition of an element is more effective than subsequent additions. For example, on the basis

---

* These apply mainly to steels containing undissolved carbides as-austenitized (41) and to low hardenability steels with low carbon contents (55). Some discrepancies between actual and calculated hardenabilities have also been encountered with complex high alloy steels and with steels containing substantial amounts of single alloying elements (56, 57, 58, 59).
** The effect of the usual amounts of phosphorus and sulphur is so small that these elements are generally not included in the calculation.
*** Factors are available for other elements. For aluminum, see (41, 60, 61). For antimony, arsenic and beryllium, see (61). For boron, see (41, 51, 60). For cobalt and columbium, see (61). For copper, see (41, 61). For germanium, see (61). For phosphorus and sulphur, see (41). For tellurium and tin, see (61). For titanium, see (60, 61, 62). For vanadium, see (41, 60). For zirconium, see (60).
† The factors for manganese, molybdenum, nickel and silicon are essentially the same on the basis of the three criteria, 99.9, 95 and 50% martensite (63).

[91]

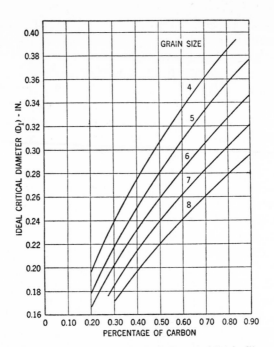

FIG 73 – Relationship between Carbon Content, Grain Size and Hardenability of Pure Iron-Carbon Alloys. The grain size figures apply to the ASTM grain size at the austenitizing temperature, not to McQuaid-Ehn grain size. The hardenability values are valid only when the carbon is completely dissolved in the austenite. Since it becomes increasingly difficult to obtain complete solution above 0.7% C, caution must be exercised in using the values shown above this carbon content (41)

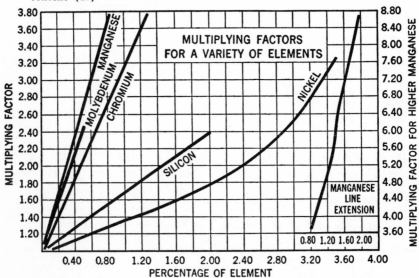

FIG 74 – Multiplying Factors for Chromium, Manganese, Molybdenum, Nickel and Silicon (55)

[92]

of the addition of the first 0.20%, the factor for manganese is 1.67. All steels contain some manganese, however, so the addition is never made to a manganese-free steel. If a content of 0.90% manganese is taken, and an addition of 0.20% manganese is made, then the multiplying factor for this addition is only 1.17. The calculation of the most efficient addition to obtain a given hardenability depends not only on the multiplying factors for each of the elements, but also on the cost of the added alloy and the possible recovery from scrap (65).

Like all calculations, the Grossmann method also requires a certain amount of practical experience for proper evaluation of the results. Some theoretically feasible and attractive steels on paper may be impractical commercially, because of difficulties in melting, processing or fabrication.

Applications

The medium carbon alloy steels are used for a wide variety of machine parts, and most of the standard grades are used for parts of the same sort. Hardenability has been emphasized here because it is the first criterion in the choice of a steel to be quenched and tempered, as are most of the alloy engineering steels.* Other factors are involved in the selection of the most suitable steel from the various grades that have the requisite minimum hardenability for the application. Among these factors are fabricating properties, forgeability, susceptibility to flaking (see pp 37, 38), machinability (see pp 13, 14), weldability, distortion during quenching, hardening practice, and temper brittleness (see pp 4-9). Changes from one grade of alloy steel to another are often made from time to time because of changes in cost factors or improvements in fabricating methods. Hence, any list of specific applications for the various grades of steel would not only be repetitive but might also soon become obsolete.

Nitriding Steels

One group of engineering steels, the nitriding steels, generally in the medium carbon class, is rather unique in composition**, treatment and application. Molybdenum is recognized as a very important constituent of these steels because of its demonstrated ability to increase hardenability and diminish susceptibility to temper brittleness. The latter contribution is particularly significant as the usual

---

* Although a minimum hardenability is required to obtain full hardening and consequently the optimum mechanical properties in any given part, "high hardenability, it should be noted, has no value in itself" (66). Unnecessarily high hardenability usually not only means higher cost of the steel but also might lead to more difficulty in processing and greater susceptibility to temper brittleness.

** The special nitriding steels discussed here are not the only wrought alloy engineering steels that are nitrided. Some of the regular AISI-SAE steels, such as 4130, 4140, 4340, 8630, 8640 and 9440, are also nitrided for improved wear resistance and fatigue properties. The maximum hardness of the nitrided case, however, is appreciably less than is obtained with the aluminum-containing nitriding steels (67).

nitriding temperature (975 F) is in the range most likely to impair the impact properties of steels susceptible to temper brittleness. Likewise, molybdenum additions to nitriding steels are stated to improve the toughness of the case without affecting its hardness. Therefore, all the nitriding steels in common use today contain molybdenum (Table 14).

The general practice is to heat treat the steel prior to nitriding. The hardenability of the steel and the quenching medium used should be chosen with the aim of producing as nearly a fully hardened structure as possible. The presence of free ferrite will have a deleterious effect on the impact strength of the core and will also increase the growth during nitriding and the possibility of spalling after nitriding. The usual heat treatment temperatures are indicated in Table 14. Since the nitriding operation is carried out at about 975 F, the minimum tempering temperature normally used is 1000 F. When the steels are fully hardened, the same approximate relationships are found between hardness and tempering temperature, and hardness and other mechanical properties as are discussed on pp 55-66. Nitrided steels show exceptional resistance to fatigue and low notch sensitivity. These characteristics are sometimes attributed to the development of compressive stresses on the surface (22, 68).

Prior to nitriding, sufficient stock should be removed from the surface to eliminate all decarburization. If this is not done, the nitrided case will be very brittle and will tend to spall in service. The steels may be machined in the annealed condition when a large amount of machining is to be done. However, these steels have such good machinability in the heat treated condition that they are normally machined after quenching and tempering. If a considerable amount of machining has been done after heat treatment, a stabilizing treatment is desirable before nitriding to minimize distortion. The usual treatment is to reheat the rough machined part to about 1000 to 1200 F for one to six hours before final machining. The subsequent distortion during nitriding will be negligible in most cases although slight distortion may occur in some sections because of unequal growth. Allowance must be made for a small growth in nitriding.

The hardness–depth curves of nitrided steels show a gradual transition from the hard surface to the core. The hardness of the case will vary somewhat with the steel. All the steels containing aluminum will give a case hardness of about 1050 to 1150 Diamond Pyramid, except for the 3.5% nickel type which will have a slightly lower case hardness of about 950 to 1050. The case hardness of the steels without aluminum in Table 14 will be approximately 600 to 900 Diamond Pyramid. While the case hardness of the steels containing aluminum

TABLE 14

Compositions and Heat Treatment Temperatures for Nitriding Steels

Nitralloy	Typical Compositions							Annealing*		Hardening	
	%C	%Mn	%Si	%Al	%Cr	%Mo	%Other	cool slowly from F	typical resultant Brinell hardness	quench in	from F
H (125).........	0.25	0.6	0.3	1.0	1.1	0.20	....	1650 to 1700	217	{ water ** / oil **	1700 to 1750
G (135).........	0.35	0.6	0.3	1.0	1.2	0.20	....	1650 to 1700	228	{ water ** / oil	1700 to 1750
EZ.............	0.35	0.8	0.3	1.0	1.2	0.20	0.2 Se	1650 to 1700	228	{ water *** / oil	1700 to 1750
G Modified..... (135 Modified)	0.42	0.6	0.3	1.0	1.6	0.40	....	1650 to 1700	235	oil	1700 to 1750
N.............	0.25	0.6	0.3	1.0	1.2	0.25	3.5 Ni	1500 to 1550†	217	oil	1625 to 1675
Graphitic.......	1.25	0.5	1.3	1.4	0.2	0.25	....	....	...	oil	1625 to 1675
....	0.30	0.5	0.2	...	1.0	1.20	0.6 Ni	1450 to 1500	235	oil	1550 to 1600
....	0.40	0.5	0.2	...	2.0	0.30	....	1450 to 1500	...	oil	1600 to 1650
....	0.15	0.5	0.2	...	3.2	0.55	(0.2 V opt)	1500 to 1550	...	oil	1625 to 1675
....	0.25	0.5	0.2	...	3.2	0.55	(0.2 V opt)	1500 to 1550	238	oil	1625 to 1675
....	0.40	0.6	0.2	...	3.0	0.95	0.2 V	1500 to 1550	...	oil	1650 to 1700

* if a normalizing treatment is desired, as for some forgings, air cool from about 1800 F
** usually water quenched if over one inch round
*** usually water quenched if over two inches round
† steel must be cooled rapidly below 1150 F to avoid rehardening because of precipitation

is substantially independent of the prior heat treatment, that of nitrided steels having chromium as the principal alloying element is affected appreciably by prior treatment (69). There appears to be a constant hardness differential between the core and case hardness of these latter steels, so higher tempering temperatures will result in lower case hardness after nitriding.

Except in the case of the 3.5% nickel steel, nitriding causes little change in the mechanical properties of the core. As shown in Table 15, however, there is a decrease in the elongation and reduction of area of nitrided specimens due to the effect of the nitrided case. The 3.5% nickel steel will precipitation harden during the nitriding operation to give a core hardness of about 415 Brinell. Consequently, the toughness of the core of this steel will decrease during nitriding in proportion to the amount of precipitation hardening.

TABLE 15
Effect of Nitriding on Mechanical Properties (70)

Heat Treatment	Tensile Strength 1000 psi	Yield Point 1000 psi	Elongation percent*	Reduction of Area percent	Izod Impact ft lb
(1)	145.2	142.0	23.5	65.6	88
(2)	146.7	140.7	24.5	63.6	87
(3)	142.5	141.6	11.0	18.4	..

* in 2 in. on a 0.564 in. diameter specimen
Analysis: 0.33% C, 0.87% Cr, 1.03% Mo, 0.65% Ni
Heat Treatment:
   (1) Oil quenched from 1600 F and air cooled from 1240 F
   (2) Oil quenched from 1600 F, air cooled from 1240 F, stabilized by furnace cooling from 1100 F, tinned all over to prevent nitriding and subjected to nitriding process
   (3) Oil quenched from 1600 F, air cooled from 1240 F, stabilized by furnace cooling from 1100 F and nitrided to a depth of 0.02 in.

Nitrided steels are being used in many applications where a hard wear resistant case*, increased fatigue strength, decreased notch sensitivity, and improved corrosion resistance are advantageous. Among these uses are automobile and aircraft crankshafts, aircraft engine cylinders and cylinder liners, pump shafts and dies for molding plastics. The choice of a satisfactory steel depends mainly upon the desired case hardness, the hardenability necessary to avoid free ferrite where possible, and the core strength required to support the nitrided case in service.

Normalized Sheet and Tubing

Although the medium carbon alloy engineering steels are used mainly in the quenched and tempered condition, some have been widely employed in the form of normalized or stress relieved sheet

---

* The presence of about 0.8% graphitic carbon in the graphitic type (see Table 14) as heat treated is said to offer added benefits where lubricated wear resistance is important (71).

and tubing. The 0.3% carbon steels of the 4130 and 8630 types have been particularly popular for applications such as aircraft fuselages. The carbon content in these steels is low enough to permit good weldability while the alloy content confers the required strength for many applications without the necessity of quenching. Naturally, when higher strength is needed, these steels are quenched and tempered.

When normalizing is used, it is often followed by a temper at about 900 F to raise the relatively low as-normalized yield point (Table 16). Stress relieving or subcritical annealing is sometimes preferred as the possibility of scaling and decarburization is minimized at the lower temperatures. Also, some tests have indicated that the ratio of endurance limit to tensile strength is higher for stress relieved than for normalized tubing of this type (73).

TABLE 16

Effect of Tempering on the Tensile Properties of Normalized 4130
and 8630 Tubes (72)

Type	Tube Size in.	Normalized from 1650 F			Tempered at 900 F after Normalizing		
		Tensile Strength 1000 psi	0.2% Offset Yield Strength 1000 psi	Elongation percent*	Tensile Strength 1000 psi	0.2% Offset Yield Strength 1000 psi	Elongation percent*
4130	¾ x 0.035	127.2	66.5	18	113.9	91.0	23
	¾ x 0.035	117.6	76.0	17	112.6	88.5	15
	2¼ x 0.25	103.0	69.2	36	104.2	75.7	37
	2¼ x 0.25	94.6	63.5	43	95.0	63.4	42
8630	½ x 0.037	111.6**	57.0**	20**	100.7†	82.4†	22†
	1 x 0.063	107.9†	60.4†	25†	100.5†	80.3†	26†
	2 x 0.25	95.5**	60.6**	43**	93.2**	68.9**	27**

* in 2 in.
** average of two determinations
† average of four determinations
Note: All stress-strain curves for normalized specimens were smooth, while all curves for normalized and tempered specimens showed a definite break preceded by a slight elongation

LOW CARBON ALLOY ENGINEERING STEELS

Carburizing Steels

One of the first considerations in the selection of a carburizing steel is the attainment of adequate core properties.

The core hardenability may be determined by various means, including most of those outlined on pp 76-80. For example, tensile tests may be made on specimens taken from heat treated bars of various sizes (see, for example, some of the values in Table 17) or hardness traverse curves may be determined (Figure 75). The most widely used method at present, however, appears to be the Jominy end-quench hardenability test (Figure 76). The hardness values expected in various positions of carburized parts may be deduced from the Jominy hardenability curve by the use of Table 10 (p 75),

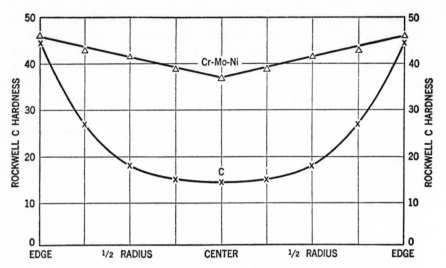

FIG 75 – Hardness Traverse Curves of Two Carburizing Steels. One inch diameter specimens water quenched from 40 to 50 F over the Ac3 (74)

	Bar Analyses						McQuaid-Ehn Grain Size
	%C	%Mn	%Si	%Cr	%Mo	%Ni	
C..........................	0.20	0.48	0.22	0.12	0.02	0.19	7 to 8
Cr–Mo–Ni.................	0.17	0.67	0.25	0.50	0.25	1.73	6 to 8

Figure 71 (p 88) and the other procedures discussed on pp 80, 90. As with medium carbon steels, it must be realized that there will be a certain amount of variation in hardenability from one heat to another of the same grade.

Uniform core hardness in finished parts having varying or heavy sections can be attained by using carburizing steels with relatively high alloy and low carbon contents. The effect of alloy content is illustrated by the hardness traverse curves in Figure 75. It is seen that the alloy steel gives a rather narrow range of hardness throughout the section, whereas the hardness values of the carbon steel drop markedly from the surface to the center. The core hardness of the high alloy steel is thus fairly independent of section thickness, while that of the carbon and, to a lesser degree, low alloy steels is very sensitive to section thickness. When the alloy content of the steel is high enough to insure almost full martensitic hardening, the hardness is determined by the carbon content and approaches the maximum values in Figure 41 (p 56).*

---

* The mechanical property charts for tempered medium carbon alloy martensite are not reliable for low carbon martensite such as may be obtained in the core of carburizing steels.

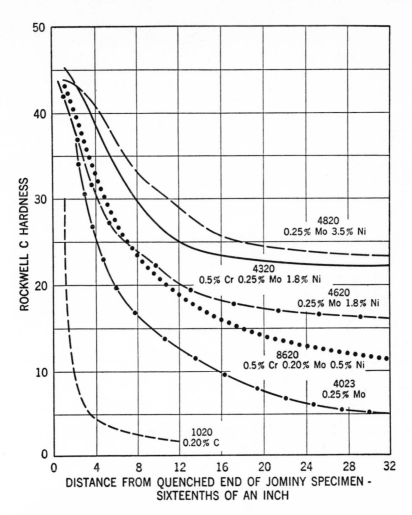

FIG 76 – Jominy End-Quench Hardenability Curves for Various Carburizing Steels

The properties of carburizing steels are conventionally characterized by the mechanical properties of the core after treatments simulating those to be used in practice (Table 17). The carbon content exerts a marked influence on these properties, as shown by Figures 77 and 78. It will be observed that the combination of high strength and high toughness in the core can be obtained only with the higher alloy steels. Higher strengths than those indicated may be obtained in parts, such as gear teeth, where the sections are considerably thinner than those included in Table 17, and Figures 77 and 78.

The resistance of gear teeth to pitting depends on various factors,

TABLE 17

Core Properties of Various Carburizing Steels

Type	%C	%Mn	%Cr	%Mo	%Ni	Heat Treatment* oil quenched from F	tempered at F	Size Treated in.	Tensile Strength 1000 psi	Yield Point 1000 psi	Elongation percent**	Reduction of Area percent	Izod Impact ft lb	BHN	Ref
4023	0.20	0.8	...	0.25	...	pot	325	0.53	170	120†	13	34		311	(75)
	0.22	0.8	...	0.21	...	pot	:::	1.0	114	89	20	55	68	217	:::
						1425		1.0	111	87	18	36	10	228	
						1525		1.0	111	91	19	48	25	217	
"4119"	0.19	0.8	0.5	0.25	...	pot	350	1.0	140	120	18	50	42	300	:
4820	0.17	0.6	0.5	0.25	1.8	pot, 1500	450	0.565	178	142	18	53	29	363	(11)
						1500+, 1425	450	0.565	129	92	19	60	58	262	(11)
	0.20	0.6	0.5	0.25	1.8	pot	300	1.0	180	160	13	52	40	:	(76)
						1425	300	1.0	155	125	12	24	28	:	(76)
						1475	300	1.0	180	160	13	45	42	:	(76)
						1525	300	1.0	185	160	13	52	50	:	(76)
4615	0.17	0.5	0.1	0.28	1.9	pot, 1500	450	0.565	140	124	16	54	48	285	(11)
						1525+, 1475	450	0.565	124	106	18	61	76	255	(11)
	0.15	0.6	...	0.25	1.8	1550+, 1425	450	0.565	124	83	22	61	71	248	(11)
4620	0.20	0.6	...	0.25	1.8	1425	300	1.0	130	90	17	45	25	212	(77)
						1475	300	1.0	130	95	18	52	42		(77)
						1525	300	1.0	135	105	19	55	52		(77)
4815	0.15	0.6	...	0.25	3.5	pot	300	1.0	180	155	17	55	37	:	(76)
						1425	300	1.0	165	140	17	57	40	:	(76)
						1475	300	1.0	155	140	18	60	43	:	(76)
						1525	300	1.0	170	150	17	55	38	:	(76)
4820	0.21	0.5	0.2	0.24	3.5	pot, 1475	300	0.565	205	166	13	53	33	415	(11)
						1500+	300	0.565	208	167	14	52	44	415	(11)
						1450	300	0.565	204	166	14	53	31	415	(11)

TABLE 17 — (Continued)

Type	Compositions					Heat Treatment*		Size Treated in.	Tensile Strength 1000 psi	Yield Point 1000 psi	Elongation percent**	Reduction of Area percent	Izod Impact ft lb	BHN	Ref
	%C	%Mn	%Cr	%Mo	%Ni	oil quenched from F	tempered at F								
4820	0.21	0.5	0.2	0.24	3.5	pot 1475	450	0.565	200	170	13	53	30	401	(11)
						1500+	450	0.565	205	184	13	53	47	415	(11)
						1450	450	0.565	196	172	13	53	29	401	(11)
8620	0.20	0.8	0.5	0.20	0.5	pot	300	0.530	173	142	14	46	53‡	375	(78)
						1525	300	0.530	146	123	15	48	55‡	321	(78)
						1550	300	0.530	144	116	15	49	57‡	311	(78)
8720	0.20	0.8	0.5	0.25	0.5	pot	300	1.0	146	114	16	47	50	321	(78)
						1525	300	1.0	137	103	16	50	53	302	(78)
						1550	300	1.0	133	102	18	53	60	293	(78)
						pot	300	0.530	176	148	13	45	54‡	388	(78)
						1525	300	0.530	147	125	14	46	58‡	331	(78)
						1550	300	0.530	146	119	15	49	61‡	321	(78)
						pot	300	1.0	150	120	16	46	52	321	(78)
						1525	300	1.0	139	107	17	49	54	311	(78)
						1550	300	1.0	136	103	18	51	59	302	(78)
	0.22	0.9	0.5	0.22	0.5	pot 1550	450	0.565	199	166	14	52	23	415	(11)
						1550+	450	0.565	187	162	14	49	28	388	(11)
						1475	450	0.565	130	88	23	58	62	269	(11)
9310	0.11	0.5	1.2	0.11	3.2	pot 1450	300	0.565	180	144	15	59	57	375	(11)
						1475+	300	0.565	173	135	15	60	61	363	(11)
						1425	300	0.565	174	189	15	62	54	363	(11)
						pot 1450	450	0.565	178	146	15	60	46	363	(11)
						1475+	450	0.565	168	138	16	60	39	341	(11)
						1425	450	0.565	170	188	15	62	63	352	(11)
9820	0.20	0.5	1.2	0.11	3.2	1420	300	1.0	180	155	12	45	....	....	(77)
						1470	300	1.0	210	180	12	48	....	....	(77)
						1520	300	1.0	220	185	12	45	....	....	(77)

* all specimens carburized or pseudo-carburized prior to single or double reheat
** in 2 in. on a 0.505 in. diameter specimen
† 0.2% yield strength
‡ treated in 0.894 in. sq

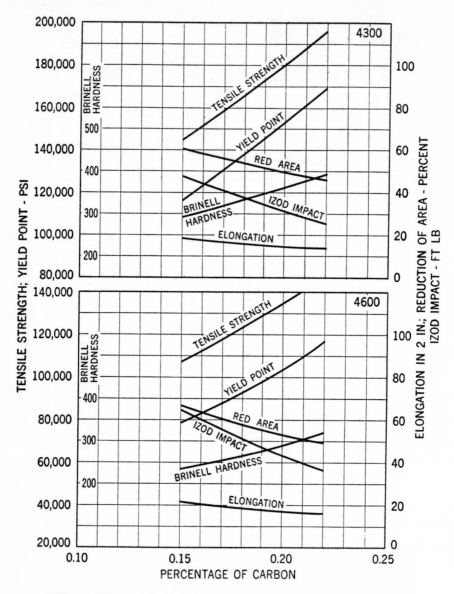

FIG 77 – Effect of Carbon Content on the Core Properties of Direct Quenched 4300 and 4600 Steels. These properties represent the average properties obtained on one inch bars of medium to fine grained steel, pseudo-carburized at 1650 to 1700 F, direct quenched into oil and tempered at 300 F (77)

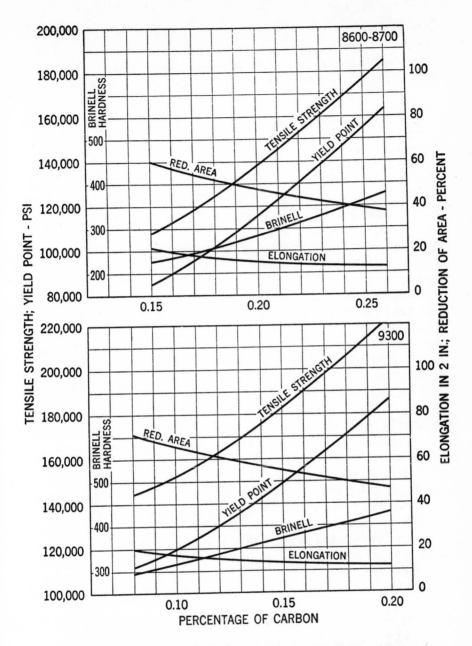

FIG 78 – Effect of Carbon Content on the Core Properties of Direct Quenched 8600-8700 and 9300 Steels. These properties represent the average properties obtained on one inch bars of medium to fine grained steel, pseudo-carburized at 1650 to 1700 F, direct quenched into oil and tempered at 300 F (77)

including accuracy of tooth form, finish, rigidity of mounting and the applied compressive stress. Gear teeth are considered unlikely to fail by pitting in service if the applied compressive stress based on the Hertz formula* does not exceed the following values: (77)

Type	Permissible Compressive Stress — psi
3100, 8600, 8700, "9400"	180,000
2300, 4600, "9900"	200,000
2500, 3300, 4800, 9300	215,000

Any alloy steel that will give the desired core properties will, in general, have adequate case hardenability. It is usually desirable to have a case hardness of about Rockwell C 60. Retained austenite** results in low hardness readings but is not objectionable for certain applications. It is even considered by some to add toughness to the case.

The case hardenability of low alloy carburizing steels, however, may not be adequate to give the required hardness in all instances. This is particularly evident in large parts (80) and in articles quenched in fixtures coming in contact with the part. Low case hardenability not only gives soft spots but may also unduly decrease the residual compressive stresses at the surface.† These stresses are believed by certain investigators to be a major factor in the improved fatigue properties of carburized parts under imposed torsion or bending stresses (22).

The quantitative expression of the hardenability of the case involves several variables including the carbon content of the case, surface removal, and the final temperature from which the part is quenched. A Jominy end-quench hardenability test with a specimen carburized and treated under conditions analogous to those to be used in practice may be employed to determine the hardenability of the carburized case (Figure 79). Although carburizing steels with high core hardenability generally have high case hardenability, the comparative hardenability rating is not always the same, because the higher carbon does not have an identical effect on the harden-

---

* Permissible compressive stress $= \sqrt{\dfrac{PE \, (1 + \rho)}{1.75 \, Df \sin 2\theta}}$

    where P = tangential force at the pitch circle in lb
        E = modulus of elasticity (30,000,000 psi for steel)
        ρ = ratio between the numbers of teeth in the gear and pinion
        D = pitch diameter of the gear in in.
        f = face width in in.
        θ = pressure angle
    The permissible stresses given assume good carburizing and heat treatment practice, adequate case depth and absence of carbide network. Core carbon content, section thickness and quenching technique can influence these stresses appreciably (77).
** It is possible to use subzero treatments to complete the transformation of this austenite and thus increase the case hardness (79).
† Because of the higher carbon content and lower Ar″ temperature, the martensite formed in the carburized layer has a greater specific volume than that formed in the core, thus promoting surface compressive stresses (68).

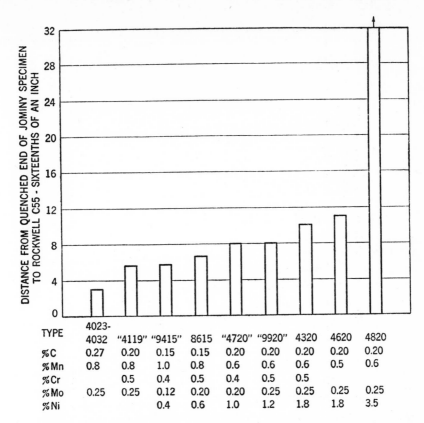

FIG 79 – Case Hardenability of Various Carburizing Steels. Jominy end-quench hardenability test specimens carburized at 1700 F for eight hours, quenched in oil, reheated to 1480 F and end-quenched in water; 0.008 in. removed from surface before hardness tests. McQuaid-Ehn grain size 5 to 8 (81)

TYPE	4023-4032	"4119"	"9415"	8615	"4720"	"9920"	4320	4620	4820
%C	0.27	0.20	0.15	0.15	0.20	0.20	0.20	0.20	0.20
%Mn	0.8	0.8	1.0	0.8	0.6	0.6	0.6	0.5	0.6
%Cr		0.5	0.4	0.5	0.4	0.5	0.5		
%Mo	0.25	0.25	0.12	0.20	0.20	0.25	0.25	0.25	0.25
%Ni			0.4	0.6	1.0	1.2	1.8	1.8	3.5

ability of all compositions. Also, the hardenability of the case of any specific type steel is unaffected by the carbon content of the core, although the latter has a marked effect on the core hardenability. The change in case hardenability with reheating temperature, which is of considerable practical importance, is illustrated in Figure 80.

Carburizing and Heat Treatment Practices. Normal carburizing practices may be employed with all the AISI-SAE steels listed in Appendix A. The required depth and structure of the case are generally determined on the basis of experience or service tests on finished parts. High carbon concentrations — even as high as 2.5% — may be found at the surface of some carburized steels containing chromium. This high carbon content and the resultant free carbides give a case of very high wear resistance, but such high carbon cases cannot be employed in some applications because of their rather low

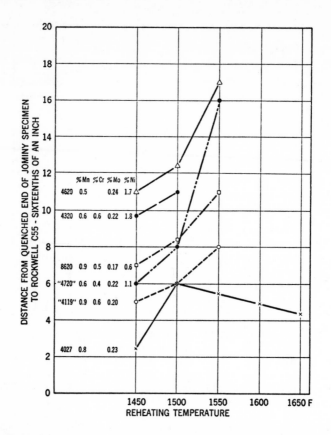

FIG 80 – Effect of Reheating Temperature on Case Hardenability of Various Carburizing Steels. Jominy end-quench hardenability test specimens carburized at 1680 F for eight hours, quenched in oil, reheated to indicated temperature and end-quenched in water; 0.008 in. removed from surface before hardness tests. McQuaid-Ehn grain size 5 to 8 (81)

resistance to chipping and spalling. Lower carbon cases may be obtained on such steels by the use of special solid carburizing media (such as the coke with 15% barium discussed by (82)) or by a diffusion treatment.

Various combinations of heat treatments are possible with carburized parts. Of these, the direct quench ("pot quench") and single reheat methods are the most popular while the double reheat method is seldom used in the U.S.A. Tempering temperatures for all methods range from 200 to 450 F.

A direct quench from the carburizing operation has the advantages of simplicity and economy. It also avoids any possible decarburization such as frequently occurs during slow cooling after carburizing. It will generally give the maximum core hardness as well as prevent the precipitation of carbides in high carbon cases. Steels with a high content of alloying elements that depress the Ar'' temperature may have so much retained austenite in the case after a pot quench that they will be unacceptable for many applications. Even moderately alloyed steels may retain too much austenite to be suitable for some applications where scuffing is a factor. If the temperature of the part is uniform before quenching, the distortion will probably be less than with a single or double reheat. Modifications of this method involve equalization of the temperature, or air cooling to just above the upper critical temperature, before quenching. Both minimize distortion while the latter reduces austenite retention.

The single reheat method is widely used, particularly where it is impracticable to direct quench. It is also chosen for many parts, such as transmission and ring gears, where it is desirable to quench in a press or fixture to decrease distortion.* In this method, the carburized steel is cooled from the carburizing treatment, reheated and quenched. The steel may be oil quenched or slowly cooled from

TABLE 18

Typical Applications of Various Carburizing Steels

Type	Approximate Alloy Content			Applications
	%Cr	%Mo	%Ni	
....	...	0.25	...	(rimmed steel) cross chains for tires
4017	...	0.25	...	drag length balls and steering knuckle pivot pins for passenger automobiles
4023, 4024	...	0.25	...	automobile countershafts, inside differential gears, spline gears, transmission shafts
4027, 4028	...	0.25	...	pinions, pinion shafts, ring and side gears and spline shafts for light trucks and passenger automobiles
4032	...	0.25	...	transmission gears and transmission drive pinions for passenger automobiles; light gears for trucks
4317, 4320	0.5	0.25	1.8	airplane camshafts, cam gears, chain pins, gudgeon pins, heavy duty gears and worms, pinions, rear axle gears and pinions, roller bearing races and rollers for heavy railroad bearings, spider forgings for heavy duty trucks, supercharger gears
4615 to 4621	...	0.25	1.8	camshafts, differential axles for trucks, free wheeling cams, gears, gudgeon pins, pinions, ring gears, rock bit cutters, roller bearing races and rollers for passenger automobiles, shafts, spider forgings for passenger automobiles, sprockets, sucker rod couplings; higher carbon contents are used for heavier sections
4812 to 4820	...	0.25	3.5	chain pins, differential axles for trucks, free wheeling shells, gears, piston rods, rock bit cutters, roller bearings, spider forgings for heavy duty trucks, steering knuckle pins; higher carbon contents are used for heavier sections
8615 to 8622	0.5	0.20	0.5	gears, pins; higher carbon contents are used for heavier sections
8720	0.5	0.25	0.5	gears, pins
9310 to 9317	1.2	0.12	3.2	aircraft gears and pinions; higher carbon contents are used for heavier sections

* Such quenching procedures are apt to involve air cooling for a variable period of time before the part can be placed in the fixture and immersed in the quenching bath. Therefore, molybdenum steels are often selected because of the retarding effect of the molybdenum on the formation of proeutectoid ferrite and pearlite.

the carburizing treatment. Oil quenching is favored for steels with a very high carbon, hypereutectoid case as slow cooling will cause the excess carbides to form a network which is hard to re-dissolve. Slow cooling, however, gives less distortion. The reheating temperature may be any temperature from just over the Ac1 temperature of the case to just over the Ac3 temperature of the core. The last is the most common practice. The higher the reheating temperature, the better are the strength and toughness of the core, but the greater is the possibility of retained austenite in high alloy steels. Excessive austenite retention in high alloy hypereutectoid cases is sometimes minimized by a preliminary treatment at around 1200 F prior to reheating for hardening.

The double reheat treatment involves quenching from just above the Ac3 temperature of the core followed by quenching from just above the Ac1 temperature of the case. Since the general adoption of steels with a fine McQuaid-Ehn grain size, this treatment is rarely used.

Applications. It is impossible to give an all-inclusive summary of the applications of the various carburizing steels because—in addition to the type of part—service conditions, economics and section are involved. Table 18, however, shows a few typical uses of some of the carburizing steels.

Sucker Rods

The low carbon molybdenum-nickel steels of the 4600 and 4800 types (frequently with slight modifications in composition) are also used uncarburized for oil well sucker rods. These steels are preferred to unalloyed rods where corrosive conditions are severe, or in deep wells where their higher yield point and tensile strength are valuable. The usual treatment is a normalize from about 1600 to 1650 F with a temper at 1000 to 1200 F (Table 19). As indicated by Table 20, the molybdenum-nickel steel has a greater endurance limit, under corrosive conditions such as might exist in an oil well, than carbon steel of approximately the same tensile strength. The 0.25% molybdenum – 3.5% nickel composition is advocated especially for wells producing severely corrosive oils with high sulphide contents.

TABLE 19
Typical Compositions and Mechanical Properties of Steels for Oil Well Sucker Rods (Normalized and Tempered Condition)

Compositions					Tensile Strength 1000 psi	Yield Point 1000 psi	Elongation percent in		Reduction of Area percent	Izod Impact ft lb
%C	%Mn	%Si	%Mo	%Ni			2 in.	8 in.		
0.20	0.70	0.25	0.25	1.80	85	70	38	20	65	95
0.16	0.50	0.25	0.25	3.50	90	75	38	20	70	100

TABLE 20
Effect of Corrosive Conditions on the Endurance Limit of Carbon
and Molybdenum-Nickel Steels for Sucker Rods (83)

	C	Mo–Ni
Analysis:		
% Carbon	0.37	0.18
% Manganese	0.83	0.51
% Silicon	0.11	0.23
% Phosphorus	0.018	0.012
% Sulphur	0.033	0.006
% Molybdenum	.....	0.24
% Nickel	.....	1.57
Heat Treatment	none	1600 F air cool
Mechanical Properties:		
Tensile Strength, psi	88,500	91,300
Yield Point, psi	55,500	53,200
Elongation, percent*	31.3	28.0
Reduction of Area, percent	56.4	55.7
Brinell Hardness Number	169	185
Endurance Limit (Rotating Beam):		
(1) In Air, psi	40,600	48,600
(2) In Oil Well Brine in Absence of Air, psi	24,600	33,100
(3) In Oil Well Brine, Saturated with Hydrogen Sulphide Gas, in Absence of Air, psi	10,600	19,900
Ratio of Endurance Limit to Tensile Strength:		
(1) In Air	0.46	0.53
(2) In Oil Well Brine in Absence of Air	0.28	0.36
(3) In Oil Well Brine, Saturated with Hydrogen Sulphide Gas, in Absence of Air	0.12	0.22

* in 2 in. on a 0.505 in. diameter specimen

Chains

Heavy chain, as for dredge, sling and billet chains, represents another application where low carbon steels are used in the uncarburized condition. The most popular of the various steels being used are 4615, 4620 and 8620. All the fittings (hooks, joining links and rings) are generally made of the same steel as the chain links proper. The entire unit is then heat treated by water quenching from above the upper critical temperature. Alloy steel chain offers various advantages over unalloyed steel or wrought iron. The strength of the alloy chain is appreciably higher, thus permitting the use of less bulky chains or higher loads for the same size chain. An additional advantage in the case of chains that may be subjected to elevated temperatures in service is that the alloy steels retain their strength better under such conditions than do the wrought iron and unalloyed steel.

Low Alloy High Strength Steels

These steels have been called by various terms, such as low alloy high tensile, low alloy structural and low alloy constructional. They are characterized by low carbon contents to provide for good forming and welding properties and by the use of suitable alloying elements to give a high yield point and tensile strength as compared with carbon steels. The low alloy high strength steels were developed primarily to meet the needs of the transportation industry. The compositions of some of these steels are such that their corrosion resistance is about four to six times that of carbon steel in normal atmospheric service. A number of different types containing molybdenum are being produced in this category (Table 21).

TABLE 21
Low Alloy High Strength Steels

Chemical Compositions*										Mechanical Properties of Hot Rolled Sheet and Plate up to ½ in. thick			Ref
C %	Mn %	Si %	P %	S %	Cr %	Cu %	Mo %	Ni %	Other %	Tensile Strength 1000 psi	Yield Point 1000 psi	Elongation percent	
0.12 max	0.50 to 1.00	.....	0.04 max	0.05 max	.....	0.50 to 1.00	0.10 min	0.50 to 1.10	.....	70 min	50 min	22 **(a) min	(84)
0.30 max	0.50 to 1.00	.....	0.04 max	0.04 max	.....	0.50 to 1.50	0.10 min	0.50 to 1.25	.....	90 min	70 min	15 ** min	(85)
0.20 max	1.25 max	0.30 max	0.10 max	0.05 max	.....	0.60 max	0.10 max (b)	1.00 max	.....	65 to 80	50 min	(c)	(86)
0.12 max	0.15 to 0.40	0.35 to 0.75	0.08 to 0.15	0.05 max	.....	0.35 to 0.60	0.16 to 0.28	.....	.....	70 min	50 min	22 **(a) min	(84)
0.10 to 0.18	0.60 to 0.75	0.65 to 0.90	0.04 max	0.04 max	0.50 to 0.65	0.25 max	0.15 max (d)	0.10 to 0.25	0.10 to 0.15 Zr	76	52	27***	(87)
0.12 max	0.50 to 0.90	0.15 max	0.05 to 0.12	0.05 max	.....	0.95 to 1.30	0.08 to 0.18	0.45 to 0.75	0.12 to 0.27 Al	70 min	55 min	20*** min	(88)
0.16	1.09	.....	.....	.....	0.07	.....	0.26	0.45	.....	88	64	16***	(89)

* producers may adjust the composition depending on the gage and the application to obtain the desired mechanical properties
** in 2 in.
*** in 8 in.
(a) does not apply on thicknesses under ³⁄₁₆ in.
(b) usually about 0.08% Mo present
(c) 1,500,000 min in 8 in.; for thicknesses under ¹⁄₁₆ in., 25% min in 2 in.
    $$\frac{}{TS}$$
(d) usually about 0.10% Mo present

Most of these steels are furnished in the hot rolled or hot rolled and tempered condition. A majority of the compositions can be welded with no precautions other than those that would be necessary for carbon steels. Stress relieving may be desirable in complex structures. Since the strength of the high copper steels can be increased by precipitation hardening, this strengthening is often expeditiously combined with stress relieving after fabrication (Table 22).

In general, a weight saving of about 25% can be realized by the use of these low alloy high strength steels in place of ordinary carbon steels. Typical applications, primarily in the form of sheets, plates

TABLE 22
Stress Relieved Properties of High Copper Steels

C %	Mn %	Si %	P %	S %	Al %	Cu %	Mo %	Ni %	Condition	Tensile Strength 1000 psi	Yield Point 1000 psi	Elongation percent*	Ref
0.10	0.69	0.07	0.092	0.027	0.16	1.09	0.15	0.63	as rolled +4 hr 1000 F	76.1 87.8	56.9 70.8	45.8 34.0	(90) (90)
0.16 max	0.60 to 0.90	....	0.04 max	0.04 max	....	0.90 to 1.10	0.20 to 0.30	1.30 to 1.60	as rolled +4 hr 1100 F	135 max	70 min	....	(91)

* in 2 in.

and structural shapes, are underframes and sheathing of railroad passenger cars, freight car bodies, automobile bumper face bars, dump wagons and truck bodies.

Copper-molybdenum ingot iron may be considered with this class although its strength is appreciably lower (Table 23). It resembles the other types in having a resistance to atmospheric attack superior to that of mild carbon steel (93). The small molybdenum content is said to make effective the addition of more copper than is normally used in molybdenum-free iron (92) and to increase the corrosion resistance (94).

TABLE 23
Mechanical Properties of Copper-Molybdenum Ingot Iron (92)

Typical Composition: 0.03% C, 0.12% Mn, 0.005% Si, 0.45% Cu, 0.07% Mo
Typical Mechanical Properties:

Tensile Strength, psi	50,000
Yield Point, psi	35,000
Elongation, percent*	35
Reduction of Area, percent	65

* in 2 in. on a 0.505 in. diameter specimen

HIGH CARBON ALLOY ENGINEERING STEELS

The foremost use of these steels is for springs and torsion bars.* Hardenability is again important because experience has shown that fully hardened springs have the maximum resistance to taking a permanent set (sagging) in service.

The silicon-manganese spring steels have better hardenability than carbon spring steels, but ". . . they are peculiarly subject to decarburization and are inclined to have excessive quantities of non-metallic inclusions, thus requiring extra processing of billets. . . . Such extra processing is not always carried out, with the result that seamy material is produced and sometimes escapes detection." (95) In view of the increasing recognition by the users of springs that fatigue

---

* Molybdenum is also used in high carbon steels for other types of applications. For example, 0.2 to 0.8% molybdenum is added to the larger sizes of 52100 bearing steel to improve the hardenability. Likewise, molybdenum is frequently present in forged, high carbon, wear resistant steels, as in crusher rolls which may contain 0.7% carbon, 0.7% manganese, 1.5% chromium, 0.3% molybdenum and 0.7% nickel.

strength is decreased significantly by the presence of surface defects such as decarburization and seams, the reason for the trend to superior spring materials is evident. Prominent among these are the 4000 and 8600 types.

The molybdenum steels (4063 and 4068) have been used for some time in springs of relatively light section, especially leaf and coil springs for passenger automobiles. The chromium-molybdenum-nickel steels (8650, 8655 and 8660) have come into use in the past few years for heavy leaf and coil springs such as those in heavy trucks, tractors, road machinery and railroad passenger cars. To quote a recent article "its use (the 8650-8660 type) is increasing among some of the larger users of heavy springs. . . . It appears, in the light of our present knowledge, to be the best low alloy steel for heavy springs." (95)

These two types of molybdenum steels offer numerous advantages over the silicon-manganese steels. They have better surface quality with greater freedom from defects such as seams, inclusions and decarburization. The ductility and toughness characteristics for a given hardness and tensile strength are higher (Tables 24 and 25). They have equal hardenability or, in the case of the chromium-molybdenum-nickel steel, considerably greater hardenability (Figure 81). The austenitizing temperatures are lower, which is desirable from the standpoint of decreased scale formation, decarburization and distortion.

TABLE 24

Comparative Mechanical Properties of Molybdenum and Silicon-Manganese Spring Steels

	Mo	Si–Mn
Chemical Composition:		
% Carbon	0.75	0.63
% Manganese	0.80	0.82
% Silicon	0.36	1.94
% Chromium	0.09	0.14
% Molybdenum	0.25	0.03
% Nickel	0.10	0.14
Heat Treatment:*		
Oil Quenched from	1480 F	1600 F
Tempered two hours at	920 F	960 F
Mechanical Properties:		
Tensile Strength, psi	208,100	205,100
0.2% Offset Yield Strength, psi	193,200	184,900
Proof Strength (0.01% permanent set), psi	169,100	168,300
Elongation, percent**	12.0	12.5
Reduction of Area, percent	36.0	30.8
Rockwell C Hardness	43.3	43.2
Charpy Impact (V notch), ft lb		
75 F	13.9	9.2
0 F	11.5	7.9
−40 F	9.7	4.9
−90 F	8.9	3.4

* tensile specimens heat treated in 0.525 in. gage section; impact specimens heat treated in ½ in. section
** in 2 in. on a 0.505 in. diameter specimen

TABLE 25

Comparative Mechanical Properties of Chromium-Molybdenum-Nickel and Silicon-Manganese-Chromium Spring Steels

	Cr–Mo–Ni	Si–Mn–Cr
Composition Limits of Heats:		
% Carbon	0.51 to 0.60	0.58 to 0.72
% Manganese	0.80 to 1.00	0.90 to 1.18
% Silicon	about 0.80	1.96 to 2.25
% Phosphorus	0.015 to 0.028	0.012 to 0.031
% Sulphur	0.014 to 0.033	0.021 to 0.034
% Chromium	0.42 to 0.54	0.32 to 0.44
% Molybdenum	0.18 to 0.27	....
% Nickel	0.46 to 0.64	....
Number of Heats Tested	11	18
Heat Treatment:*		
Oil Quenched from	1500 to 1550 F	1600 F
Tempered at	925 to 1000 F	1025 to 1080 F
Mechanical Properties (average):		
Tensile Strength, psi	183,000	193,000
0.2% Offset Yield Strength, psi	161,000	157,000
Elongation, percent**	15	13.2
Reduction of Area, percent	48	27
Charpy Impact, ft lb***	30.0	16.1†
Rockwell C Hardness on impact specimen	42	40.7

* heat treated in test specimen size. Si–Mn–Cr test specimens were left in oil only 60 sec for the tensile specimens and 30 sec for the impact specimens
** in 2 in. on a 0.505 in. diameter specimen
*** on a Charpy impact specimen, 0.394 x 0.630 in with a keyhole notch
† average of six heats only

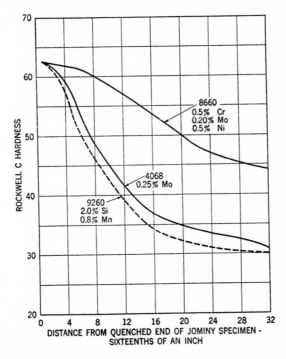

FIG 81 – Jominy End-Quench Hardenability Curves for Various Spring Steels

Table 26, based upon the opinions of competent spring makers and users, gives a schedule of limiting spring sections for various steels. It applies to average spring hardening practices. Experience in individual shops may indicate slightly different limiting sections in accordance with local conditions.

TABLE 26
Suggested Schedule of Maximum Sections for Various Spring Steels

Type	Type Compositions							Limiting Sections—in.	
	%C	%Mn	%Si	%Cr	%Mo	%Ni	%V	rounds	flats
4068	0.68	0.85	0.25	....	0.25	....	....	1	5/16
9260	0.60	0.85	2.00	....	....	....	....	1	5/16
9261	0.60	0.85	2.00	0.20	....	....	....	1¼	3/8
8650	0.50	0.85	0.25	0.50	0.20	0.55	....	1⅜	7/16
6152	0.52	0.80	0.25	0.95	....	....	0.10**	1½	½
9262	0.60	0.85	2.00	0.35	....	....	....	1⅝	7/8
8660	0.60	0.85	0.25	0.50	0.20	0.55	....	1¾	1
"8662"*	0.62	0.85	0.25	0.50	0.20	0.55	....	1⅞	1⅜

* "8662" is not yet a standard composition but is numbered according to the AISI–SAE system
** minimum

The impact properties in Tables 24 and 25 are especially note-worthy*, since some spring failures have been associated with low notched bar impact values. It will be noted that the impact of the chromium-molybdenum-nickel steel is nearly twice that of the silicon-manganese steel. In Table 24**, the superior toughness of the molybdenum steel is again outstanding, particularly the better retention of toughness at low temperatures. These low temperature impact values mean good toughness under severe service conditions at room temperature (pp 3, 4) as well as at the low temperatures which might be encountered in vehicles operating in winter.

LOW TEMPERATURE PROPERTIES

A major factor in the selection of a steel for low temperature service is its toughness at the temperature in question, because hardness and strength† increase as the temperature decreases. While it is generally recognized that low temperatures are apt to lead to brittle failures, it is not so widely appreciated that the actual temperature at which this occurs depends upon several factors, some

---

* In some cases, better toughness values are obtained in high carbon steels at hardnesses over about Rockwell C 48 by austempering than by conventional quenching and tempering. This treatment is generally limited to light sections. Austempered springs, however, have a lower fatigue life than quenched and tempered or martempered springs (96).
** The carbon content of the molybdenum steel in Table 24 is appreciably higher than that of the present 4068 type which has 0.63 to 0.70% carbon. This makes its superior ductility and toughness all the more significant.
† This applies to the strength as determined on the usual unnotched test specimens. The "notch strength", measured by tensile tests on circumferentially notched specimens, is affected by temperature in the same way as is the impact value. Notch strength-test temperature curves show a transition temperature (97) and are similar in appearance to the schematic diagram of Figure 2 (p 3).

mechanical (presence and type of notch, rate and type of loading, transverse constraint — shape, size — and direction of loading relative to direction of rolling) and some metallurgical (melting practice, composition, microstructure and embrittlement, particularly temper brittleness). Furthermore, there is often a marked individuality among heats of the same composition with the same thermal treatment (98). This difference among supposedly duplicate heats is particularly noticeable at temperatures below –100 F. Therefore, it is impractical to discuss low temperature properties of engineering steels from the standpoint of the exact impact properties likely to be found with a specific composition at a specific temperature. Instead, brief consideration will be given to some general principles that affect low temperature toughness.

Some of the mechanical factors have already been discussed (pp 2-4). The presence and type of notch have a great bearing on the temperature at which the transition from a ductile to brittle fracture occurs (Figure 82). Even with a specific type of specimen, however,

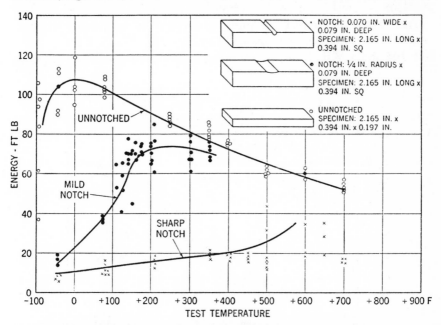

FIG 82 – Effect of Shape of Piece and Testing Temperature on Energy Absorbed in Breaking Specimens (26)
Composition of Steel: 0.52% C, 0.85% Mn, 0.24% Si, 0.016% P, 0.023% S, 1.01% Cr, 0.14% Cu, 0.20% Mo, 0.06% Ni
Heat Treatment: oil quenched from 1600 F, tempered at 400 F

there is no exact impact level at which the fracture changes sharply from tough to brittle. The amount of transverse constraint (determined by the size and shape of the part) and manner of loading have a pronounced influence on the possibility of a brittle fracture in service. A part may, therefore, show a brittle fracture in service even though the steel gives a tough fracture in an impact test at the same temperature. The reverse may also be true. The tendency towards brittleness shown by impact tests is not revealed by unnotched tensile tests. For example, the transition temperature of steels with a pearlitic structure is generally in the range from –150 to +210 F, but these steels usually do not break in a brittle manner in a tensile test until the temperature has dropped to around –310 F (99). Since notched bar impact tests rarely duplicate service conditions, it is clear that low temperature impact tests, while valuable in some respects, serve only as a qualitative rather than a quantitative guide to the suitability of steel for low temperature service. By the same token, low temperature impact tests may also be useful as an indication of room temperature toughness under severe conditions of loading (31). Similarly, the toughness at low temperatures (as determined in a slow bend test on a notched, welded specimen) has been used as a criterion of weldability since "the essence of the weldability problem is ductility of the weldment". (100)

The important effect of microstructure on toughness at low temperature has been emphasized recently (24, 31, 36, 99, 101, 102, 103, 104, 105). All other factors being equal, the transition tempera-

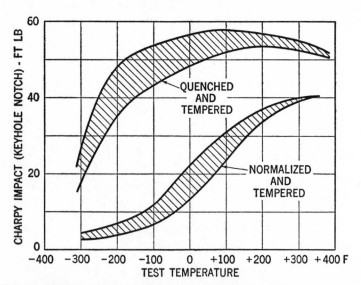

FIG 83 – Effect of Heat Treatment on the Low Temperature Impact Properties of a Chromium-Molybdenum-Nickel Steel (101)

Bar Analysis: 0.36% C, 0.70% Mn, 0.30% Si, 0.011% P, 0.028% S, 0.023% Al, 0.018% Al₂O₃, 0.66% Cr, 0.38% Mo, 1.71% Ni

McQuaid-Ehn Grain Size: 7 to 8

Thermal Treatment: (0.42 in. sq)
  Quenched and Tempered: oil quenched from 1525 F, tempered one hour at 1200 F. Rockwell C Hardness 29 to 30
  Normalized and Tempered: air cooled from 1525 F, tempered one hour at 1000 F. Rockwell C Hardness 31 to 33

ture of a steel is lowered as the structure is changed from coarse pearlite through tempered bainite to tempered martensite. Therefore, quenching and tempering gives better low temperature impact properties than normalizing and tempering* (Figure 83), and normalizing and tempering gives superior properties to annealing. The transition temperature of tempered martensite depends to a certain degree on hardness; harder specimens show no transition temperature on the temperature-impact curve but rather a gradual decrease of impact values with decreasing temperature (Figure 84). The harder specimens do, however, have a transition temperature range as evidenced by a change from ductile to brittle fractures.

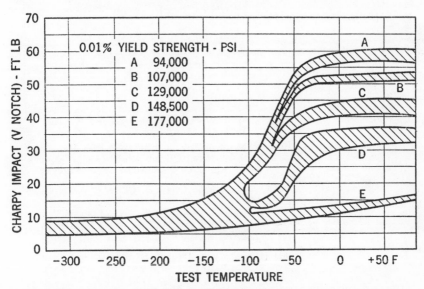

FIG 84 – Effect of Hardness of Tempered Martensite on the Low Temperature Impact Properties of a 0.45% Carbon Steel Containing Chromium, Molybdenum and Vanadium (99)

Incomplete hardening, resulting in the presence of bainite, pearlite, or proeutectoid ferrite in addition to martensite, moves the transition towards higher temperatures (Figure 85). Pearlite causes a greater change than bainite, while bainite formed at higher temperatures appears to be more harmful than bainite formed at lower temperatures. Therefore, the importance of using a steel that will harden fully in the section to be heat treated is clear. The efficacy of molybdenum in increasing hardenability economically has already been covered (p 54). Even in sections where it is not feasible to add sufficient alloying elements to obtain full hardening, molybdenum has an advantage since it retards the formation of pearlite more than that of

* This obviously does not apply if the steel is hardenable enough to harden fully on air cooling.

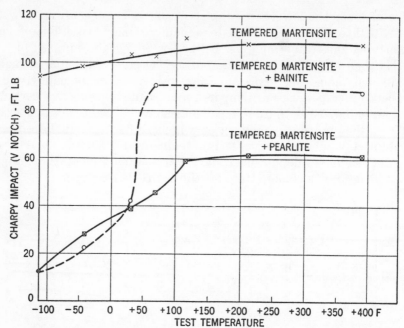

FIG 85 – Effect of Microstructure on the Low Temperature Impact Properties of a Chromium-Molybdenum-Nickel Steel (8735) at a Tensile Strength of Approximately 125,000 psi (data from Figures 3, 8 and 10 of (24))

Analysis: 0.34% C, 0.95% Mn, 0.26% Si, 0.014% P, 0.018% S, 0.56% Cr, 0.24% Mo, 0.66% Ni

Heat Treatment: (⅝ in. rd)

Tempered Martensite: water quenched from 1650 F, tempered at 1210 F

Tempered Martensite + Bainite: water quenched from 1650 F and held for five seconds; transferred to salt pot at 750 F and held for five minutes; water quenched to room temperature; cooled in liquid nitrogen and tempered at 1095 F

Tempered Martensite + Pearlite: austenitized at 1650 F; transferred to salt pot at 1110 F and held for 115 min; water quenched to room temperature; tempered at 1160 F

bainite and thus ensures the absence of the more injurious pearlite.

Carbon within the usual limits for engineering steels has a minor effect on the low temperature impact values of quenched and tempered steels. Provided the steels have the same grain size, little difference will be noticed in the low temperature impact properties of a steel with 0.25% and one with 0.40% carbon, fully hardened and tempered to the same hardness. In the normalized and tempered, normalized, annealed and hot worked conditions, however, better low temperature toughness will be obtained with lower carbon contents.

Temper brittleness will cause a serious impairment of low temperature impact strength as indicated by Figures 3 and 6 (pp 5 and 8). It will be recalled that this temper brittleness may be found not only in heat treated but also in normalized or annealed or hot rolled steels if they have been held in the embrittling temperature range. The addition of proper amounts of molybdenum is the simplest means of minimizing temper brittleness (pp 6-9).

The position of the transition zone is significantly affected by steel making practice. For example, the phosphorus content and the method and completeness of deoxidation may have more effect on the low temperature impact properties than the nominal composition of the steel. Phosphorus shifts the transition towards higher temperatures, so low phosphorus contents are desirable for optimum retention of low temperature toughness. In general, steels with a fine grain size as heat treated have low temperature impact characteristics superior to those of similar steels with a coarse actual grain size (Figure 86). There is some indication that the low temperature impact strength may be impaired by incipient grain coarsening caused by heating slightly below the coarsening temperature, even though the grain size is not perceptibly coarsened. This actual grain size is not always the same as the McQuaid-Ehn grain size. A steel with a fine McQuaid-Ehn grain size may often be coarsened by heating over 1700 F, while a steel with a coarse McQuaid-Ehn grain size will have a fine actual grain size if heated just over the critical. It is commonly believed, however, that differences among supposedly duplicate heats are mini-

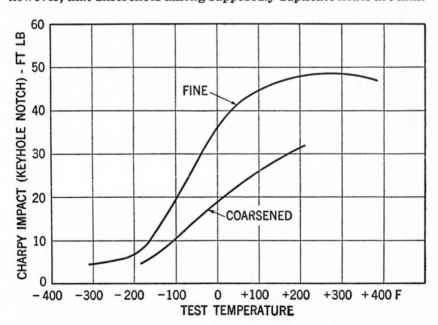

FIG 86 – Effect of Actual Grain Size on the Low Temperature Impact Properties of Normalized and Tempered Chromium-Molybdenum Steel (4130) (101)

Bar Analysis: 0.30% C, 0.51% Mn, 0.23% Si, 0.011% P, 0.023% S, 0.043% Al, 0.015% Al₂O₃, 0.91% Cr, 0.18% Mo, 0.024% Ni
McQuaid-Ehn Grain Size: 7 to 8
Thermal Treatment: (0.42 in. sq)
 Coarsened: held 30 min at 2200 F, cooled to 1625 F, air cooled, tempered one hour at 900 F. Rockwell C Hardness 14 to 16
 Fine: air cooled from 1625 F, tempered one hour at 900 F. Rockwell C Hardness 19 to 21

mized if the steels are melted so as to produce a fine grain size with a high coarsening temperature (101). Unless otherwise noted, all the curves given are based on aluminum deoxidized steel and do not necessarily apply to fine grained steels obtained by other means.

Figure 87 and 88 show comparative low temperature impact properties of various medium carbon alloy steels in the quenched and tempered and in the normalized and tempered conditions. Low carbon molybdenum-nickel and nickel steels, normalized and tempered, are

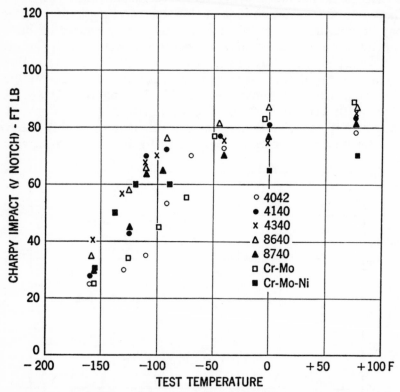

FIG 87 – Comparative Low Temperature Properties of Martensitic Steels (Individual Heats) Tempered to Approximately Rockwell C 30. McQuaid-Ehn grain size 5 to 8 for all heats

	Bar Analyses							Quenched* from 1550 F and Tempered Two Hours at F**	Rockwell C Hardness
	%C	%Mn	%Si	%P	%Cr	%Mo	%Ni		
4042	0.41	0.77	0.23	0.017	0.02	0.24	0.05	1060	30 to 31
4140	0.39	0.79	0.26	0.016	0.95	0.20	0.24	1180	31 to 32
4340	0.42	0.77	0.27	0.008	0.91	0.22	1.58	1175	30 to 31
8640	0.39	0.74	0.25	0.021	0.52	0.24	0.56	1140	30.5 to 32
8740	0.43	0.95	0.27	0.026	0.46	0.27	0.52	1150	30 to 31
Cr-Mo	0.38	0.65	0.32	0.010	0.57	0.15	0.08	1050	28 to 29
Cr-Mo-Ni	0.43	0.81	0.28	.....	0.97	0.25	0.59	1175	30 to 31

* all specimens oil quenched except 4042 which was water quenched
** specimens quenched from tempering temperature

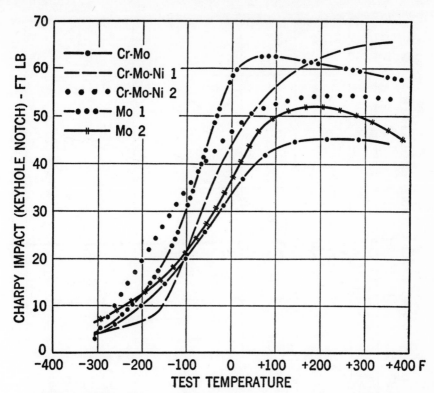

FIG 88 – Comparative Low Temperature Impact Properties of Normalized and Tempered Alloy Steels (101)

	Bar Analyses									Mc-Quaid-Ehn Grain Size	Rockwell B Hardness
	C %	Mn %	Si %	P %	S %	Al %	Al₂O₃ %	Cr %	Mo %	Ni %	
Cr–Mo.........	0.30	0.51	0.23	0.011	0.023	0.043	0.015	0.91	0.18	0.024	7 to 8	88 to 92
Cr–Mo–Ni 1....	0.22	0.90	0.28	0.010	0.028	0.031	0.011	0.53	0.27	0.50	8	95 to 96
Cr–Mo–Ni 2....	0.21	0.89	0.43	0.014	0.027	0.065	0.033	0.33	0.12	0.31	7 to 8	86 to 88
Mo 1...........	0.20	0.76	0.25	0.011	0.020	0.07	0.011	0.04	0.23	0.15	6 to 8	81 to 83
Mo 2...........	0.31	0.72	0.29	0.012	0.018	0.034	0.014	0.12	0.45	0.019	7 to 8	91 to 96

Thermal Treatment: (0.42 in. sq)
Cr–Mo: air cooled from 1625 F, tempered one hour at 1000 F
All others: air cooled from 1600 F, tempered one hour at 1000 F

sometimes used at low temperatures when the shape of the part or the available equipment makes quenching undesirable and where high strength is not required (Figure 89).

MACHINABILITY*

It is generally most economical to machine steel in the annealed condition when an appreciable amount of machining is to be done. If the steel has a high alloy content, it is often expedient to use a sub-critical temper as an excessive time might be required for full anneal-

---

* See pp 13, 14.

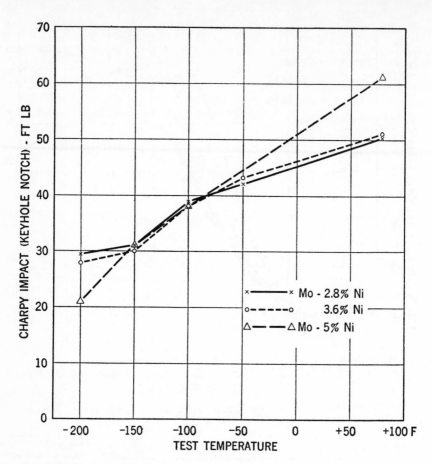

FIG 89 – Comparative Low Temperature Impact Properties of Low Carbon-High Nickel Steels (106)

	Analyses					
	%C	%Mn	%Si	%Mo	%Ni	
Mo–2.8% Ni............	0.17	(0.60)*	(0.15)*	0.31	2.83	0.08% Al added in ladle
3.6% Ni...............	0.17	(0.60)*	(0.15)*	....	3.61	0.08% Al added in ladle
Mo–5% Ni.............	0.09	0.86	0.22	0.34	5.35	7 McQuaid-Ehn grain size

* aim

	Size, in.	Air Cooled from F	Tempered at F	Tensile Strength 1000 psi	0.01% Yield Strength 1000 psi
Mo–2.8% Ni............	⅞ x 1¼	1525	1200	81.5	67.5
3.6% Ni...............	⅞ x 1¼	1525	1200	74.0	50.5
Mo–5% Ni.............	2½ rd	1575	1200	108.0	51.0

ing (see pp 35, 36). On the other hand, lower alloy steels may be annealed relatively readily to produce either spheroidal or lamellar structures. Therefore, it is possible to develop any desired structure. As recently stated "it is necessary to arrive at a compromise between tool wear and surface finish, adjusting the annealing treatment to give good surface finish and reasonable tool life. The exact condition of the particular cutting operation involved and the importance of surface finish obtained will determine in each particular case where the compromise must be struck." (107) One suggested schedule of optimum structures is reproduced in Table 27. Machinability is frequently improved by cold drawing and sometimes by a grain coarsening treatment. When various types of machining operations are to be performed, the efficiency of one machining operation may have to be sacrificed for another, or an intermediate treatment may be advisable (109).

TABLE 27
Effect of Carbon Content and Microstructure on the Machinability
of Alloy Steels (108)

%C	Condition	Microstructure	Comparative Machinability			
			turning	forming	drilling	broaching
0.08 to 0.30	normalize + temper	blocky ferrite	good	good	good	good
0.30 to 0.50	anneal	spheroidal	good	poor	fair	poor
	anneal	lamellar	fair	good	good	good
	quench + temper	tempered martensite	fair	fair	fair	fair
0.50 to 0.80	anneal	spheroidal	good	good	good	fair
	anneal	lamellar	fair	poor	poor	poor
	quench + temper	tempered martensite	good	fair	good	good

Notes: Low carbon steels with over about 3.5% total alloy content may show an acicular structure after the normalize + temper, but the comparative machinability values will be about as indicated in the table for blocky ferrite. Milling and threading more or less follow the suggestions given for forming and broaching

Uniformity of structure is important in all cases. Marked banding and heavy ferrite segregation in normalized and annealed steels will definitely affect tool life and produce a rough, torn surface. The magnitude of the effect will depend on the kind of machining operation and the direction of the cutting relative to the bands (109). Uniformity is of particular importance in steels to be machined in the heat treated condition. Steels with low hardenability are apt to have poor machining characteristics, especially at high hardnesses (110). The reason appears to be twofold. The hardness of low hardenability steels is likely to be non-uniform across the section with the higher hardness at the surface where the machining is to be done. Secondly, the non-martensitic constituents may have a deleterious effect on machinability. For example, free ferrite in a structure of tempered martensite may cause tearing and a poor surface finish due to a built-up edge on the tool.

[123]

Section IV — Bibliography

(1) Standard Steels, issued by the AISI (October 30, 1947)

(2) Contributions to the Metallurgy of Steel—No. 11, Hardenability of Alloy Steels, published by the AISI (June 1947) and supplement of September 20, 1947

(3) G. R. Bolsover and S. Barraclough "The Influence of Tin on Alloy Steels" Journal of the Iron and Steel Institute, Vol. CXLVI, No. II (1942)

(4) J. L. Burns, T. L. Moore and R. S. Archer "Quantitative Hardenability" Transactions, ASM, Vol. 26 (1938)

(5) J. M. Hodge and M. A. Orehoski "Relationship between Hardenability and Percentage of Martensite in Some Low-alloy Steels" Transactions, AIME, Vol 167 (1946)

(6) W. E. Cooper and N. P. Allen "Observations on the Relationship between Hardenability and the Mechanical Properties of Quenched and Tempered Steels" Section VID of Symposium on the Hardenability of Steel, Iron and Steel Institute Special Report No. 36, published by the Iron and Steel Institute, London, England (1946)

(7) SAE Handbook, published by the SAE (1947)

(8) J. H. Hollomon and L. D. Jaffe "Time-temperature Relations in Tempering Steel" Transactions, AIME, Vol 162 (1945)

(9) G. K. Manning and G. P. Krumlauf "Effect of Tempering on Mechanical Properties" Iron Age, Vol 158 (1946)

(10) Army-Navy Aeronautical Specification AN-QQ-H-201 (February 7, 1942) and Amendment 2 (November 14, 1942)

(11) Properties of Frequently Used Carbon and Alloy Steels, published by the Bethlehem Steel Company, Bethlehem, Pennsylvania (1946)

(12) Battelle Memorial Institute, Prevention of the Failure of Metals under Repeated Stress, published by John Wiley and Sons, Inc. (1941)

(13) Data from Verein deutscher Ingenieure and Karpov, reproduced in Battelle Memorial Institute (12)

(14) H. F. Moore "A Study of Size Effect and Notch Sensitivity in Fatigue Tests of Steel" Proceedings, ASTM, Vol 45 (1945)

(15) R. E. Peterson, discussion of H. F. Moore (14)

(16) P. O. Johnson and C. Lipson "Fatigue Strength of Steel Parts" Product Engineering, Vol 18 (1947)

(17) J. O. Almen "Shot Blasting to Increase Fatigue Resistance" SAE Journal, Vol 51 (1943)

(18) O. J. Horger "Mechanical and Metallurgical Advantages of Shot Peening" Iron Age, Vol 155 (1945)

(19) H. F. Moore "Shot Peening and the Fatigue of Metals" published by the American Foundry Equipment Company, Mishawaka, Indiana (1944)

(20) O. J. Horger and C. H. Lipson "Automotive Rear Axles and Means of Improving Their Fatigue Resistance" Symposium on Testing of Parts and Assemblies, Technical Publication No. 72, published by the ASTM (1946)

(21) H. F. Moore "The Problem Defined" Surface Stressing of Metals, published by the ASM (1947)

(22) J. O. Almen "Fatigue of Metals as Influenced by Design and Internal Stresses" Surface Stressing of Metals, published by the ASM (1947)

(23) P. R. Kosting "Progressive Stress-Damage" Surface Stressing of Metals, published by the ASM (1947)

(24) J. H. Hollomon, L. D. Jaffe, D. E. McCarthy and M. R. Norton "The Effects of Microstructure on the Mechanical Properties of Steel" Transactions, ASM, Vol 38 (1947)

(25) H. Malcor "Special Replacement Steels for Mechanical Construction and Their Future" Circulaire d'Informations Techniques, Centre de Documentation Sidérurgique (1946)

(26) M. A. Grossmann "Toughness and Fracture of Hardened Steels" Transactions, AIME, Vol 167 (1946)

(27) W. G. Patton "Mechanical Properties of NE, S.A.E. and Other Hardened Steels" Metal Progress, Vol 43 (1943)

(28) Federal Specification QQ-M-151a (November 27, 1936)

(29) E. J. Janitzky and M. Baeyertz "The Marked Similarity in Tensile Properties of Several Heat Treated S.A.E. Steels" Metals Handbook, published by the ASM (1939)

(30) W. Crafts and J. L. Lamont "The Izod Impact Strength of Heat-Treated Alloy Steel" AIME TP 2134; Metals Technology, Vol 14 (1947)

(31) S. A. Herres and A. F. Jones "A Method for Evaluating Toughness of Steel" Metal Progress, Vol 50 (1946)

(32) A. L. Boegehold "Selection of Automotive Steel on the Basis of Hardenability" SAE Journal, Vol 52 (1944)

(33) Alloy Steel Reference Book, published by Joseph T. Ryerson & Son, Inc. (1947)

(34) Private communication from Dr. E. C. Bain, Carnegie-Illinois Steel Corporation, Pittsburgh, Pennsylvania (November 24, 1947)

(35) H. Allsop "The Significance of Variation in Jominy Hardenability with Respect to the Mechanical Properties of Some Hardened and Tempered B.S. En Steels" Section VA of Symposium on the Hardenability of Steel, Iron and Steel Institute Special Report No. 36, published by the Iron and Steel Institute, London, England (1946)

(36) A. J. K. Honeyman "On the Relation between the As-Quenched Hardness and the Mechanical Properties of Quenched and Tempered Steel" Section VIC of Symposium on the Hardenability of Steel, Iron and Steel Institute Special Report No. 36, published by the Iron and Steel Institute, London, England (1946)

(37) W. Crafts and J. L. Lamont "Addition Method for Calculating Rockwell C Hardness of the Jominy Hardenability Test" Transactions, AIME, Vol 167 (1946)

(38) Wrought Steels (Carbon and Alloy Steels) T.A.C. 1-33 Steels En 1-58, B.S. 971, issued by the British Standards Institution, London, England (1944)

(39) W. T. Griffiths, L. B. Pfeil and N. P. Allen "The Intermediate Transformation in Alloy Steels" Second Report of the Alloy Steels Research Committee, Iron and Steel Institute Special Report No. 24, published by the Iron and Steel Institute, London, England (1939)

(40) M. A. Grossmann, M. Asimow and S. F. Urban "Hardenability, its Relation to Quenching, and some Quantitative Data" Hardenability of Alloy Steels, published by the ASM (1939)

(41) M. A. Grossmann "Hardenability Calculated from Chemical Composition" Transactions, AIME, Vol 150 (1942)

(42) Suiting the Heat Treatment to the Job, published by the United States Steel Corporation, Pittsburgh, Pennsylvania (1946)

(43) The Tensile and Impact Properties of Quenched and Tempered Nickel Alloy Steels in Different Sizes, published by the International Nickel Company, Inc., New York City, New York (1946)

(44) J. H. G. Monypenny "British EN Alloy Specifications" Iron Age, Vol 156 (1945)

(45) Wrought Steels, British Standard 970:1947, issued by the British Standards Institution, London, England (1947)

(46) D. A. Oliver "Résumé of the Activities of the Hardenability Sub-Committee and Suggestions for Future Research" Section IX of Symposium on the Hardenability of Steel, Iron and Steel Institute Special Report No. 36, published by the Iron and Steel Institute, London, England (1946)

(47) P. Klain and C. H. Lorig "Hardness Characteristics of Some Medium Carbon S.A.E. Steels" Transactions, ASM, Vol 28 (1940)

(48) J. Erb "Extending the Jominy Scale" Iron Age, Vol 157 (1946)

(49) J. Welchner, E. S. Rowland and J. E. Ubben "Effect of Time, Temperature and Prior Structure on the Hardenability of Several Alloy Steels" Transactions, ASM, Vol 82 (1944)

(50) E. S. Rowland, J. Welchner, R. G. Hill and J. J. Russ "The Effect of Carbon Content on Hardenability" Transactions, ASM, Vol 35 (1945)

(51) G. D. Rahrer and C. D. Armstrong "The Effect of Carbon Content on the Hardenability of Boron Steels" Transactions, ASM, Vol 40 (1948)

(52) A. L. Boegehold "Hardenability of N.E. 8600 H Steels" Metal Progress, Vol 50 (1946)

(53) ASTM Specification A 304-47T

(54) A. L. Boegehold "Use of Hardenability Tests for Selection and Specification of Automotive Steels" SAE Journal, Vol 49 (1941)

(55) Contributions to the Metallurgy of Steel— No. 12, Calculation of the Standard End-Quench Hardenability Curve from Chemical Composition and Grain Size, published by the AISI (1946)

(56) W. Steven "The Effect on the Hardenability of Small Additions of Chromium and Molybdenum to a Grain-Size-Controlled 0.9% Nickel Steel" Journal of the Iron and Steel Institute, Vol. CXLIX, No. I (1944)

(57) G. R. Brophy and A. J. Miller "An Appraisal of the Factor Method for Calculating the Hardenability of Steel from Composition" Transactions, AIME Vol 167 (1946)

(58) I. R. Kramer, S. Siegel and J. G. Brooks "Factors for the Calculation of Hardenability" Transactions, AIME, Vol 167 (1946)

(59) J. Glen "The Effect of the Major Alloying Elements and of Boron on the Hardenability of Steel" Section VIIA of Symposium on the Hardenability of Steel, Iron and Steel Institute Special Report No. 36, published by the Iron and Steel Institute, London, England (1946)

(60) W. Crafts and J. L. Lamont "Effect of Some Elements on Hardenability" Transactions, AIME, Vol 158 (1944)

(61) I. R. Kramer, R. H. Hafner and S. L. Toleman "Effect of Sixteen Alloying Elements on Hardenability of Steel" Transactions, AIME, Vol 158 (1944)

(62) G. F. Comstock "The Influence of Titanium on the Hardenability of Steel" Transactions, AIME, Vol 167 (1946)

(63) J. M. Hodge and M. A. Orehoski "Hardenability Effects in Relation to the Percentage of Martensite" Transactions, AIME, Vol 167 (1946)

(64) J. Field "Calculation of Jominy End-Quench Curve from Analysis" Metal Progress, Vol 43 (1943)

(65) H. E. Hostetter "Determination of Most Efficient Alloy Combinations for Hardenability" Transactions, AIME, Vol 167 (1946)

(66) N. P. Allen, L. B. Pfeil and W. T. Griffiths "The Determination of the Transformation Characteristics of Alloy Steels" Second Report of the Alloy Steels Research Committee, Iron and Steel Institute Special Report No. 24, published by the Iron and Steel Institute, London, England (1939)

(67) P. A. Haythorne "Nitriding of Aircraft Steels" Iron Age, Vol 157 (1946)

(68) J. O. Almen "Some Needed Precautions When Induction and Flame Hardening" Metal Progress, Vol 46 (1944)

(69) C. C. Hodgson and H. O. Waring "A Note on the Relationship between Preliminary Heat Treatment and Response to Nitriding of some Nitriding Steels" Journal of the Iron and Steel Institute, Vol. CLI, No. I (1945)

(70) J. L. F. Vogel and W. F. Rowden, Molybdenum Steels, published by the High Speed Steel Alloys Limited, Widnes, England (1935)

[125]

(71) C. F. Floe "The Nitriding of Steel" Metal Progress, Vol 50 (1946)

(72) M. Hill "Tests on NE 8630 Steels for Welded Air Frames" Metal Progress, Vol 43 (1943)

(73) G. Sachs and G. Espey "Fatigue Strength Properties of SAE X4130 Tubing" Iron Age, Vol 153 (1944)

(74) W. H. Bruckner "The Hardenability of Carburizing Steels" University of Illinois Engineering Experiment Station Bulletin Series No. 320 (1939)

(75) Supplementary Information on Alloy Steel, Section 10 — Sheet 64, issued by the AISI (June 16, 1942)

(76) U.S.S. Carilloy Steels, published by the Carnegie-Illinois Steel Corporation, Pittsburgh, Pennsylvania (1938)

(77) The Case Hardening of Nickel Alloy Steels, published by the International Nickel Company, New York City, New York (1946)

(78) NE National Emergency Steels, published by the Republic Steel Corporation, Cleveland, Ohio (1943)

(79) H. C. Amtsberg "Sub-Zero Treatment of Steel" Iron Age, Vol 155 (1945)

(80) O. W. McMullan "Utility of the Hardenability Test on Steels for Carburizing" Metal Progress, Vol 45 (1944)

(81) A. S. Jameson "Hardenability Behavior of Carburizing Grades of NE and Automotive Alloy Steels" Steel, Vol 116 (1945)

(82) G. K. Manning "Carburizing Characteristics of 0.20% Carbon Alloy and Plain Carbon Steels" Transactions, ASM, Vol 31 (1943)

(83) Private information from the Gulf Research and Development Company, Pittsburgh, Pennsylvania

(84) Three Republic High Strength Steels, published by the Republic Steel Corporation, Cleveland, Ohio (1947)

(85) Republic Double Strength Steel, published by the Republic Steel Corporation, Cleveland, Ohio (1940)

(86) "Low-Alloy, High-Strength Steels" Materials and Methods, Vol 26 (1947)

(87) Properties and Characteristics of N-A-X High Tensile, published by the Great Lakes Steel Corporation, Detroit, Michigan (1940)

(88) Hi-Steel, Supplement to Engineering Bulletin No. 11, published by the Inland Steel Company, Chicago, Illinois (1945) ; also private communication from the Inland Steel Company

(89) A. J. K. Honeyman and J. Erskine "Developments in Low Alloy Steels for Welding Construction" Metallurgia, Vol 34 (1946)

(90) J. W. Halley, U.S.A. Patent No. 2,402,135 (1946)

(91) H. Miller "The Development of High Strength Welding Quality Alloy Steels and Their Postwar Applications" Welding Journal, Vol 25 (1946)

(92) Sheet Iron—A Primer, published by the Republic Steel Corporation, Youngstown, Ohio (1934)

(93) Anonymous "Copper-Molybdenum Steel" Cuivre et Laiton, Vol 5 (1932)

(94) F. Eisenkolb "Weathering Experiments with Thin Sheets of Mild Steel" Korrosion und Metallschutz, Vol 10 (1934)

(95) H. C. Keysor "Carbon and Alloy Steel Materials for Hot-Formed Springs" Product Engineering, Vol 17 (1946)

(96) F. P. Zimmerli "Proper Use of Spring Materials" SAE Quarterly Transactions, Vol 2 (1948)

(97) W. F. Brown, Jr., L. J. Ebert and G. Sachs "Distribution of Strength and Ductility in Welded Steel Plate as Revealed by the Static Notch Bar Tensile Test" Welding Research Supplement to the Journal, AWS, Vol 26 (1947)

(98) S. J. Rosenberg and D. H. Gagon "Effect of Grain Size and Heat Treatment upon Impact Toughness at Low Temperatures of Medium Carbon Forging Steel" Transactions, ASM, Vol 30 (1942)

(99) J. H. Hollomon "The Problem of Fracture. The Failure of Welded Steel Structures and Recommended Research" Welding Research Supplement to the Journal, AWS, Vol 25 (1946)

(100) A. B. Kinzel "Ductility of Steels for Welded Structures" Metal Progress, Vol 52 (1947)

(101) H. W. Gillett and F. T. McGuire, Report on Behavior of Ferritic Steels at Low Temperatures, published by the ASTM (1945)

(102) P. C. Rosenthal and G. K. Manning "Heat Treatment of Heavy Cast Steel Sections" Foundry, Vol 74 (1946) ; also Steel, Vol 119 (1946)

(103) J. H. Hollomon "Temper Brittleness" Transactions, ASM, Vol 36 (1946)

(104) W. S. Pellini and B. R. Queneau "Development of Temper Brittleness in Alloy Steels" Transactions, ASM, Vol 39 (1947)

(105) S. I. Sakhin and V. Ya. Vetrov "Fundamental Principles of Improved Alloy Construction Types of Steel" Stal, No. 4-5 (1946)

(106) T. N. Armstrong and A. P. Gagnebin "Impact Properties of Some Low Alloy Nickel Steels at Temperatures Down to — 200 Degrees Fahr." Transactions, ASM, Vol 28 (1940)

(107) C. Sykes "Machinability and Structure of Ferrous Materials" Engineering, Vol 161 (1946)

(108) G. P. Witteman "Studies on the Machinability of Carbon and Alloy Steels" Mechanical Engineering, Vol 67 (1945)

(109) N. E. Woldman "Good and Bad Structures in Machining Steel" Materials and Methods, Vol 25 (1947)

(110) O. W. Boston and L. V. Colwell "The Effect of Hardness on the Machinability of Six Alloy Steels" Transactions, ASM, Vol 31 (1943)

SECTION V

WROUGHT CORROSION
RESISTANT STEELS

THE "18-8" TYPE WITH MOLYBDENUM*

The basic "18-8" with approximately 18% chromium and 8% nickel has long been known as a corrosion resistant or "stainless" steel. It was found soon after its introduction, however, that there were many applications where it did not have sufficient corrosion resistance for commercial use. With the discovery of the efficacy of molybdenum additions in improving the corrosion resistance of 18-8, new fields of application were opened. As discussed in Section VI, the utility of the 18-8 type with molybdenum is further enhanced by the fact that it has elevated temperature properties considerably better than those of the basic 18-8. Therefore, today, the 18-8 type with molybdenum is widely used both for its superior corrosion resistance and for its high elevated temperature strength.

Originally, this grade was actually an 18-8 with molybdenum as it was produced with approximately 18% chromium, 8% nickel and 3% molybdenum. The composition was not wholly austenitic but contained appreciable amounts of delta ferrite. This duplex structure caused difficulties in hot working. Moreover, on stress relieving or long time holding at about 1400 to 1600 F, it was likely to be embrittled by the transformation of the delta ferrite to the hard, brittle sigma phase. Consequently, the composition was eventually modified for most applications to give an essentially austenitic steel which is much easier to hot work and is not embrittled by holding at 1400 to 1600 F. As a matter of convenience, however, these steels will still be referred to as 18-8 type with molybdenum.

---

* Electrodes of this general composition are used for welding hardenable steels as they minimize cracking in the hardened zone of the latter. This application is not discussed here since the value of these electrodes is due to their structure, not their corrosion resistance. It is noteworthy, however, that the presence of molybdenum appears to overcome tendencies towards weld metal cracking not only by forming some ferrite in the weld metal but also by strengthening the austenite (1). Even the completely austenitic chromium-nickel weld metals are less susceptible to cracking when they contain molybdenum (1). For example, austenitic Type 316 weld metal with about 3% molybdenum is the least sensitive to cracking of any of the standard, fully austenitic steels (1).

It is possible to change the composition in various ways and still obtain an austenitic structure as long as the austenite formers (carbon, manganese, nickel and nitrogen) are increased sufficiently to compensate for the ferrite-forming tendencies of the chromium, molybdenum and silicon. Figures 90 through 93 show the effect of varying percentages of chromium and nickel on the structures present in steels with about 2 and 3% molybdenum as softened and as stress relieved for four hours at 1600 F. With the aid of these diagrams, it is possible to predict the composition balance needed for a substantially austenitic steel.

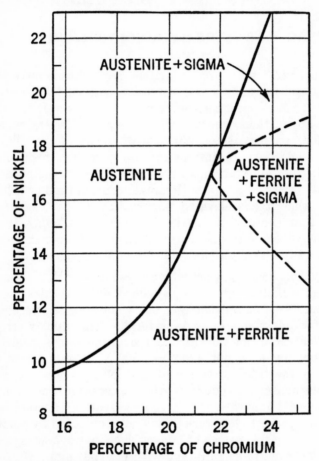

FIG 90 – Structural Diagram for Chromium-Nickel Steels with 1.75 to 2.25% Mo, 0.10% C max, about 1.5% Mn and 0.5% Si, as Air Cooled from 2010 to 2100 F (2)

The AISI has adopted the following two composition ranges as standard (3) for all wrought products except electrodes and tubes, for which the limits are slightly different:

AISI Type	%C max	%Mn max	%Si max	%P max	%S max	%Cr	%Ni	%Mo
316	0.10	2.00	1.00	0.040	0.030	16.00 to 18.00	10.00 to 14 00	2.00 to 3.00
317	0.10	2.00	1.00	0.040	0.030	18.00 to 20.00	11.00 to 14.00	3.00 to 4.00

The susceptibility of the basic 18-8 to intergranular corrosion as a result of welding or otherwise sensitizing (by exposure to temperatures of 900 to 1500F) is well known. The susceptibility of the 18-8

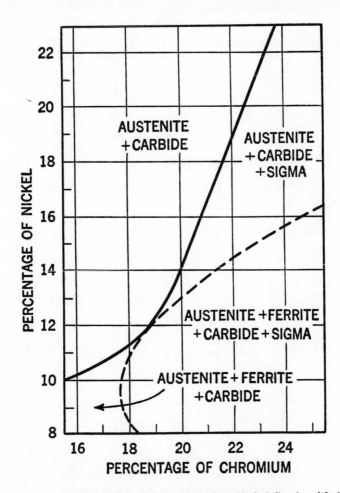

FIG 91 – Structural Diagram for Chromium-Nickel Steels with 1.75 to 2.25% Mo, 0.10% C max, about 1.5% Mn and 0.5% Si, as Air Cooled from 2010 to 2100 F, Reheated Four Hours at 1600 F and Air Cooled (2)

type with molybdenum to intergranular corrosion after welding or holding at about 900 to 1500 F depends on its structure. If a fair amount of delta ferrite is present, the alloy will show at the most a slight susceptibility to intergranular corrosion when tested in the conventional boiling 10% sulphuric acid–10% copper sulphate solution. If the alloy is fully austenitic, it is susceptible to intergranular corrosion, as shown by this test, even though the carbon is as low as 0.04%. It should be remembered that this test is severe and may be more stringent than the actual service conditions.

If welded 18-8 with molybdenum having an austenitic structure is to be used in applications involving exposure to aqueous corrosive media, intergranular corrosion may be encountered unless the part is fully softened after welding. In cases where this is undesirable from the standpoint of the size of the article, distortion or residual stresses,

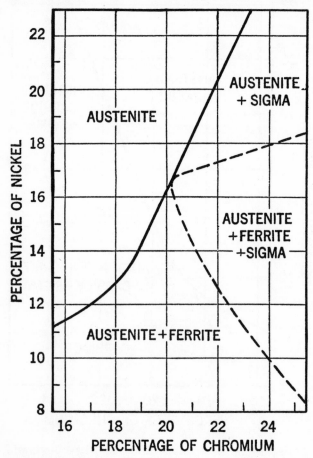

FIG 92 – Structural Diagram for Chromium-Nickel Steels with 2.75 to 3.25% Mo, 0.10% C max, about 1.5% Mn and 0.5% Si, as Air Cooled from 2010 to 2100 F (2)

the 18-8 type with molybdenum may be rendered completely resistant to intergranular corrosion by the addition of columbium (at least about ten times the carbon content) or titanium (at least about five times the carbon content). These modifications combine the excellent corrosion resistance of the 18-8 type with molybdenum and the resistance to intergranular corrosion of 18-8 with columbium or titanium. The titanium modification is not suitable for a welding rod since most of the titanium is lost during welding. Therefore, a welding rod with columbium and, of course, molybdenum, should be used with both these modifications.

The physical properties of the 18-8 type with molybdenum are very similar to those of 18-8. Representative properties are shown in Table 28. It is generally non-magnetic as softened but slightly mag-

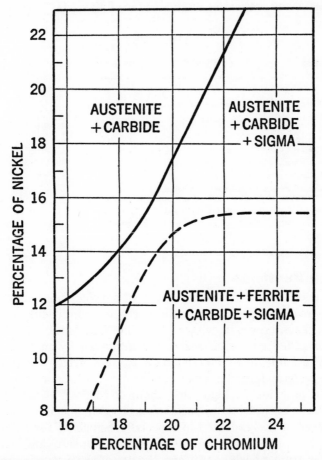

FIG 93 – Structural Diagram for Chromium-Nickel Steels with 2.75 to 3.25% Mo, 0.10% C max, about 1.5% Mn and 0.5% Si, as Air Cooled from 2010 to 2100 F, Reheated Four Hours at 1600 F and Air Cooled (2)

netic when cold worked. Cold working will also decrease the **modulus** of elasticity, but stress relieving at about 400 to 750 F will tend to restore the value shown in Table 28 for the softened condition.

Table 29 gives representative mechanical properties for various forms and conditions. The 18-8 type with molybdenum is generally furnished as fully softened by cooling rapidly from 1850 to 2050 F. It is similar to the basic 18-8 in that it is not hardenable by heat treatment but only by cold work. It will be noted from the table that high tensile strengths may be obtained in small sections if they are given sufficient cold reduction. The proportional limit and yield strength are not increased by cold working to the same extent as is the tensile strength. A stress relieving treatment for at least eight hours at about 400 to 480 F will improve these elastic properties without impairing the other properties or the surface finish (5).

TABLE 28

Physical Properties of Type 316 in Fully Softened Condition (4)

Density, lb per cu in.	0.29
Mean Coefficient of Thermal Expansion, per degree F	
32 to 212 F	8.9×10^{-6}
32 to 600 F	9.0×10^{-6}
32 to 1000 F	9.7×10^{-6}
32 to 1200 F	10.3×10^{-6}
32 to 1500 F	11.1×10^{-6}
Melting Point Range	2500 to 2550 F
Modulus of Elasticity in Tension, psi	28.0×10^{6}
Specific Electrical Resistance at Room Temperature, microhm-cm	74
Specific Heat, BTU per lb per degree F (32 to 212 F	0.12
Thermal Conductivity, BTU per hr per sq ft per ft per degree F	
212 F	9.4
932 F	12.4

Corrosion Resistance

18-8 is satisfactory for many types of service, particularly those involving oxidizing media and mild corrosive conditions. There are numerous cases, however, where 18-8 is not adequately resistant and where the added corrosion resistance imparted by molybdenum is needed. The addition of molybdenum to 18-8 greatly improves its corrosion resistance under most conditions. As has been mentioned above, the addition is generally about 2 to 3%, although larger amounts have been found to be advantageous in special applications. The presence of molybdenum is especially beneficial for exposure to sulphuric, sulphurous and organic acids, halogen salts and sea water. Even under atmospheric conditions, the use of the molybdenum modification may be indicated where the rusting of 18-8 in marine and industrial environments is excessive, either from the standpoint of

TABLE 29
Mechanical Properties of Type 316 (4)

Form and Treatment	Tensile Strength 1000 psi	Yield Strength (0.2% offset) 1000 psi	Elongation in 2 in. percent	Reduction of Area percent	Impact Strength, ft lb		Hardness Number		Endurance Limit 1000 psi	Cold Bend, deg	Cupping Tests	
					Charpy	Izod	Brinell (3000 kg load 10 mm ball)	Rockwell			Erichsen mm	Olsen in.
Sheet												
Annealed............	90	40	50a	....	....	....	....	B85	39	180	10 to 14	0.4 to 0.5
Strip												
Annealed............	90	40	50a	....	....	....	....	B85	....	180	10 to 14	0.4 to 0.5
Cold rolled												
30 percent......	145	120	10a	....	...	...	...	...	...	...	...	...
40 percent......	160	135	5a									
Wire												
Annealed............	90	30	55b	....	....	....	....	B85	....	180	...	...
Cold drawn												
20 percent......	130	100	20b	...	...	...	...	C25	...	...	...	...
40 percent......	170	140	10b					C33				
60 percent......	205	180	5b					C88				
Plate												
Annealed............	85	30	60	70	80	100	150	B80	39	180	...	...
Bars												
Annealed............	85	30	60	70	80	100	150	B80	38	180	...	...
Cold drawn												
30 percent......	140	115	15	60	...	...	....	C29	...	...	...	...

(a) elongation values vary with thickness, being higher with greater thicknesses
(b) elongation values vary with diameter, being higher with larger diameters

appearance (6, 7) or actual service life (8). The wide use of the 18-8 type with molybdenum includes the paper, chemical, rayon and dye industries.

The improved corrosion resistance of the 18-8 type with molybdenum is evident from Table 30. In the use of this table as a guide to the selection of the proper type, consideration must be given to the fact that other constituents may be present in the actual corrosive media. Some of these may have an inhibiting action, as is displayed for example by copper in sulphuric acid solutions. Others, such as ferric or chloride ions, may accelerate corrosion. Since most of these results are based on tests with pure chemicals, they cannot be used as a final criterion of the precise corrosion rate to be expected.

All the 18-8 steels have their best corrosion resistance in the fully softened condition. Subsequent reheating to lower temperatures, as may be used to stress relieve large vessels after fabrication, will tend to have a deleterious effect on the general corrosion resistance (as distinguished from intergranular corrosion). The extent of this loss in resistance will depend upon the corrosive conditions as well as on the time and temperature of reheating. The 18-8 type with molybdenum retains its superiority over 18-8 even after such treatments (Figure 94). In some cases, the addition of columbium, and probably titanium, in the amounts previously mentioned, to 18-8 with molybdenum will minimize the loss in general corrosion resistance after such stress relieving treatments.

Although failures due to stress corrosion have been reported, the 18-8 steels seem to be quite resistant to this form of attack. The combination of high stresses with the corrosive action of fairly concentrated chloride solutions appears to be most unfavorable. Preliminary results in a large scale investigation (10) indicate that the addition of molybdenum tends to decrease the susceptibility to stress corrosion. In the standard test adopted in this work, samples stressed to 90% of their yield strength are exposed to a boiling solution of hydrated 60% magnesium chloride acidified with hydrochloric acid to a pH of 4. Plain 18-8, either with or without addition of titanium and columbium, failed in 20 to 52 hours while four heats of 18-8 with 1.90 to 3.00% molybdenum did not fail in 300 hours, at which time the tests were discontinued. In a subsequent study with a stress of 40,000 psi and a boiling solution of 42% calcium chloride, an austenitic 18-8 with 2.55% molybdenum failed, but the presence of 3.65% molybdenum and a low enough nickel content to give about 30% ferrite were found to eliminate stress corrosion (11).

In addition to its favorable action in increasing general corrosion resistance, molybdenum also improves the resistance of 18-8 to

TABLE 30

Guide to the Selection of Corrosion Resistant Steels (9)

Code
A   fully resistant   (under 0.1 g per sq m per hr)
B   satisfactorily resistant (0.1 to 1.0 g per sq m per hr)
C   fairly resistant   (1.0 to 8.0 g per sq m per hr)
D   non resistant   (over 3.0 g per sq m per hr)
*   subject to pitting at air line or if allowed to dry

Corroding Medium	Percent Concentration[1]	Temperature F	18–8 Type	18–8 Type with Molybdenum
Acetic acid	any	85	A	A
	50	boiling	C	B
	80	boiling	D	B
	100	boiling	C	B
Acetic acid condensate	80	boiling	D	A
	glacial	boiling	C	A
Acetic anhydride	..	85	A	A
	..	boiling	A	A
Acetone	..	70	A	A
	..	boiling	A	A
Acetylating solutions for rayon	..	..	C	A
Alcohol, ethyl	..	70	A	A
	..	boiling	A	A
Alcohol, methyl	..	70	A	A
	..	160	C*	B
Aluminum chloride	5	70	C	B
Aluminum potassium sulphate	2	70	A	A
	10	70	A	A
		boiling	B	A
	saturated	boiling	C	B
Aluminum sulphate (neutral)	10	70	A	A
		boiling	B	A
	saturated	70	A	A
		boiling	C	B
Ammonium chloride	5	70	B	A
Ammonium sulphate + 0.5% sulphuric acid	..	70	D	A
Blood (meat juices)	..	70	A*	A
Boric acid	..	70	A	A
Calcium chloride, alkaline	dilute	70	B*	A*
	concentrated	70	B*	A*
Calcium hydroxide	10	boiling	A	A
	20	boiling	A	A
	50	boiling	C	B
Calcium hypochlorite	5° Be	105	C*	B*
	70 g Cl₂ per l	35	D*	A*
	150 g Cl₂ per l	35	D*	A*
Carbolic acid	..	boiling	A	A
Carbon tetrachloride (pure)	..	70	A*	A
Chloracetic acid	..	70	D	C
Chlorinated water	saturated	70	C*	B*
Chlorine gas, dry	..	70	C	B
Chlorine gas, moist	..	70	D	C
Chromic acid, pure	5	70	A	A
	10	boiling	C	B

[1] in aqueous solution

TABLE 30 – (Continued)

Corroding Medium	Percent Concentration[1]	Temperature F	18–8 Type	18–8 Type with Molybdenum
Chromic acid, with traces of sulphur trioxide (commercial chromic acid)	50	boiling	D*	C
Citric acid..........................	5	70	A	A
		160	A	A
	10	70	A	A
		boiling	A	A
	15	70	A	A
		boiling	B	A
	25	70	A	A
		boiling	D	A
	50	70	A	A
		boiling	D	A
Copper chloride..................	1	70	B*	A*
	5	70	C*	B*
Copper sulphate..................	saturated	boiling	A	A
Developing solutions...............	..	70	A	A
Ether.............................	..	70	A	A
Ethyl chloride......................	..	70	A	A
Ferric chloride.....................	1	70	B*	A*
		boiling	D*	C*
	10	70	C*	A*
Ferric sulphate....................	1	70	A	A
		boiling	A	A
	5	70	A	A
		boiling	B	A
Ferrous sulphate..................	al	70	B	A
Food products.....................	..	..	A	A
Formic acid.......................	all	70	B	A
	1	140	A	A
		boiling	D*	A
	10	140	C	A
		boiling	D*	B
	50	140	D	A
		boiling	D	B
	90	140	B	A
		boiling	D	C
	100	140	A	A
		boiling	A	A
Fuel oil...........................	..	..	A	A
Glue, dry..........................	..	70	A	A
Glue, acid solution.................	..	70	B*	A
	..	140	B*	A
Hydrochloric acid..................	0.5	60	B	A
		105	D	A
		boiling	D	D
	1	60	B	A
		105	D	A
		140	D	D
	2	60	B	A
		140	D	D
	5	60	C	B
		140	D	D
Hydrofluoric acid..................	..	70	D	D
Hydrogen peroxide.................	..	70	A	A
	..	boiling	B	A
Hydrogen sulphide, dry............	..	70	A	A
Hydrogen sulphide, wet............	..	70	B	A
Ink...............................	..	..	B*	A

[1] in aqueous solution

[136]

TABLE 30 – (Continued)

Corroding Medium	Percent Concentration[1]	Temperature F	18-8 Type	18-8 Type with Molybdenum
Iodine.............................	..	70	C	B
Iodoform dressing..................	..	..	C	A
Lactic acid........................	5	70	A	A
		150	B	A
	10	150	C	B
		boiling	D	B
Magnesium chloride................	1	70	A*	A
	5	70	A*	A
Malic acid.........................	all	70	B	A
Nitric acid........................	all	70	A	A
	50	boiling	A	A
	65	boiling	B	B
	fuming	boiling	D	D
Nitrous acid.......................	5	70	A	A
Oleic acid.........................	all	70	A*	A
Oxalic acid........................	2.5	70	A	A
		140	B	A
		175	C	A
		boiling	D	B
	5	70	A	A
		boiling	D	B
	10	70	A	A
		boiling	D	B
	25	boiling	D	B
	50	35	B	A
		175	C	B
		boiling	C	B
Phosphoric acid................,.....	1	70	A	A
		boiling	A	A
	10	70	C	A/B
		boiling	A	A
	45	boiling	A	A
	80	70	..	A
		140	A	A
		230	D	C
Potassium bromide.................	..	70	B*	A*
Potassium carbonate...............	..	70	A	A
Potassium hydroxide...............	all	70	A	A
	27	boiling	A	A
	50	boiling	B	A/B
Potassium nitrate..................	50	70	A	A
		boiling	A	A
Pyrogallic acid....................	all	70	A	A
Quinine bisulphate, dry.............	all	70	B	A
Sea water..........................	..	70	A*	A
Silver bromide.....................	..	70	B*	A*
Sodium acetate, moist..............	..	70	A*	A
Sodium bicarbonate................	all	70	A	A
Sodium carbonate..................	5	70	A	A
Sodium chloride, aerated............	5	70	A*	A
		150	A*	A
	20	70	A*	A
	saturated	70	A*	A
		boiling	B*	A
Sodium fluoride....................	5	70	B*	A*

[1] in aqueous solution

TABLE 30 – (Continued)

Corroding Medium	Percent Concentration[1]	Temperature F	18–8 Type	18–8 Type with Molybdenum
Sodium hydroxide....................	0.5	70	A	A
		boiling	A	A
	50	70	A	A
		boiling	A	A
Sodium hypochlorite.................	5	70	B	B
Sodium hyposulphite.................	..	70	A*	A
Sodium nitrate......................	..	fused	C	B
Sodium sulphate....................	all	70	A	A
Sodium sulphide....................	saturated	70	B*	A
Sodium sulphite....................	5	70	A	A
	10	150	A	A
Stannous chloride...................	saturated	70	C	A
Steam..............................	..	..	A	A
Sulphate liquor (paper industry)......	..	..	B/C	A
Sulphite liquor (paper industry).......	..	..	..	A
Sulphur dioxide gas, moist...........	..	70	B	A
Sulphuric acid......................	0.5	70	B	A
		boiling	D	B
	1	70	B	A
		boiling	D	C
	5	70	B	A
		boiling	D	C
	10	70	C	A
		boiling	D	D
	25	70	C	A
		boiling	D	D
	50	70	D	C
		boiling	D	D
	95	70	B	A
		105	B	A
	concentrated	70	A	A
		boiling	D	D
	fuming	70	C	B
Sulphurous acid....................	saturated	70	B	A
	5 to 8 atm	320	C	A
	10 atm	355	C	A
	15 atm	390	C	B
	20 atm	390	C	B
Sulphur, wet.......................	..	70	B*	A*
Tannic acid........................	50	70	A	A
		boiling	B	A
Tartaric acid.......................	50	60	A	A
		105	A	A
		boiling	C	A
Vinegar fumes......................	..	..	B	A
Zinc chloride.......................	5	70	C	B
		boiling	D	B*
Zinc sulphate......................	5	70	B	A

[1] in aqueous solution

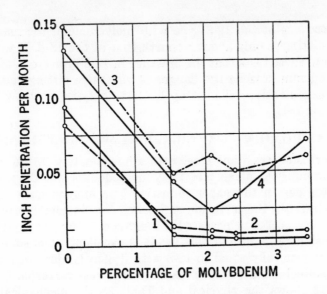

FIG 94—Effect of Heat Treatment and Molybdenum Content on the
Corrosion Rate of "18-8" with 0.05 to 0.08% C in 10% Sulphuric Acid
at 160 F (2)

Curve 1 — Heated five minutes at 2010 to 2100 F and air cooled
Curve 2 — Heated five minutes at 2010 to 2100 F and air cooled; reheated four
    hours at 1600 F and air cooled
Curve 3 — Heated five minutes at 2010 to 2100 F and air cooled; reheated four
    hours at 1600 F and air cooled; reheated four hours at 1200 F and air cooled
Curve 4 — Heated five minutes at 2010 to 2100 F and air cooled; reheated four
    hours at 1200 F and air cooled

pitting. Pitting is likely to occur in 18-8 in certain media, such as
concentrated chloride brines, even though the general attack is
negligible.

Molybdenum makes 18-8 substantially immune to the localized
corrosion that develops on the surface of 18-8 under foreign deposits
which prevent access of oxygen. A severe example of this type of
corrosion, variously called crevice or contact or differential aeration
corrosion, is the pitting that occurs on 18-8 in sea water under bar-
nacles. Table 31 shows results of tests on 18-8 and 18-8 with molybdenum in sea water at low velocity under conditions permitting the
attachment and growth of marine organisms. In spite of the much

TABLE 31

Corrosion Tests in Sea Water at Kure Beach, North Carolina (12)

Composition				Duration years	Maximum Pitting in.
%C	%Cr	%Ni	%Mo		
0.05	18.5	9.0	...	1.88	0.130
0.05	18.8	10.2	2.7	5.26	0.037

longer exposure of the 18-8 type with molybdenum, the maximum depth of pitting is only about a fourth that of the 18-8. It was concluded from these tests that the presence in 18-8 type steels of about 3% molybdenum lessens the danger of excessive pitting caused by oxygen concentration cells set up by certain types of sea growths (12, see also 13).

27% CHROMIUM – 4% NICKEL – 1.5% MOLYBDENUM*

This corrosion resistant steel with approximately 0.10% carbon, 27% chromium, 4% nickel and 1.5% molybdenum was developed in Sweden for use in the paper industry. The molybdenum addition serves to improve the corrosion resistance and, in combination with the nickel, is reported to increase the toughness by four to eight times. The corrosion resistance of this grade is excellent. It is superior to 18-8 and is generally equal to 18-8 with 3% molybdenum. Furthermore, this steel is stated to be resistant to stress corrosion (14).

Table 32 shows the physical and Table 33 the mechanical properties in the softened condition.

TABLE 32

Physical Properties of 27% Chromium – 4% Nickel – 1.5% Molybdenum Steel in Fully Softened Condition (15,16)

Typical Composition: 0.08% C, 27.5% Cr, 4.5% Ni, 1.5% Mo	
Mean Coefficient of Thermal Expansion, per degree F	
0 to 600 F	6.1×10^{-6}
0 to 1000 F	6.6×10^{-6}
0 to 1500 F	7.2×10^{-6}
Melting Point (approximate)	2500 F
Modulus of Elasticity in Tension, psi	28.0×10^{6}
Specific Electrical Resistance at 68 F, microhm-cm	72
Specific Gravity	7.69
Specific Heat, BTU per lb per degree F	0.11
Temperature Coefficient of Specific Electrical Resistance, per degree F	
68 to 1500 F	0.26×10^{-3}

This composition is unique in that it does not fit into the usual classification of "austenitic", "ferritic" and "martensitic" corrosion resistant steels. As softened by cooling rapidly from a high temperature, the structure consists of ferrite and austenite. On holding at about 1400 F it is hardened by the transformation of the soft ferrite to the hard sigma phase. The extent of this hardening and the time required depend upon the balance of composition (17). In general, if the chromium is under 26%, the nickel under 3.5% and the molyb-

---

* This steel is often called Type 329 as it was formerly so designated in the AISI list. This nomenclature is still used in specifications, such as ASTM A 268-44T.

denum under 1.5%, no significant hardening occurs on short time holding. If the chromium, nickel and molybdenum are on the high side, the hardness can be increased to approximately Rockwell C 40 or even higher by holding at 1400 F for 4 to 48 hours. Cold working prior to heating accelerates the hardening reaction (17). Since the hardening occurs during the holding at temperature, the steel may

TABLE 33

Mechanical Properties of 27% Chromium – 4% Nickel – 1.5% Molybdenum Steel in Fully Softened Condition (15)

Typical Composition: 0.08% C, 27.5% Cr, 4.5% Ni, 1.5% Mo
Thermal Treatment:

single treatment – cooled rapidly from 1700 F

double treatment – held 48 hr at 1350 F, furnace cooled, reheated to 1700 F and cooled rapidly

Mechanical Properties: (except for impact strength, the same properties apply for either a single or double treatment)

Tensile Strength, psi	105,000
Yield Point, psi	80,000
Elastic Limit, psi	70,000
Elongation, percent in 2 in.	20
Reduction of Area, percent	50
Brinell Hardness Number	230
Izod Impact, ft lb	
single treatment	8
double treatment	16

then be air cooled to room temperature. It is impossible to decrease the hardness by subsequent tempering since the steel once hardened does not soften on reheating to temperatures below about 1325 F.* If intermediate hardnesses are desired, it is necessary to adjust the holding time at 1400 F or to vary the temperature slightly to obtain the lower hardness. The hardening operation decreases the toughness and ductility, but it does not affect the corrosion resistance. Therefore, this steel, as hardened, is suitable for applications requiring a higher hardness than can be obtained in the 18-8 steels and a higher corrosion resistance than is shown by any of the stainless steels that can be hardened by quenching.

Long time holding at about 850 F should be avoided since it will embrittle the alloy and may make it susceptible to a form of intergranular corrosion. The original mechanical properties can be restored by a relatively short heating at a temperature over 930 F (17).

SPECIAL PURPOSE CORROSION RESISTANT STEELS

A number of corrosion resistant steels have been developed for special applications where the 18-8 type with molybdenum is not sufficiently resistant. Most of these steels contain both copper and

---

* The original microstructure and mechanical properties may be restored by heating to a temperature over 1650 F (17).

molybdenum while in many cases the chromium and nickel are appreciably higher than in 18-8. The copper appears to augment the beneficial effect of molybdenum in increasing the corrosion resistance, particularly to sulphuric acid. Table 34 gives typical compositions of wrought steels of this type. Sometimes, the alloy content is increased to such an extent that the materials are no longer malleable enough to be hot worked commercially and therefore are used in the form of castings. These modifications are discussed in Section VIII (pp 245-247). Nonferrous corrosion resistant alloys are covered in Section X (pp 332-334).

TABLE 34

Typical Compositions of Special Purpose Wrought Corrosion Resistant Steels

%C	%Mn	%Si	%Cr	%Ni	%Cb	%Cu	%Mo
0.08	1.2	0.4	24	13	0.9	1.1	1.2
0.25	0.7	3.2	20	21	...	1.2	1.2
....	...	...	18	8	...	1.5	1.5
0.05	...	...	18	8	...	1.0	2.5
0.06	0.6	3.5	20	24	...	1.5	3.0
0.08	2.0	0.7	20	27	...	2.0	3.0
0.15	0.2	0.3	18	8	...	2.2	3.5
0.07	0.7	0.5	19	22	...	1.0	3.5
0.03	1.2	0.3	20	25	...	1.5	4.3
0.06	1.5	0.5	20	26	0.6	...	4.5

In general, the physical and mechanical properties of these wrought steels are similar to those of the 18-8 with molybdenum except that the ductility and toughness tend to be somewhat lower. The corrosion resistance naturally varies with the composition. Figures 95 and 96 show the results of tests of a representative composition in various hydrochloric and sulphuric acid solutions.

HIGH CHROMIUM STEELS WITH MOLYBDENUM

Molybdenum increases the corrosion resistance of steels with 12 to 30% chromium and up to 3% nickel. It is widely used in the free machining and cutlery types. In the latter case, it has been stated that the molybdenum addition also improves the ability to hold a cutting edge.

Non-hardenable ferritic chromium steels with the following approximate chemical compositions have been used considerably in Europe for their corrosion resistant properties:

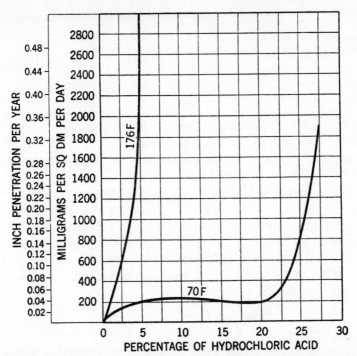

FIG 95 – Results of Laboratory Tests in Aerated Hydrochloric Acid on a Steel Containing about 20% Cr, 24% Ni, 1.5% Cu, 3.0% Mo and 3.5% Si (18)

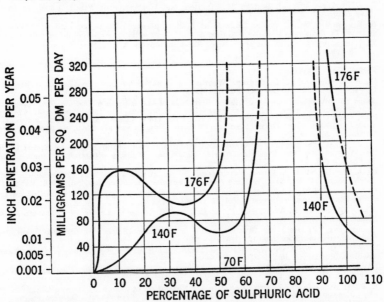

FIG 96 – Results of Laboratory Tests in Aerated Sulphuric Acid on a Steel Containing about 20% Cr, 24% Ni, 1.5% Cu, 3.0% Mo and 3.5% Si (18)

%C	%Mn	%Si	%Cr	%Mo	%Ti
0.09	0.5	0.4	17	1.5	...
0.09	0.5	0.4	17	1.5	0.7
0.15	0.3	0.4	25	2.5	1.7
0.12	0.6	1.0	23	3.4	1.2

The first three steels are stated to have a corrosion resistance to air, salt water and dilute bleaching solutions equal to that of 18-8. The last steel is highly resistant to a number of chemicals, notably phosphoric acid.

The 17% chromium compositions have a high degree of cold formability. Sigma is one of the stable phases in the higher chromium steels. Nevertheless, these compositions can be successfully hot and cold worked by avoiding the formation of sigma phase during hot working. If sigma phase is formed by hot working below 1700 F or by reheating to about 1600 F, it can be retransformed to the ductile ferrite by air cooling from about 1800 F (19).

Section V — Bibliography

(1) R. D. Thomas, Jr. "Crack Sensitivity of Chromium-Nickel Stainless Weld Metal" Metal Progress, Vol 50 (1946)

(2) R. Franks, W. O. Binder and C. R. Bishop "The Effect of Molybdenum and Columbium on the Structure, Physical Properties and Corrosion Resistance of Austenitic Stainless Steels" Transactions, ASM, Vol 29 (1941)

(3) Steel Products Manual, Section 24, Stainless and Heat-resisting Steels, Supplementary Information, issued by the AISI (April 16, 1947)

(4) Steel Products Manual, Section 24, Stainless and Heat-resisting Steels, issued by the AISI (May 1946)

(5) R. Franks and W. O. Binder "Effects of Low-temperature Heat-treatment on Elastic Properties of Cold-rolled Austenitic Stainless Steels" Transactions, AIME, Vol 140 (1940)

(6) W. Mutchler "Corrosion-Resistant Steel Sheet in Marine Atmospheres" Proceedings, ASTM, Vol 46 (1946)

(7) G. L. Snair, Jr. "Atmospheric Corrosion Tests on Corrosion-Resistant Steel" Proceedings, ASTM, Vol 46 (1946)

(8) W. A. Wesley and H. R. Copson "Weathering Behavior of Corrosion-Resistant Steel Insect Screens" Proceedings, ASTM, Vol 46 (1946)

(9) Based on information in the published literature of the Allegheny-Ludlum Steel Corporation, Brackenridge, Pennsylvania; Carpenter Steel Company, Reading, Pennsylvania; Crucible Steel Company of America, New York City, New York; Climax Molybdenum Company, New York City, New York; Crane Company, Chicago, Illinois; Eastern Stainless Steel Corporation, Baltimore, Maryland

(10) M. A. Scheil, O. Zmeskal, J. Waber and F. Stockhausen "First Report on Stress Corrosion Cracking of Stainless Steel in Chloride Solutions" Welding Research Supplement to the Journal, AWS, Vol 22 (1943)

(11) M. A. Scheil and R. A. Huseby "Studies on Stress Corrosion Cracking of Austenitic Stainless Steels, Types 347 and 316" Welding Research Supplement to the Journal, AWS, Vol 23 (1944)

(12) C. P. Larrabee "Corrosion of Steels in Marine Atmospheres and in Sea Water" Transactions of the Electrochemical Society, Vol 87 (1945)

(13) E. H. Wyche, L. R. Voigt and F. L. LaQue "Corrosion in Crevices" Transactions of the Electrochemical Society, Vol 89 (1946)

(14) Anonymous "Proposal for Standardization of Stainless Steels" Meddelande fran Stal-och Metallnormskommitten No. 12 (1947)

(15) Working Data for Carpenter Stainless Steels, published by the Carpenter Steel Company, Reading, Pennsylvania (1946)

(16) Corrosion and Heat Resisting Steels, published by the Crucible Steel Company of America, New York City, New York

(17) E. Börje Bergsman and C. Ericsson "On the Formation of Sigma Phase and Other Embrittlement Reactions in Stainless and Heat Resistant Steels" Värmländska Bergsmannaföreningen Annaler (1942)

(18) Technical Information on Worthite, published by the Worthington Pump and Machinery Corporation, Harrison, New Jersey

(19) F. B. Foley "The Sigma Phase in Certain High-Chromium Steels" Metallurgia, Vol 34 (1946)

SECTION VI

WROUGHT STEELS FOR
ELEVATED TEMPERATURE SERVICE

Molybdenum has been repeatedly shown to be a very effective addition for increasing the elevated temperature strength of all types of steel. Consequently, molybdenum is added to most steels used in applications requiring high strength at elevated temperatures. Confirmation of the practical benefits of such additions from the standpoint of the designer is found in the maximum allowable working stresses at various temperatures as specified by the ASME codes for unfired pressure vessels and boilers (Appendix E). Molybdenum has the additional advantage of reducing the embrittlement in service of low alloy steels (pp 12, 13). It also promotes the formation of the Widmanstätten or upper bainitic structures found to be propitious for high elevated temperature strength up to about 1000 F (1).

CARBON-MOLYBDENUM STEELS*

Low carbon steels with 0.5% molybdenum are widely used for pipe, valves, flanges and fittings in superheated steam plants, in superheater tubing and in cracking furnace tubes where the corrosion resistance of carbon steel is satisfactory.** They are also utilized for large boilers and other types of pressure vessels where their higher strength, as compared with unalloyed steels of the same carbon content, makes possible a reduction in wall thickness with a consequent weight saving. The wide use of these steels is mainly the result of their excellent elevated temperature strength and good weldability.

---

* Maximum allowable working stresses under the ASME code are given in Appendix E.
** There are some indications that molybdenum may improve the corrosion resistance in super-heated steam. Laboratory tests for 500 to 1300 hours at 1100 and 1200 F showed no significant difference between unalloyed and carbon-molybdenum steel (2) ; but, much longer tests, lasting for about 16,000 hours, showed a marked reduction in the corrosion rate of carbon-molybdenum steels as compared with unalloyed steels under average power plant conditions in 1100 F steam (3).

Figures 97, 98, 99 and 100 depict graphically the superior creep and rupture strengths obtained in commercial steels by the addition of 0.5% molybdenum.* The creep strength is further increased by larger amounts of molybdenum (Figures 100 and 101). Figure 9 (p 11) indicates that the same holds true for short time tensile strength at elevated temperatures. Although intergranular cracks have been observed in these steels under certain conditions of stress and temperature, it appears that they may be avoided by limiting the maximum permissible creep to a value under 0.5 to 1% (6, 14).

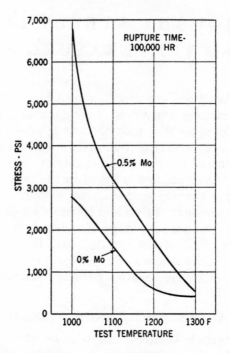

FIG 97 – Effect of Molybdenum on the Stress Rupture Strength of Annealed Steel (4)

	Analyses			
	%C	%Mn	%Si	%Mo
0% Mo....................................	0.15	0.46	0.28	....
0.5% Mo....................................	0.13	0.49	0.25	0.52

* Microstructure and actual grain size are particularly important at temperatures around 900 to 1000 F. A coarse Widmanstätten structure, such as is formed in coarse grained carbon-molybdenum steel by normalizing from over about 1750 F and in fine grained steel by normalizing from over about 1875 F (9), has considerably higher elevated temperature strength than a fine pearlitic structure (see, for example (10)). There is, however, a tendency for all structures to approach a common rupture and creep strength after extremely long exposures at 900 and 1000 F (11, 12).

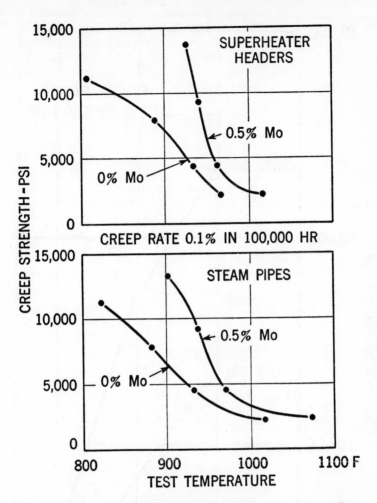

FIG 98 – Effect of Molybdenum on the Creep Strength of Superheater Header and Steam Pipe Steels (data on carbon steels from (5);
data on carbon-molybdenum steels from (6))

	Analyses								Condition
	%C	%Mn	%Si	%P	%S	%Cr	%Mo	%Ni	
Superheater Headers									
0% Mo........	0.24	0.61	0.10	0.040	0.032	....	....	....	1650 F air cooled
0.5% Mo.....	0.26	0.51	0.11	0.038	0.032	....	0.47	....	1690 F air cooled; tempered 1220 to 1240 F
Steam Pipes									
0% Mo........	0.135	0.47	0.18	0.028	0.037	....	....	....	hot rolled
0.5% Mo.....	0.09	0.52	0.22	0.023	0.034	0.08	0.50	0.26	1690 F air cooled

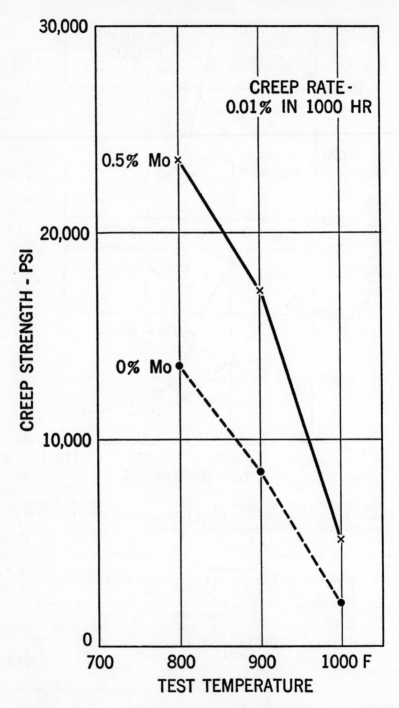

FIG 99 – Effect of Molybdenum on the Creep Strength of Annealed
Steel with 0.10 to 0.20% C and 0.50% Si max (7)

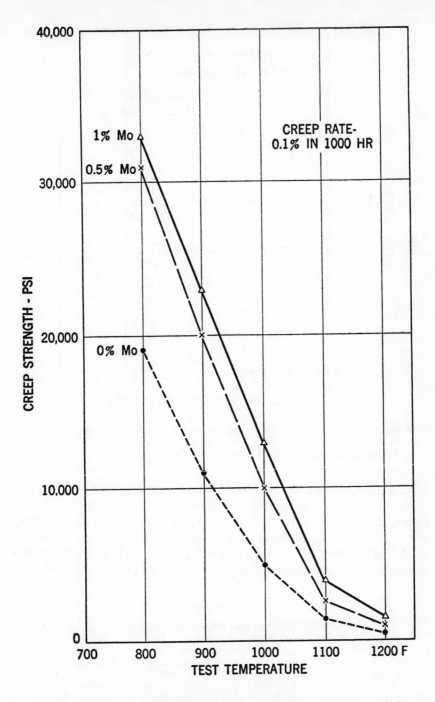

FIG 100 – Effect of Molybdenum on the Creep Strength of Annealed Steel with 0.08 to 0.20% C and 0.50% Si max (8)

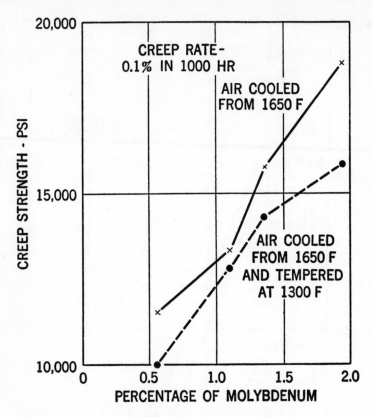

FIG 101 – Effect of Molybdenum and Prior Treatment on the Creep Strength at 1000 F of Steels with 0.13 to 0.21% C and 0.16% Si max (actual grain size ASTM 8 to 9) (13)

Hydrogen, at the high pressures and temperatures encountered in many chemical processes and in some oil refining operations, causes rapid decarburization of unalloyed steel as well as embrittlement. Molybdenum increases the resistance to attack by hydrogen, so the safe operating limits of molybdenum steels in contact with hydrogen are higher than those for unalloyed steel (Table 35).

TABLE 35

Operating Limits of Unalloyed and Carbon-Molybdenum Steels in Contact with Hydrogen at High Temperatures and Pressures (15)

	Maximum Temperature F for a Pressure of				
	100	500	1000	2000	15,000 psi
Unalloyed......................	975	530	495	455	430
0.5% Mo......................	975	885	690	640	620

Welding

A certain amount of hardening may occur during welding when no preheat is used. A minimum preheating temperature of 300 F has been recommended. A range of 300 to 600 F is frequently given, as with an intermittent form of preheating—such as a removable induction coil—it is possible to heat to 600 F and allow welding to proceed until the temperature drops to 300 F, when the preheating coil is again replaced. A welding rod depositing metal of the same composition as the parent metal is generally used. The welded joints are frequently stress relieved at 1200 to 1300 F.

Graphitization

In recent years, as a result of a failure in a power plant, a great deal of attention has been given to the subject of graphitization at about 850 to 1100 F. The operating temperatures of carbon steel are generally so low that graphitization does not occur in service. Random graphitization, however, has been observed in carbon steel cracking still tubes operating at an estimated temperature of about 1100 F (16). Since the carbon-molybdenum steels are used more widely than unalloyed steel at the temperatures where graphitization may occur, power plant engineers and metallurgists have studied the phenomenon chiefly in connection with molybdenum steels. The usual amounts of molybdenum impart some resistance to graphitization (17, 18). Investigations have indicated that the use of aluminum for deoxidation is conducive to graphitization, so many specifications now limit the amount added to ½ lb per ton. The addition of chromium appears to be a useful means of retarding or preventing graphitization (19, 20). Whether or not graphitization occurs in a given steel appears to depend on a combination of factors, including prior heat treatment, processing (welding, hot upsetting), stress relief after welding, residual stresses, and service conditions (temperature, time, stress). Random graphitization has little effect on the properties of the steel and is not a serious problem. Under certain critical combinations of the factors mentioned above, however, graphitization may occur in the form of chains or "eyebrows", which are detrimental to the ductility of the steel.

A tentative specification has been set up calling for about 0.15% carbon, 0.5% chromium and 0.5% molybdenum (21). A low aluminum addition for deoxidation is assured by specifying a McQuaid-Ehn grain size of one to five. This requirement, along with the chromium content, is an additional safeguard against graphitization. Regardless of deoxidation practice, no graphite has been found in chromium-molybdenum steels with 0.50% chromium or more after 10,000 hours at 900, 1050 and 1200 F (20). Despite the chromium addition, it is believed by some that this steel will be satisfactory only up to 950 F. No one composition has yet been agreed upon for nominal operating temperatures of 1000 F*, although attention has been focused on various molybdenum-vanadium steels with 0.5 to 1.25% molybdenum. As normalized, a 0.5% molybdenum – 0.2% vanadium steel has somewhat better creep strength than carbon-molybdenum steel in the same condition (Table 36). As normalized and tempered, the molybdenum-vanadium steel has significantly better stress rupture strength (Figure 102) and creep strength (Figure 103) than either the carbon-molybdenum or a low chromium-molybdenum steel. At higher temperatures, the higher chromium-molybdenum steels to be discussed next are most generally considered.

TABLE 36
Comparative Creep Properties of Molybdenum and Molybdenum-Vanadium Steels (14)

Temperature F	Stress for Rupture in 100,000 hr 1000 psi		Stress for 0.2% Creep in 100,000 hr 1000 psi	
	Mo	Mo-V	Mo	Mo-V
915	21.1	32.5	15.7	19.3
970	11.4	20.2	7.4	11.6
1020	6.0	12.3	3.6*	4.5*

* approximate

	Analyses										Condition
	%C	%Mn	%Si	%P	%S	%Cr	%Cu	%Mo	%Ni	%V	
Mo	0.09	0.66	0.24	0.026	0.022	0.27	0.05	0.49	tr	....	1785 F, air cooled
Mo–V	0.14	0.47	0.16	0.02	0.016	0.10	0.06	0.54	0.07	0.20	1830 F, air cooled

CHROMIUM-MOLYBDENUM STEELS**

Chromium-molybdenum steels with 1 to 9% chromium have proved to be invaluable as intermediate steels for applications where better oxidation and corrosion resistance are needed than are obtainable with carbon-molybdenum steels but where the more highly alloyed steels such as the 18-8 with molybdenum are not required. The economic advantages of these steels have been widely recognized as attested by their use in steam plants, oil refineries, hydrogenation processes and other elevated temperature work.

* It is interesting to note that a chromium-molybdenum steel (0.15% carbon – 0.8% chromium – 0.55% molybdenum) and a molybdenum-vanadium steel (0.12% carbon – 0.55% molybdenum – 0.25% vanadium) have been used in Great Britain for piping for service at temperatures over 950 F (22).
** Maximum allowable working stresses under the ASME code are given in Appendix E.

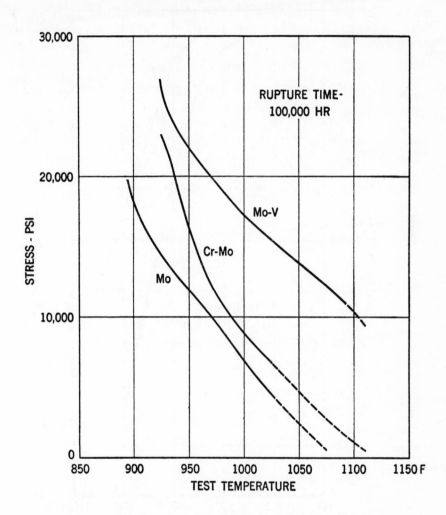

FIG 102 – Comparative Stress Rupture Strengths of Molybdenum, Chromium-Molybdenum and Molybdenum-Vanadium Steels (23)

	Type Compositions						Condition
	%C	%Mn	%Si	%Cr	%Mo	%V	
Mo......................	0.15*	0.60	0.3*	0.25*	0.55	....	1720 F air cooled
Cr–Mo........	0.15*	0.50	0.3*	0.80	0.55	....	1720 F air cooled
Mo–V..................	0.13*	0.60	0.3*	....	0.55	0.28	1760 F air cooled; tempered five hours at 1275 F

*max

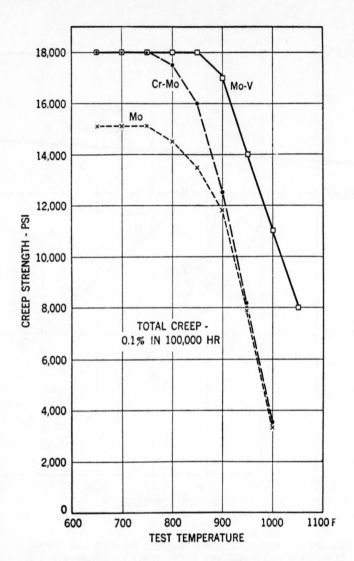

FIG 103 – Comparative Creep Strengths of Molybdenum, Chromium-Molybdenum and Molybdenum-Vanadium Steels (24)

	Type Compositions						Condition
	%C	%Mn	%Si	%Cr	%Mo	%V	
Mo.....................	0.15*	0.60	0.3*	0.25*	0.55	....	1720 F air cooled
Cr–Mo.................	0.15*	0.50	0.3*	0.80	0.55	....	1720 F air cooled
Mo–V...................	0.13*	0.60	0.3*	....	0.55	0.28	1760 F air cooled; tempered five hours at 1275 F

* max

The first attempts to use intermediate chromium steels for elevated temperature service showed the necessity for molybdenum additions to minimize temper brittleness. Tubes with 5% chromium but no molybdenum were introduced for oil refinery service. Although the original impact strength was high, the room temperature impact strength became so low after prolonged holding at high temperatures that there were numerous brittle failures on cleaning the tubes during shut-downs (25). As indicated by Figure 104,

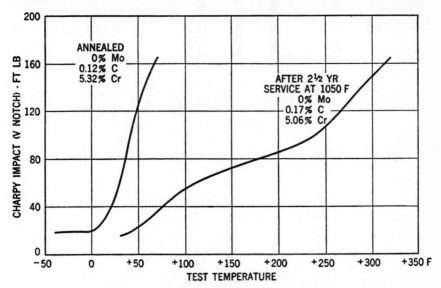

FIG 104 – Effect of Service at 1050 F on the Temperature-Impact Curve of 4 to 6% Cr Steel without Molybdenum (26)

the effect of the elevated temperature service (in this case at 1050 F) was to produce typical temper brittleness (see pp 4-9). Molybdenum has proved so effective as a practical cure for this temper brittleness (Figure 105), that today it is specified in substantially all the intermediate chromium steels.

Molybdenum plays a dual role as it also produces a notable improvement in the elevated temperature strength of the chromium steels, as illustrated by the effect of 0.5% molybdenum in raising the creep strength of the 4 to 6% chromium steel (Figure 106). Although the most common molybdenum addition is about 0.5%, larger amounts, up to 2% at least, progressively increase the elevated temperature strength. This improvement is found in short time tensile tests (Figure 107) as well as in long time stress rupture tests (Figure 108). The combined effect of chromium and molybdenum on the creep and rupture strengths is shown in Figures 109, 110 and 111.

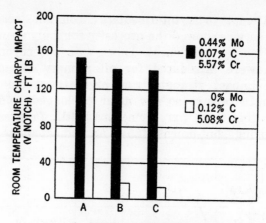

A - ORIGINAL CONDITION - ANNEALED

B - AFTER 3452 HR EXPOSURE AT
    700 F IN CRACKING STILL

C - AFTER 3147 HR EXPOSURE AT
    810 F IN CRACKING STILL

FIG 105 – Effect of Molybdenum on the Embrittlement of 4 to 6% Cr Steel by Holding at 700 and 810 F (26)

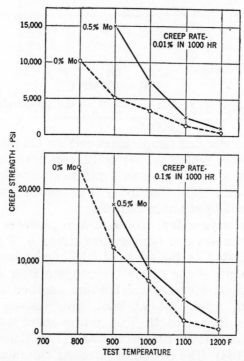

FIG 106 – Effect of Molybdenum on the Creep Strength of Annealed Steel with 4 to 6% Cr (steel with 0% Mo – 0.21% C; steel with 0.5% Mo – 0.15% C max. both steels have 0.5% Si max) (7)

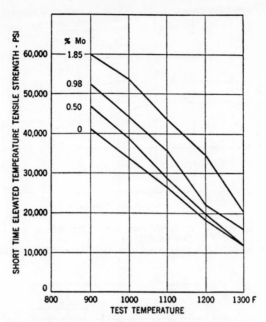

FIG 107 – Effect of Molybdenum on the Short Time Elevated Temperature Tensile Strength of Annealed Steel with 0.15% C max, 0.50% Si max and 9% Cr (7)

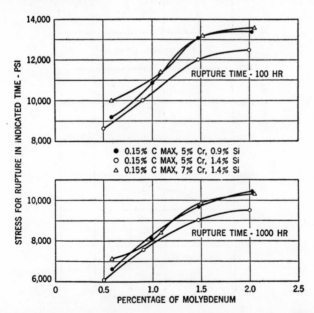

FIG 108 – Effect of Molybdenum on the Stress Rupture Strength at 1200 F of 5 and 7% Cr Steels (5% Cr – 0.5 and 1% Mo steels were annealed by slow cooling from 1550 F; all others steels were air cooled from 1750 F, reheated to 1500 F for six hours and air cooled) (27)

[157]

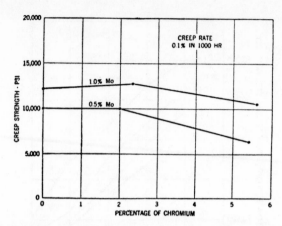

FIG 109 – Effect of Molybdenum and Chromium on the Creep
Strength at 1000 F of Steels with 0.16% C max and 0.50% Si max.
Prior treatment: 1650 F air cool plus temper at 1300 to 1380 F (13)

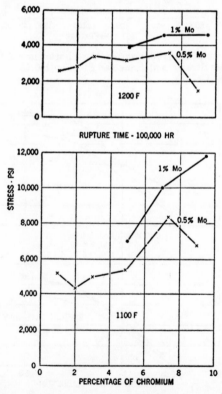

FIG 110 – Effect of Molybdenum and Chromium on the Stress Rupture Strength of Annealed Steel with 0.15% C max (about 0.75% Si
in 7 and 9% Cr steels; about 1.2 to 1.5% Si in all others) (data on
1% Cr – 0.5% Mo, 9% Cr – 0.5% Mo and 7% Cr – 1% Mo from (28);
all other data from (4))

[158]

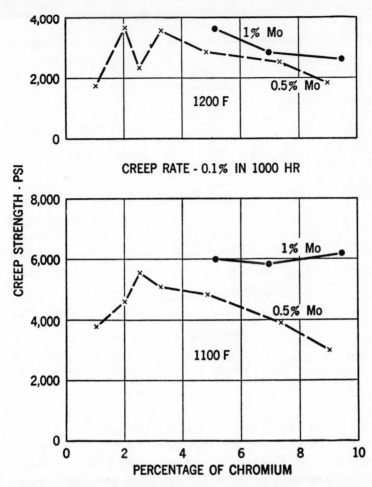

FIG 111 – Effect of Molybdenum and Chromium on the Creep Strength of Annealed Steel with 0.15% C max (about 0.75% Si in 2.5, 7 and 9% Cr steels; about 1.2 to 1.5% Si in all others) (data on 1% Cr – 0.5% Mo and 9% Cr – 0.5% Mo from (28); data on 7% Cr – 1% Mo from (29); all other data from (4))

The primary function of the chromium in these steels is to increase the corrosion and oxidation resistance at elevated temperatures. As shown in Figure 112, the corrosion resistance improves progressively with increasing chromium content although the amount of improvement varies with the corroding conditions. In general, however, the 4 to 6% chromium-molybdenum steel is found to be about four to ten times as corrosion resistant as carbon steel, while the 7% chromium-molybdenum steel is about twice, and the 9% chromium-molybdenum steel is about four times as resistant as the 4 to 6% chromium-molybdenum grade. The oxidation resistance also

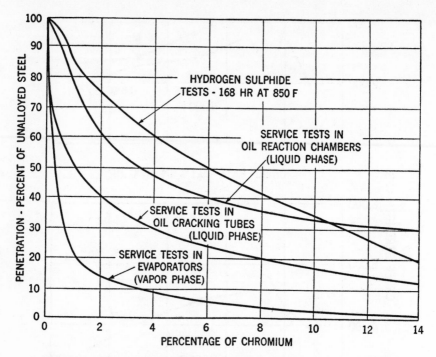

FIG 112 – Effect of Chromium on the Rate of Corrosion at Moderate Temperatures under Various Conditions (service tests represent averages of tests made at ten refineries) (30)

increases with the chromium content (Figure 113) as does the resistance to attack and decarburization by hydrogen (Table 37). Consequently, for any specific service, a steel must be chosen with sufficient chromium to resist the corrosion and oxidation at the temperature involved. At least about 0.5% molybdenum is usually present to minimize temper brittleness and to increase the elevated temperature strength.

While molybdenum steels with 0.5% molybdenum have many excellent characteristics, they break with relatively low elongation, particularly at about 950 to 1000 F, when rupture occurs after a prolonged time period. The addition of chromium will minimize this low hot ductility (31). For example, stress rupture tests of 0.5% molybdenum steel showed an elongation of about 5% for a fracture time of 1500 hours at 1000 F, while a 4 to 6% chromium-molybdenum steel had an elongation of about 48% (32). This low elongation at rupture is often attributed to a lack of sufficient oxidation resistance so this effect of chromium seems to be related to its action in increasing oxidation resistance.

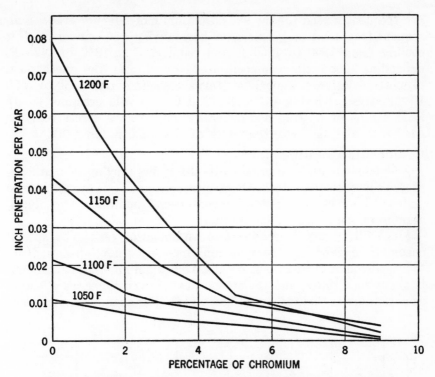

FIG 113 – Effect of Chromium on the Oxidation Resistance of Steel.
Based on 1000 hr test in air (all steels contain 0.15% C max, 0.50%
Si max and 0.45 to 1.50% Mo) (7)

TABLE 37

Operating Limits of Unalloyed and Chromium-Molybdenum Steels in Contact
with Hydrogen at High Temperatures and Pressures (15)

	Maximum Temperature F for a Pressure of				
	100	500	1000	2000	15,000 psi
Unalloyed......................	975	530	495	455	430
1% Cr–0.5% Mo..............	1140	1095	1040	650	620
2% Cr–0.5% Mo..............	1190	1150	1110	770	750
3% Cr–0.5% Mo..............	1280	1190	1150	1050	....
6% Cr–0.5% Mo..............	1800	1250	1195	1130	....

Welding

Hardening on welding increases roughly with the chromium
content. For the lower chromium-molybdenum steels, preheating
at 300 to 600 F is stated to be quite suitable. For the steels with
4% chromium or more, preheating is essential except for small
diameter tubes. A minimum preheating temperature of about 500
F is desirable. Welding rods depositing the same composition as
the parent metal are usually used, although austenitic electrodes

[161]

are frequently used for the 9% chromium-molybdenum grade. Subsequent treatment may consist of normalizing and tempering (air cooling from 1600 to 1800 F and tempering at 1250 to 1425 F, depending upon the composition involved and the mechanical properties desired), annealing (furnace cooling from 1550 to 1650 F) or stress relieving (1300 to 1350 F). In field erection, where local means of heating are generally employed, a stress relief is used with at least twice the width of the weld heated (33).

Composition Modifications

Molybdenum and chromium are the basic alloying constituents of these intermediate steels. Other elements, however, are sometimes added. The most common of these special additions are silicon, aluminum, columbium and titanium.

Since silicon and aluminum improve oxidation resistance, special chromium-molybdenum compositions have been developed with up to 2% silicon or with 1% silicon and 0.5% aluminum. The aluminum is about four times, and the silicon about seven times, as effective as chromium in this respect (Figure 114). For example, an increase

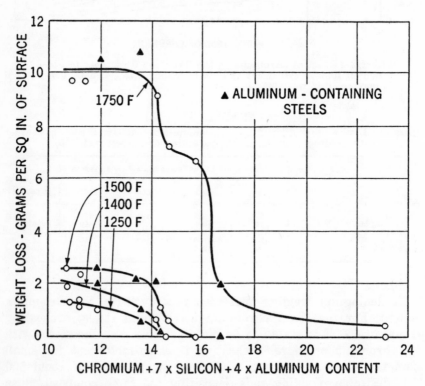

FIG 114 – Effect of Chromium, Silicon and Aluminum on the Oxidation Resistance of Steel. Based on 1000 hr test in air (34)

in the silicon content from 0.2 to 1.2% in a 2.5% chromium – 0.5% molybdenum steel increases the initial temperature of rapid oxidation in air by about 90 F (35). The silicon appears to be more effective in higher chromium steels. The addition of 1 to 2% silicon to a 5% chromium – 0.5% molybdenum steel makes it possible to raise the maximum service temperature under oxidizing conditions from 1200 to 1500 F (4). Service data from certain refineries indicate that the aluminum addition and the increased silicon improve the resistance to hot petroleum products (36). The drawback of these additions is that they lower the creep strength of chromium-molybdenum steels (13).

Columbium and titanium are added to minimize air hardening. If columbium is present in an amount equal to seven to nine times the carbon content or titanium equal to five to seven times the carbon content, hardnesses over about 200 Brinell will not be obtained in the chromium-molybdenum steels on air cooling from temperatures up to about 1800 F.* Their presence, therefore, prevents undesirable hardening on cooling from hot working operations. However, some hardening will occur on normalizing from higher temperatures where the columbium or titanium carbides are at least partially dissolved. The columbium and titanium do not prevent the steels from hardening during welding but the welded parts can be annealed simply by air cooling from about 1500 F whereas the chromium-molybdenum steels would otherwise require furnace cooling. These additions have little effect on the corrosion and oxidation resistance.

"18-8" WITH MOLYBDENUM**

The addition of molybdenum to "18-8" not only improves corrosion resistance (see Section V) but also is equally effective in increasing elevated temperature strength.*** This steel, therefore, offers high creep strength combined with excellent corrosion and oxidation resistance at temperatures up to about 1550 F. To avoid embrittlement after prolonged holding in the temperature range of approximately 1400 to 1600 F, the composition must be adjusted to produce a substantially austenitic structure (see pp 127, 128).

The superior short time tensile strength of "18-8" with molybdenum is accompanied by a ductility at temperature superior to that of 18-8 without molybdenum (Figure 115). There is a similar marked increase in creep strength (Figure 10, p 11) and stress rupture strength (Figure 116).

---

* Larger amounts are generally not added as they will cause a two phase structure which is likely to have poor hot working characteristics and low toughness (36).
** Maximum allowable working stresses under the ASME code are given in Appendix E.
*** Modifications of this composition used mainly in gas turbines are discussed on pp 181-192.

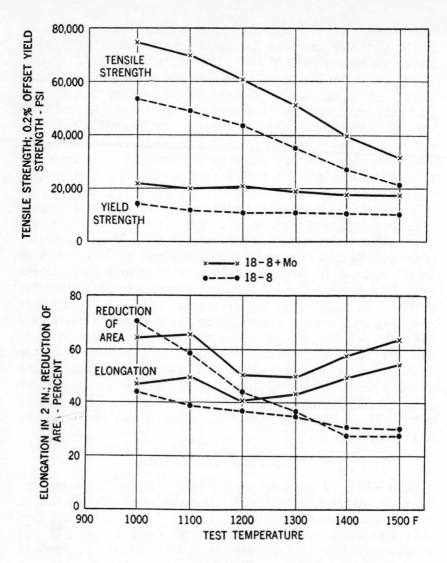

FIG 115 – Short Time Elevated Temperature Tensile Properties of 18-8 and "18-8" plus Molybdenum (4)

	Analyses					
	%C	%Mn	%Si	%Cr	%Ni	%Mo
18–8......................	0.06	0.50	0.61	17.75	9.25	....
18–8+Mo.................	0.08	1.40	0.45	16.42	13.44	2.81

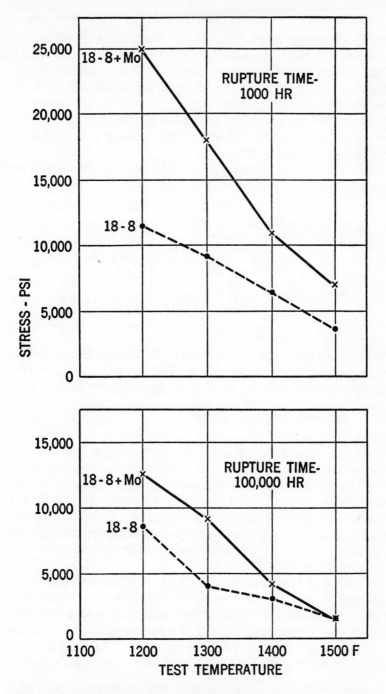

FIG 116 – Stress Rupture Strength for 18-8 and "18-8" with 2.5% Molybdenum (AISI types 304 and 316) (37)

BOLTS*

Elevated temperature bolt steels must have good mechanical properties at room as well as elevated temperatures and must remain tough after prolonged service. The molybdenum present in most of the compositions used up to about 1200 F increases the elevated temperature strength and reduces embrittlement after long periods at temperature (see pp 12, 13). Molybdenum also minimizes softening and structural changes during long holding at elevated temperatures (38).

Some widely used compositions for elevated temperature bolt steels are listed in Table 38.** Although certain of the compositions,

TABLE 38
Representative Compositions of Elevated Temperature Bolt Steels

No.	%C	%Mn	%Si	%Cr	%Mo	% Other
1	0.40	0.80	0.25	0.95	0.20	....
2	0.45	0.55	0.25	0.95	0.35*	0.25 V
3	0.45	0.55	0.65	1.25	0.50	....
4	0.20	0.45	0.35	5.00	0.50	....
5	0.40	0.80	0.25	0.60	0.50	1.10 W
6	0.40	0.80	0.25	0.95	0.60	....

* some specifications require 0.45 min

such as 4, are used at temperatures up to 1200 F, the most common service temperatures range from 750 to 1050 F. The elevated temperature properties of some of these steels are indicated by the creep values in Table 39 and the short time tensile properties in Figures 117, 118, 119, 120 and 121.

Relaxation tests*** are sometimes considered to be more indicative of the properties of elevated temperature bolt steels than creep tests since the load on a bolt decreases as the bolt stretches. When the initial stress has decreased to approximately 15,000 psi, re-tightening of the bolt is generally required to prevent leakage in the usual high pressure flanged joint (39). Figure 122 shows the results of relaxation tests on an oil quenched chromium-molybdenum steel and a normalized chromium-molybdenum-vanadium steel under an initial stress of 30,000 psi.

The effect of heat treatment will be noted in the creep values in Table 39 of the chromium-molybdenum-vanadium steel and the chromium-molybdenum-silicon steel. Figure 123 also indicates the effect of heat treatment on a slightly higher silicon modification of the chromium-molybdenum-vanadium steel. The chromium-molybdenum-vanadium steel, for example, is used in both the oil quenched

---

* Maximum allowable working stresses under the ASME code are given in Appendix E.
** A steel similar to the 5% chromium-molybdenum steel of this table is used for elevated temperature nuts. A carbon-molybdenum steel with about 0.45% carbon and 0.30% molybdenum is also used for this application.
*** A relaxation test is one in which strain rather than stress is held constant.

TABLE 39
Creep Strengths of Various Elevated Temperature Bolt Steels

No.*	Type	Heat Treatment	Creep Rate**	Creep Strength, 1000 psi				Ref
				900 F	950 F	1000 F	1100 F	
1	Cr-low Mo	oil quenched +tempered	A B	10.0 20.5	7.5 15.0	5.0 11.0	....	(39) (39)
2	Cr-Mo-V	air cooled +1200 F	A B	40.0 59.0	30.0 45.0	15.0 28.0	3.0 10.0	(39) (39)
		1650 F oil quenched +1200 F	a	....	20.4	12.4	....	(40)
3	Cr-Mo-Si	1725 F air cooled +1180 F	a b	....	....	7.8 23.0	....	(41) (41)
		1650 F oil quenched +1250 F	a	13.5	5.5	2.6	....	(42)
4	5 Cr-Mo	oil quenched +1100 F	b	....	....	....	3.0	(43)
5	Cr-Mo-W	1750 F air cooled +1270 F	b	....	....	10.0	....	(43)
6	Cr-high Mo	oil quenched +tempered	a	13.2	4.5***	....	....	(44)

* for type composition, see Table 38
** A—total creep of 1% in 100,000 hr
   B—total creep of 1% in 10,000 hr
   a —creep rate of 1% elongation in 100,000 hr
   b —creep rate of 1% elongation in 10,000 hr
*** 960 F

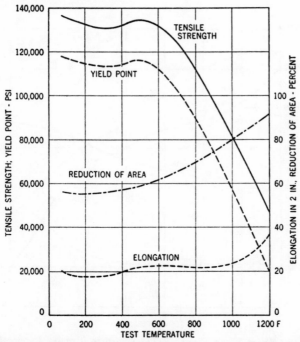

FIG 117 – Short Time Elevated Temperature Tensile Properties of Chromium-Molybdenum Steel. Type composition: 0.40% C, 0.80% Mn, 0.95% Cr, 0.20% Mo; oil quenched and tempered (39)

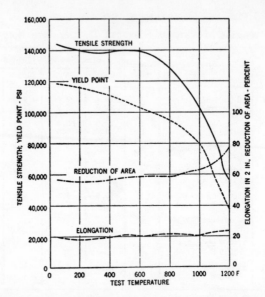

FIG 118 – Short Time Elevated Temperature Tensile Properties of
Chromium-Molybdenum-Vanadium Steel. Type composition: 0.45%
C, 0.55% Mn, 0.95% Cr, 0.35% Mo, 0.25% V. Air cooled and tempered
at about 1200 F (39)

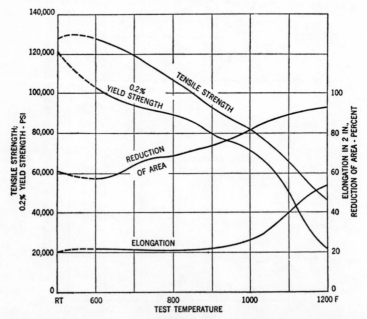

FIG 119 – Short Time Elevated Temperature Tensile Properties of
Chromium-Molybdenum-Tungsten Steel with 0.36% C, 0.76% Mn.
0.21% Si, 0.54% Cr, 0.59% Mo, 1.11% W, Oil Quenched from 1625 F
and Tempered at 1280 F (45)

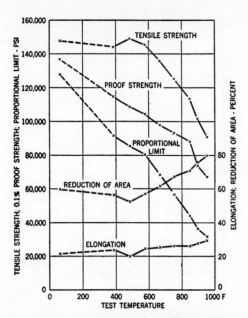

FIG 120 – Short Time Elevated Temperature Tensile Properties of
Chromium-Molybdenum Steel. Type composition: 0.40% C, 0.55% Mn,
1.25% Cr, 0.6% Mo, oil quenched and tempered at 1220 F. Rate of
stressing 1120 psi per minute up to proof strength and 1/24 in. per
minute thereafter. 1 1/8 in. diameter bars. Gage length four times
the square root of the area (44)

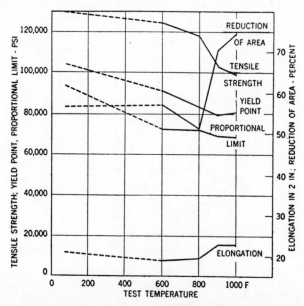

FIG 121 – Short Time Elevated Temperature Tensile Properties of
Chromium-Molybdenum Steel with 0.38% C, 0.94% Mn, 0.29% Si,
1.01% Cr, 0.46% Mo. Air cooled from 1650 F and tempered at 1185 F

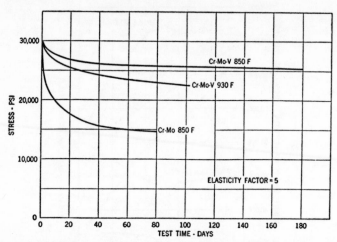

FIG 122 – Relaxation Curves on Chromium-Molybdenum and Chromium-Molybdenum-Vanadium Bolt Steels (39)

	Type Compositions					Condition
	%C	%Mn	%Cr	%Mo	%V	
Cr–Mo.................	0.40	0.80	0.95	0.20	....	oil quenched and tempered
Cr–Mo–V.............	0.45	0.55	0.95	0.35	0.25	air cooled and tempered

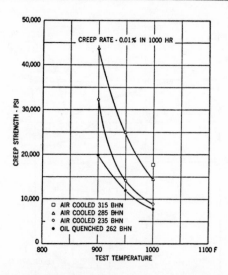

FIG 123 – Effect of Heat Treatment and Hardness on the Creep Strength of a Chromium-Molybdenum-Vanadium Steel. Bar analysis: 0.29% C, 0.46% Mn, 0.75% Si, 1.27% Cr, 0.54% Mo, 0.24% V. Air cooled specimens cooled from 1725 F and tempered six hours at 1200 F (315 Brinell), 1225 F (285 Brinell) and 1250 F (235 Brinell). Oil quenched specimens quenched from 1650 F and tempered six hours at 1275 F. Heat treated in one inch round bars (42)

[170]

and the air cooled conditions. The structure is predominantly bainite in air cooled material and in large oil quenched sections but martensite in smaller oil quenched sizes. While the tempered martensite has a lower creep strength, it has higher room temperature yield and impact strengths for the same hardness (40). Therefore, the heat treatment for any specific application must be selected on the basis of the relative importance of room and elevated temperature properties.

The tempering temperature should be at least 100 F over the service temperature but even this margin is not always enough to assure a stable structure. The stability of the structure under stress for prolonged periods at temperature must be considered as changes in structure will usually be accompanied by changes in the elevated temperature strength. In this connection, it is reported that some molybdenum steels show a decrease in creep rate during the creep test. This phenomenon is attributed by some to the formation of a fine precipitate believed to be a molybdenum-rich carbide (46).

STAYBOLTS

A molybdenum staybolt steel with under 0.1% carbon and about 0.5% molybdenum is giving good service in locomotive boilers. Staybolt materials with low elevated temperature strength tend to deform at the operating temperatures, with the result that undesirable leakage occurs at the staybolts. For example, double refined wrought iron has only a short time tensile strength of 18,400 psi and a yield point of 12,050 psi at 1000 F. The improved elevated temperature strength of the molybdenum staybolt steel (Table 40) minimizes the deformation during operation and thus decreases leakage.

TABLE 40
Room and Short Time Elevated Temperature Tensile Properties
of Molybdenum Staybolt Steel

Test Temperature	Room	1000 F
Tensile Properties:		
Tensile Strength, psi	61,800	47,800
Yield Point, psi	44,800	31,500
Elongation, percent*	34.5	26.5
Reduction of Area, percent	76.8	78.7

* in 2 in. on a 0.505 in. diameter specimen machined from an as-rolled, machine straightened bar

STEAM TURBINE ROTORS

Turbine rotors must have sufficient strength to withstand rotation and transmit heavy loads over long periods of time. Alloy steels have become necessary because of increases in operating speeds, temperature and blade loads (47). In some cases, the controlling factor in selecting the type of alloy steel is the temperature of service; in other cases, it is purely a question of obtaining sufficient strength to withstand high loads (47). In either case, molybdenum is used advantageously. ASTM A 293-46T requires 0.40 to 0.60% molybdenum when the rotors are to be used at high temperatures. In addition, molybdenum improves the hardenability and thus makes it possible to obtain the needed strength in large rotors even without liquid quenching. Table 41 lists three compositions used in this

TABLE 41
Representative Compositions of Steam Turbine Rotors

%C	%Mn	%Si	%Cr	%Mo	%Ni	%V
0.30	0.75	0.30	....	0.50	....	*
0.30	0.75	0.30	....	0.50	2.75	*
0.30	0.75	0.30	0.90	0.50	2.50	*

* a small vanadium content is sometimes present

country. The usual treatment is either a normalize or a double normalize and temper, although liquid quenching may be used for sizes under ten inches in diameter. A significant improvement in creep strength has been obtained, at least with some rotor steels, by heating to 2010 F, then cooling to 1470 F and equalizing the temperature prior to air cooling (48).

The uniformity of properties at room and elevated temperatures in rotors of a 3% chromium-molybdenum and a chromium-molybdenum-nickel steel is illustrated in Table 42. The proof strength values, both at room and elevated temperatures, are much superior to those of carbon and carbon-molybdenum steel rotors. There is no significant change in the elevated temperature tensile properties of these steels after holding for 1½ years at 750 to 930 F. The Izod impact at temperature, however, tends to increase with time. On cooling to room temperature after such long time exposure, there is some loss of notched bar toughness but not of the elongation and reduction of area values in tensile tests. The chromium-molybdenum-nickel steel has better creep strength than the chromium-molybdenum steel. For example, under a load of 35,170 psi at 840 F, various forgings of the former had an average creep rate at 500 hours of 5 x 10⁻⁷ in. per in. per hr while the equivalent rate for the latter was about 3 x 10⁻⁶ (48).

TABLE 42

Room and Short Time Elevated Temperature Properties of Turbine Rotors (48)

No.	%C	%Mn	%Si	%P	%S	%Cr	%Mo	%Ni	Type of Melting	Ingot Weight tons	Diameter of Body of Forging in.	Heat Treatment quenched in	Heat Treatment quenched from F	Heat Treatment tempered at F	Izod Impact ft lb
1	0.28	0.56	0.25	0.022	0.035	3.26	0.41	0.20	acid open hearth	36	31	air	1650	1220	23†, 23†, 19†
2	0.28	0.58	0.23	0.024	0.033	3.15	0.42	0.21	acid open hearth	21½	24	oil	1635	1245	...
3	0.25	0.54	0.21	0.027	0.030	0.38	0.43	2.23	acid open hearth	36	34	air	1560	1150	...

No.	Temperature F	Test Position*	Direction	Tensile Strength 1000 psi	Proof Strength, 1000 psi 0.1%	0.2%	0.5%	Elongation percent**	Reduction of Area percent	Izod Impact ft lb
1	room	outside	tangential	106.6	80.4	81.8	83.3	20	47	41, 34, 40
		midway	tangential	105.6	78.0	80.0	81.5	12	28	40, 41, 30
		near center	tangential	103.9	77.5	79.1	81.1	16	33	57, 63, 87
		core	longitudinal	103.9	75.8	77.1	78.8	25	61	
	750	outside	tangential	86.0	66.8	69.0	72.4	17.5	55	...
		midway	tangential	86.9	63.2	67.6	72.8	14.5	34	...
		near center	tangential	85.8	65.2	68.5	72.8	20	43	...
		core	longitudinal	84.9	63.8	67.6	71.2	20	61	...
	850	outside	tangential	79.7	62.7	66.1	69.9	21	56.5	...
		midway	tangential	79.7	62.3	65.4	69.7	19	46	...
		near center	tangential	78.8	61.8	65.4	70.8	20	49	...
2	room	outside	tangential	101.4	75.9	77.3	78.4	23	56	...
		near center	tangential	97.2	74.1	75.5	77.7	22	52	...
		core	longitudinal	98.1	70.3	74.1	78.4	26	67	...
	750	outside	tangential	88.6	62.9	65.6	69.4	18.5	51	...
		near center	tangential	78.4	59.8	63.2	68.8	18	49	...
		core	longitudinal	79.1	61.6	65.2	68.5	18.5	64	...
	850	outside	tangential	77.1	60.3	63.4	67.6	22.5	51	...
		near center	tangential	76.4	60.9	63.8	66.8	18	51	...
		core	longitudinal	72.4	58.7	62.0	65.9	24	67	...
3	room	outside	tangential	99.9	69.4	73.2	77.1	22	40	24, 15, 20
		near center	tangential	84.7	51.1	53.8	57.3	17	30	30, 34, 86
		core	longitudinal	88.3	54.9	57.8	60.5	14	18	40, 44, 44
	750	outside	tangential	85.3	56.7	62.9	69.7	23	47	...
		near center	tangential	69.4	37.4	43.0	50.8	23	51.5	...
		core	longitudinal	75.3	44.1	49.7	55.6	23	51	...

* all specimens from the mid-body
** in 2 in. on a 0.564 in. diameter specimen
† average

EXHAUST VALVES

Exhaust valve steels for internal combustion engines must have a combination of high hot hardness, resistance to stretching at operating temperatures and good resistance to the products of combustion of the fuel.

For years, the standard steels for automotive valves have been chromium-silicon compositions with about 5 to 10% chromium and 1 to 4% silicon. These steels are highly resistant to scaling and can be hardened to reduce the wear on the stem and tappet ends. Molybdenum is sometimes added to increase their elevated temperature strength (Table 43) and to decrease their susceptibility to temper brittleness (Figure 124) (51). The molybdenum appears to be most effective in minimizing temper brittleness if the silicon is under 3% (Figure 125). Where heavily leaded fuels are not used, such steels are suitable for both intake and exhaust valves on automobiles*, while the lower silicon types have even been recommended for low power aircraft engines. A nickel-containing modification with about 0.3% carbon, 1% manganese, 3.5% silicon, 7.5% chromium, 0.6% molybdenum and 1.8% nickel is used for stems of automotive exhaust valves in combination with an austenitic steel head.

Recently, there has been a trend towards more highly alloyed steels as a result of the corrosive action of the tetra-ethyl lead or other anti-knock additions used to increase the octane rating of the fuel. It is rather difficult to devise any single test that accurately duplicates service conditions. Experience has shown that the over-all indication of five tests is quite reliable: scale resistance in the products of combustion under oxidizing and reducing conditions; corrosion resistance in the exhaust condensate; hot hardness; resistance to softening after exposure at high temperatures; and relative susceptibility to attack by the anti-knock additions. The operating temperature will depend to a large extent on whether or not the valve is internally cooled with sodium. The sodium-cooled exhaust valves used on most aircraft and on some heavy duty trucks have a maximum temperature of about 1200 F while solid exhaust valves of automobiles may operate at 1300 to 1400 F or even higher. Therefore, hot hardness tests are generally made in this range to indicate the resistance to stretching in service while subsequent room temperature tests show the tendency to soften. The resistance to attack by leaded fuels in service has been correlated reasonably closely with the weight loss in molten lead oxide, bromide and sulphate salts. This latter test is of particular importance if

---

* Where service temperatures are low, automotive intake valves are commonly made of low alloy engineering steels with about 0.35 to 0.5% carbon (such as 4047, 4140, 8640).

TABLE 43

Effect of Molybdenum on Room and Elevated Temperature Tensile Properties of Chromium-Silicon Intake and Exhaust Valve Steels (49)

Compositions				Heat Treatment		Typical Mechanical Properties at Room Temperature			Typical Mechanical Properties at 1110 F**	
%C	%Si	%Cr	%Mo	Hardening F	Tempering F	Tensile Strength 1000 psi	Elongation percent*	Izod Impact ft lb	Tensile Strength 1000 psi	Elongation percent*
0.60	1.55	5.80	....	1800 air cool	1440 water or oil quench	123.2	24	15	44.8	50
0.60	1.00	6.00	0.5	1800 oil quench or air cool	1360 oil quench	143.4	23	15	56.0	50
0.45	3.30	8.50	....	1920 oil quench	1560 water or oil quench	127.7	24	9	40.3	60
0.50	3.00	7.50	0.5	1920 oil quench	1560	160.1	25	11	49.3	55

* in 2 in. on a 0.564 in. diameter specimen
** straining rate 0.028 per min

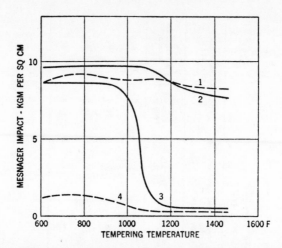

FIG 124 – Effect of Molybdenum on the Susceptibility of Chromium-Silicon Steels to Temper Brittleness (all specimens slowly cooled from tempering temperature) (50)

No.	Analyses			
	%C	%Si	%Cr	%Mo
1......................	0.40	2.26	9.07	0.31
2......................	0.40	2.75	8.44	0.39
3......................	0.48	2.73	10.21	....
4......................	0.41	3.60	8.92	....

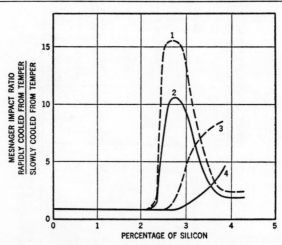

FIG 125 – Effect of Silicon and Molybdenum on the Susceptibility of Chromium-Silicon Steels to Temper Brittleness (50)

Curve 1 — 8 to 10% Cr; after six tempers
Curve 2 — 8 to 10% Cr; after one temper
Curve 3 — 8 to 10% Cr, 0.35% Mo; after six tempers
Curve 4 — 8 to 10% Cr, 0.35% Mo; after one temper

the valves are to be used without a protective hard surfacing of a chromium-cobalt-tungsten (Stellite) or a 20% chromium – 80% nickel (Brightray) alloy.

Steel 2 in Table 44 is widely used for automotive exhaust valves. As-forged or as-rolled, this steel contains ferrite and austenite. On holding for 14 hours at 1400 F, it is hardened to about Rockwell C 38 to 42 by the transformation of the ferrite to the hard sigma phase. From the comparison with the chromium-silicon steel 1, it will be noted that Steel 2 has much better hot hardness, equal or better scale resistance, and vastly improved resistance to corrosion by leaded fuels.

Steels 3 and 4 in Table 44 are intended for internally cooled valves. Steel 3 has long been standard for aircraft engine exhaust valves. Small amounts of molybdenum up to 1% are often present in this composition. Since it is austenitic and non-hardenable by heat treatment, the stem is nitrided to reduce stem wear and scuffing. The seat is faced with chromium-cobalt-tungsten (Stellite) or a 20% chromium – 80% nickel (Brightray) alloy. Steel 4 is an improvement over Steel 3 with much greater scale resistance, higher hot hardness at 1290 and 1470 F and considerably better resistance to lead attack. It is also claimed to have superior resistance to intergranular corrosion by the sodium coolant (52).

High carbon high chromium steels with molybdenum and sometimes with cobalt (similar to Types 4B and 4C in Table 54, p 196) have been used for exhaust valves in low power aviation motors as well as for intake valves and exhaust valve seats in aircraft engines.

A steel with about 0.4% carbon, 0.6% manganese, 0.3% silicon, 20% chromium, 1.4% molybdenum and 20% nickel has been used for aircraft exhaust valves in U.S.S.R. (54).

SPRINGS

A chromium-molybdenum-vanadium steel with approximately 0.4% carbon, 2.5% chromium, 0.5% molybdenum and 0.25% vanadium is used for springs that are exposed to elevated temperatures of the order of 750 to 1000 F during service. Among the applications where this steel has proved satisfactory are piston rod packing springs and by-pass valve springs on locomotives (55).

For springs to withstand higher loads or slightly higher temperatures (for example, safety valve springs in highly preheated steam), it may be necessary to employ high speed steel, such as the 6-5-4-2 type (Steel 3 in Table 62, p 216). In the case of springs, the use of a double temper is considered essential (56); usually the best results are obtained by an initial temper at 1050 F, followed by

TABLE 44
Properties of Exhaust Valve Steels (52, 53)

No.	%C	%Mn	%Si	%Cr	%Ni	%Mo	%W
1	0.45	....	3.25	8.5	....	....	....
2	0.45	0.75	0.75	24.0	4.8	3.0	....
3	0.45	....	0.55	14.0	14.0	....	2.4
4	0.45	1.00	0.55	25.0	14.0	2.5	....

Compositions

No.	Scale Resistance*		Corrosion Resistance in Exhaust Condensate	Brinell Hardness** at				Rockwell Hardness					Relative Attack***		
	oxidizing atmosphere	reducing atmosphere		930 F	1110 F	1290 F	1470 F	before test	after test at 930 F	1110 F	1290 F	1470 F	PbO. PbBr2 1550 F	PbO 1800 F	2PbO. 3PbSO4 1800 F
1	50	140	poor	174	87	39	18	C33	C32	C30	C28	C24	41	100	200
2	40	50	complete	230	167	110	63	C41	C38	C39	C39	C36	2	35	1
3	2600	1600	complete if unnitrided; poor if nitrided	162	144	98	55	C25	C25	C28	C26	C23	20	126	26
4	50	40	complete if unnitrided; poor if nitrided	....	125	113	76	B94	....	B94	B94	B94	12	47	0.3

* total loss in mg after 200 hr (300 cycles) in a special test in which samples are heated to a maximum temperature of 1800 F and cooled to 400 to 650 F in 40 min cycles. A special kerosene fuel with an anti-knock addition of 10 cc tetra-ethyl lead per gallon is burned with 15 to 16 lb dry air per lb of fuel for the oxidizing atmosphere and with 12 to 13 lb dry air per lb of fuel for the reducing atmosphere
** by mutual indentation test
*** after 6 min exposure to the molten lead salt at the indicated temperature

[178]

cooling to room temperature and a second temper at 1150 F. These springs will successfully withstand a total combined stress of 40,000 psi at 700 F and 20,000 psi at 800 F (56).

GAS TURBINE STEELS*

Molybdenum-containing steels naturally are prominent in gas turbine applications in view of the outstanding elevated temperature strength conferred by the molybdenum. The older steels, such as the 18-8 with molybdenum and the chromium-molybdenum steels of the 4140 type, are used in some of the turbosupercharger and gas turbine parts that are either not highly stressed or not subject to particularly high temperatures. But, for the vitally important wheels (disks) and blades which must withstand high stresses at high temperatures, it has been necessary in most cases to develop new alloys.

Ferritic Steels

Although the creep strength of ferritic steels generally falls rapidly above 1000 F, they can be used in two types of gas turbine wheels: 1) wheels designed so the rim temperature is under 950 F**, and 2) composite wheels with the center portion made of a ferritic steel and the hotter rim of an austenitic steel, or nonferrous alloy.

Gas turbine wheels of the first type are made of Steels 2 to 6 (Table 45). Room and elevated temperature mechanical properties of some of these steels are tabulated in Table 46. Steel 1 (Table 45) is used in large composite wheels, where it is joined by arc welding to a rim of an austenitic steel or nonferrous alloy.***

TABLE 45
Compositions of Some Ferritic Steels Used for Gas Turbine Wheels

No.	%C	%Mn	%Si	%Cr	%Mo	%Ni	%V	%W	Reference
1	0.40	0.7	0.3	0.8	0.25	1.85	....	...	(60)
2	0.2	...	...	2.8	0.4	....	0.8	...	(59)
3	0.25	0.4	0.4	3.0	0.5	....	0.75	0.5	(61)
4	0.6	0.5	1.2	6.0	0.5	....	....	...	(61)
5	0.4	0.4	0.3	1.1	0.7	....	....	...	(61)
6	0.4	0.6	0.3	3.0	0.8	....	0.2	...	(61)

In temperature ranges where ferritic steels can be used, they offer the following advantages over austenitic steels: easier forgeability†

---

* The steels are discussed here. Information on the cobalt and nickel base alloys with substantially less than 50% iron will be found in Section X, pp 320-330. In both cases the information given is based on publications through 1947. For later developments it is suggested that current literature be consulted.
** For example, the maximum rim temperature of the turbine wheel of the Goblin jet engine is stated to be under 930 F (57, 58), while the wheel temperatures of the German jet engines were claimed not to exceed 660 F (59).
*** Timken Alloy and 19-9DL (Table 47, p 182) as well as N 155 (Table 85, p 321) have been used for the rim (60, 62).
† This ease of forging is particularly advantageous in large wheels where it is hard to "warm work" austenitic steels to produce a suitable room temperature proof strength.

TABLE 46
Mechanical Properties of Some Ferritic Steels used for Gas Turbine Wheels (61)

No.*	Heat Treatment		Room Temperature Mechanical Properties				Creep Strength in 1000 psi for 1% Strain in 300 hr			
	Oil Quenched from F	Tempered at F	Tensile Strength 1000 psi	0.1% Proof Strength 1000 psi	Elongation percent**	Reduction of Area percent	980 F	1020 F	1110 F	1200 F
3	1940	1240	134.4	112.0	18	45	58.2	47.0	30.2	14.6
4	1795	1865	134.4	100.8	20	40	24.6	11.9	6.3	....
5	1580	1165	129.9	96.3	20	40	65.0	35.8	14.1	....
6	1760	1200	134.4	112.0	18	40	49.3	28.0	12.3	....

* for type composition, see Table 45

** gage length = $4\sqrt{A}$

and machinability, less stress owing to the lower thermal expansion and ready attainment by heat treatment of high room temperature proof strength values. On the disadvantageous side, apart from the necessary temperature limitations, are the generally difficult weldability and the greater notch sensitivity below 750 F* (61).

Austenitic Steels

Numerous austenitic steels have been developed for turbosuperchargers and gas turbines. They are used mainly in parts, such as wheels**, which must have high strength at temperatures from about 1000 to 1350 F. Practically all these steels contain molybdenum since "probably the most effective element in contributing high temperature strength to ferrous alloys is molybdenum" (63). Table 47 lists the compositions and applications of the steels in this category that have been used successfully or that have been seriously considered for such use.

Prior condition has an important effect upon the properties of these steels, as is indicated by Figure 126. Warm working*** markedly improves the room temperature yield strength of most of the steels of this type as well as the elevated temperature strength, for limited periods, up to about 1300 or 1350 F.† At 1200 F, for example, warm worked steels of this type usually have better load carrying ability under high stresses for short times, while solution treated or softened steels are better for longer times. The exact time at which the softened steels become superior to the warm worked steels depends upon composition but is generally over 1000 hours (64). A solution treatment prior to warm working usually produces superior rupture strengths at 1200 F but may cause low ductility in the rupture tests. There are possible difficulties in utilizing the beneficial effect of warm working as it may not be easy to warm work large parts to the desired extent. The properties of small bars, however, are reproduced in large forgings when the processing and heat treatment are equivalent (64).

At temperatures over about 1300 to 1350 F, the best elevated temperature properties are generally produced by a solution treatment, at around 2150 to 2300 F, followed by aging. The higher the solution temperature, the lower the ductility will be but the greater the elevated temperature strength. Aging at 1350 F has been stated

---

* An exception is Steel 3 of Table 45. Alternating stress fatigue tests indicate this steel is notably free from notch sensitivity (61).
** See p 179 for ferritic steels used for wheels exposed to lower temperatures.
*** Also called cold work and hot-cold work. It implies plastic deformation below the recrystallization temperature. As commercially applied, it generally involves forging or rolling in the temperature range of 1200 to 1650 F.
† All degrees of warm working are beneficial at test temperatures of 750 F and below. For test temperatures from 750 to 1290 or 1380 F, however, there appears to be an optimum degree of warm working, which is a function of composition and test temperature (65).

TABLE 47

Composition and Applications of Some Austenitic Steels for Turbosuperchargers and Gas Turbines

No.	Designation	Type Compositions											Applications
		%C	%Mn	%Si	%Cb	%Co	%Cr	%Mo	%Ni	%Ti	%W	% Other	
1	19-9WMo	0.10	0.6	0.5	0.4	....	19.0	0.50	9.0	0.3	1.5	....	Diesel turbosupercharger wheels; gas turbine blades, ducts, wheels; welding rods
2	17W (a)	0.45	0.6	1.0	...	....	13.0	1.00	20.0	...	2.2	....	airplane turbosupercharger blades (1933 to 1942 in U.S.A.), wheels (1937 to 1943 in U.S.A.)
3	19-9DL (AMS 5369— sand castings) (AMS 5526— sheet, strip) (AMS 5721 and 5722— bars and forgings)	0.30	1.0	0.5	0.4	....	20.0	1.35	9.0	0.4	1.3	....	gas turbine blades, bolts, collector rings, ducts, exhaust cones, nozzle diaphragm assemblies, tail pipes, wheels
4	CSA (b)	0.25	4.5	0.5	0.5	....	18.5	1.35	5.5	...	1.2	....	wheels (experimental)
5	G. 18B	0.4	0.8	1.0	3.0*	10.0	13.0	2.0	13.0	...	2.5	....	gas turbine blades, rotors, wheels
6	N 153 (c)	0.10	1.5	0.5	1.0	13.0	16.0	3.00	15.0	...	2.0	0.10 N	wheels (experimental)
7	Discalloy	0.04	0.5	0.5	...	....	13.0	3.00	24.5	1.8	...	0.2 Al	wheels (experimental)
8	R. ex 78	0.07	0.8	0.7	...	....	14.0	3.75	18.0	0.6	...	3.6 Cu	gas turbine blades, wheels
9	R. ex 337A	0.25	0.7	0.9	...	7.0	14.5	3.75	18.0	0.8	...	3.5 Cu	gas turbine wheels
10	Gamma Columbium	0.4	1.0	1.0	2.0	....	15.0	4.00	25.0	...	...	....	airplane turbosupercharger wheels (1941 in U.S.A.)
11	S495 (d)	0.45	1.0	0.5	4.0	....	14.0	4.00	20.0	...	4.0	....	airplane turbosupercharger blades
12	Timken Alloy (e) (AMS 5725—bars) (AMS 5726 and 5727— bars and forgings)	0.10	1.5	0.5	...	....	16.0	6.00	25.0	...	...	0.15 N	airplane turbosupercharger blades, wheels; Diesel turbosupercharger blades, wheels; gas turbine rotor assemblies, stationary blades, wheels

* Cb+Ta
(a) also made with about 0.30% C
(b) also known as 4275 Modified and 234-A-5
(c) also made with about 0.35% C
(d) also known as S588 when chromium content is increased to about 19%
(e) also known as 16-25-6

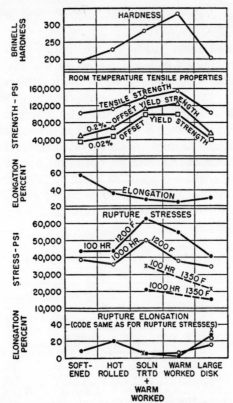

FIG 126 – Effect of Size and Condition on the Room Temperature Mechanical Properties and Elevated Temperature Rupture Strength of Steel No. 3 (19-9DL) (room temperature elongation, percent in 2 in.; rupture elongation, percent in 1 in.) (64)

Condition	Heat No.	Size	Processing
Softened...........	1	⅞ in. sq	forged, then rolled at 2100 to 1750 F; heated two hours at 2050 F, water quenched
Hot Rolled.........	1	⅞ in. sq	forged, then rolled at 2100 to 1750 F; stress relieved one hour at 1200 F
Solution Treated + Warm Worked	3	0.69 in. sq	hammer forged at 2055 to 1300 F to ⅞ in. sq bar; heated one hour at 2100 F, air cooled; heated to 1200 F and reduced 21.8% by rolling; stress relieved at 1200 F
Warm Worked.......	2	about 0.7 in.	hot rolled bar stock heated to 1200 F and reduced 20% by rolling; stress relieved one hour at 1200 F
Large Disk.........	2	19¾ in. in diameter; 3¼ in. thick	billet upset to disk at finishing temperature of 1640 F; stress relieved at 1200 F

Heat No.	Analyses								
	%C	%Mn	%Si	%Cb	%Cr	%Mo	%Ni	%Ti	%W
1..............	0.24	0.43	0.49	0.31	19.50	1.28	9.06	0.25	1.09
2..............	0.33	1.44	0.65	0.35	19.10	1.35	9.05	0.16	1.14
3..............	0.26	0.52	0.57	0.29	18.95	1.22	9.05	0.21	1.19

to be definitely superior to aging at 1500 F, even when the testing is conducted at 1500 F (66).

As will be noted from Table 48, which indicates the usual conditions in which these steels are placed in service, there are four steels that are not customarily used in the warm worked condition. In 7 (Discalloy) the high room temperature yield strength and rupture strength at 1250 F are obtained by precipitation hardening rather than warm working; 8 (R. ex 78) is given a triple treatment which has been found to improve its elevated temperature properties (48, 67); 9 (R. ex 337A) has an optimum combination of room and elevated temperature properties when solution treated and aged (48); while 11 (S495) is stated to have better elevated temperature properties when solution treated and aged than when warm worked (68).

TABLE 48

Usual Condition in which Some Austenitic Gas Turbine Steels are Placed in Service

No.*	Type	Condition
1	19–9WMo	Warm worked and stress relieved at about 1200 F
2	17W	Warm worked and stress relieved at about 1200 F
3	19–9DL	Warm worked and stress relieved at about 1200 F
4	CSA	Warm worked and stress relieved at about 1200 F
5	G. 18B	Oil quenched or air cooled from 2370 F; warm worked at 1200 to 1470 F; aged 20 hr at 1470 F
6	N 153	Warm worked and stress relieved for service temperatures below about 1300 F. Solution treated and aged for service at higher temperatures
7	Discalloy	Cooled from about 1950 F and aged for about 20 hr at 1350 F
8	R. ex 78	Air cooled from 1920 F; aged three hours at 1470 F, air cooled; aged 48 hr at 1110 F
9	R. ex 337A	Cooled rapidly from 2245 F and aged at 1290 F
10	Gamma Cb	Warm worked and stress relieved at about 1200 F
11	S495	Cooled rapidly from 2150 to 2300 F and aged at least ten hours at 1400 F
12	Timken Alloy	Mainly warm worked at 1200 to 1400 F and stress relieved at 1250 to 1275 F. Some used in form of cold rolled or cold drawn bars for blades

* for type composition, see Table 47

While elevated temperature strength is essential, there is no general consensus as to how this property is best measured, nor as to the usefulness of properties such as room temperature mechanical properties and elevated temperature endurance limit. Among the properties that have been considered by many to be significant are: room temperature mechanical properties (Table 49), short time elevated temperature tensile properties (Figure 127), stress rupture strength (Figures 128 and 129), elevated temperature endurance limit (Table 50) and creep strength as evaluated by the creep rate (Table 51) and by the total deformation (Tables 52 and 53).

TABLE 49
Room Temperature Mechanical Properties of Some Austenitic Gas Turbine Steels

No.*	Type	Condition	Tensile Strength 1000 psi	0.2% Offset Yield Strength 1000 psi	0.02% Offset Yield Strength 1000 psi	Elongation percent**	Reduction of Area percent	Reference
1	19-9WMo	1	122.9	....	79.0	26.7	....	(64)
2	17W	2	164.0	152.8	111.0	13.5	23.7	(64)
3	19-9DL	3	154.0	125.0	100.0	24.2	43.8	(64)
4	CSA	4	153.2	105.4	84.6	17.8	22.2	(64)
5	G.18B	5	107.5	62.7a	53.8b	12c	15	(69)
6	N 155	6	118.0	96.0	....	27	62	(70)
7	Discalloy	7	158.0	104.0	....	28	26	(70)
8	R. ex 78	8	94.1	46.8a	43.0b	39d	57	(48)
9	R. ex 337A	9	99.5	54.0a	44.8b	37.5d	43	(48)
10	Gamma Cb	1	160.9	....	118.0	18.2	....	(64)
11	S495	10	132.0	....	35.0	11	14	(68)
12	Timken Alloy	11	148.0	112.0	....	21	41	(71)

* for type composition, see Table 47
** in 2 in. on a 0.505 in. diameter specimen
(a) 0.2% proof strength
(b) 0.05% proof strength
(c) in $L=4\sqrt{A}$
(d) in 2 in. on a 0.564 in. diameter specimen

Conditions
1 20 to 25% reduction at 1200 F after hot rolling
2 Rolled to ⅞ in. sq bar from 2045 to 1800 F; reduced 20.8% by rolling at 1200 F; stress relieved at 1200 F
3 Hot rolled bar stock heated to 1200 F; reduced 20% by rolling; stress relieved one hour at 1200 F
4 Hammer forged; finished at 1200 F; stress relieved one hour at 1200 F
5 Warm worked disk forgings; 18 in. in diameter
6 Forged
7 1950 F cooled in air blast; aged 20 hr at 1350 F
8 1¾ in. rd bar; 1920 F air cooled; aged three hours at 1470 F, air cooled; aged 48 hr at 1110 F
9 1⅜ in. rd bar; 2245 F water quenched; aged 48 hr at 1290 F
10 2250 F water quenched; aged 16 hr at 1500 F; stress relieved four hours at 1250 F
11 1 in. rd hot rolled bar elongated 20% cold; stress relieved four hours at 1250 F

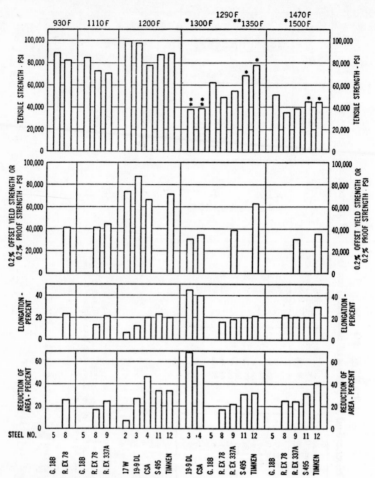

FIG 127 – Short Time Elevated Temperature Properties of Some Austenitic Gas Turbine Steels

No.*	Type	Condition	Reference
2	17W	rolled to ⅞ in. sq bar from 2045 to 1800 F; reduced 20.8% by rolling at 1200 F; stress relieved at 1200 F	(64)
3	19–9DL	(1200 F) hot rolled bar stock heated to 1200 F; reduced 20% by rolling; stress relieved one hour at 1200 F (1350 F) a billet was upset to a disk 19¾ in. in diameter by 3¼ in. thick at a finishing temperature of 1640 F; stress relieved at 1200 F	(64)
4	CSA	(1200 F) hammer forged; finished at 1200 F; stress relieved one hour at 1200 F (1350 F) a disk 20½ in. in diameter by 3⅛ in. thick was forged from 2100 to 1400 F; stress relieved four hours at 1200 F	(64)
5	G.18B	....	(72)
8**	R. ex 78	1920 F air cooled; aged three hours at 1470 F, air cooled; aged 48 hr at 1110 F	(67)
9**	R. ex 337A	1⅛ in. rd bar; 2245 F water quenched; aged 48 hr at 1290 F	(48)
11	S495	2250 F water quenched; aged 16 hr at 1500 F	(68)
12	Timken Alloy	hot rolled bars, elongated 20% at room temperature; stress relieved four hours at 1250 F	(68)

* for type composition, see Table 47
** values for No. 8 and No. 9 are 0.2% proof strength; all others are 0.2% offset yield strength

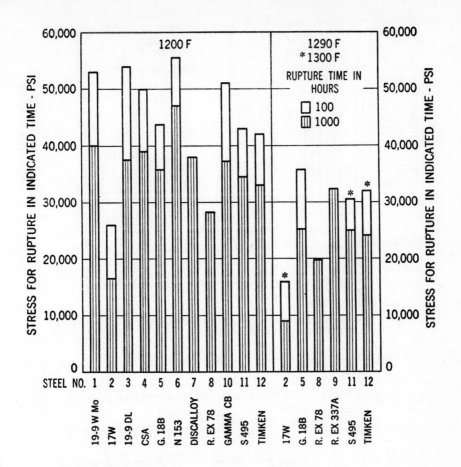

FIG 128 – Stress Rupture Strengths at 1200, 1290 and 1300 F of Some Austenitic Gas Turbine Steels

No.*	Type	Condition	Reference
1	19–9WMo	20 to 25% reduction at 1200 F after hot rolling	(64)
2	17W	warm worked below 1200 F	(73)
3	19–9DL	hot rolled bar stock heated to 1200 F; reduced 20% by rolling; stress relieved one hour at 1200 F	(64)
4	CSA	hammer forged; finished at 1200 F; stress relieved one hour at 1200 F	(64)
5	G. 18B	2370 F solution treated	(69)
6	N 153	forged	(70)
7	Discalloy	1950 F cooled in air blast; aged 20 hr at 1350 F	(70)
8	R. ex 78	1920 F air cooled; aged three hours at 1470 F, air cooled; aged 48 hr at 1110 F	(67)
9	R. ex 337A	2245 F solution treated; aged at 1290 to 1380 F	(48)
10	Gamma Cb	20 to 25% reduction at 1200 F after hot rolling	(64)
11	S495	(1200 F) 2250 F water quenched; aged 16 hr at 1400 F (1300 F) 2250 F water quenched; aged 16 hr at 1500 F	(68)
12	Timken Alloy	solution treated	(63)

* for type composition, see Table 47

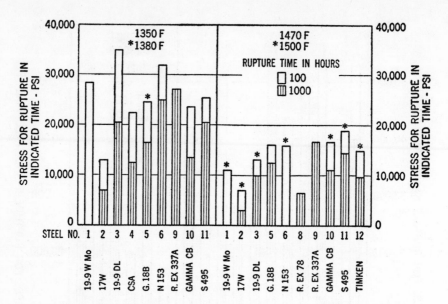

FIG 129 – Stress Rupture Strengths at 1350, 1380, 1470 and 1500 F
of Some Austenitic Gas Turbine Steels

No. *	Type	Condition	Reference
1	19-9WMo	(1350 F) 20 to 25% reduction at 1200 F after solution treatment	(64)
2	17W	(1500 F) warm worked; aged 50 hr at 1500 F	(66)
		warm worked below 1200 F	(73)
3	19-9DL	(1350 F) forged to ⅞ in. sq bar from 2055 to 1300 F; 2100 F air cooled; heated to 1200 F; reduced 21.3% by rolling; stress relieved at 1200 F	(64)
4	CSA	(1500 F) 2250 F oil quenched; aged 50 hr at 1500 F	(66)
		hammer forged; finished at 1200 F; stress relieved one hour at 1200 F	(64)
5	G. 18B	2370 F solution treated	(69)
6	N 153	(1350 F) forged	(70)
		(1500 F) 2200 F water quenched; aged 50 hr at 1500 F	(66)
8	R. ex 78	1920 F air cooled; aged three hours at 1470 F, air cooled; aged 48 hr at 1110 F	(67)
9	R. ex 337A	2245 F solution treated; aged at 1290 to 1380 F	(48)
10	Gamma Cb	(1350 F) 20 to 25% reduction at 1200 F after solution treatment	(64)
		(1500 F) 2250 F oil quenched; aged 50 hr at 1500 F	(66)
11	S495	2250 F water quenched; aged 16 hr at 1500 F	(68)
12	Timken Alloy	solution treated	(63)

* for type composition, see Table 47

TABLE 50

Elevated Temperature Endurance Limits of Some Austenitic Gas Turbine Steels

No.*	Type	Condition	Endurance Limit in 1000 psi at				Reference
			1110 F	1200 F	1290 F	1500 F	
3	19-9DL	1	....	43.0a	....	17.0a	(70)
5	G. 18B	2	±40.3b	±33.6b	±29.1b	±19.0b†	(70)
		3	44.8±19.0e	31.4±22.4c	26.9±18.8c	13.4±12.8c†	(74)
6	N 155	4	....	....	....	22.0a	(69)
8	R. ex 78	5	26.9±22.4c	26.9±18.6c	20.2±12.8c	....	(75)
10	Gamma Cb	6	....	....	....	20.0a	(67)
11	S495	7	....	41.5a	....	....	(75)
		8	....	46.0a	....	....	(68)
12	Timken Alloy	9	....	....	....	19.0a	(70)
		10	....	....	....	....	(70)

* for type composition, see Table 47
† 1470 F
(a) cantilever specimens, tested in reversed bending, for 100 x 10^6 cycles
(b) 40 x 10^6 cycles (about 300 hr)
(c) Haigh type test, with alternating stress superimposed on tensile stress, for 40 x 10^6 cycles (about 300 hr)

Conditions
1   2100 F air cooled; stress relieved four hours at 1200 F
2   2100 F air cooled; reduced 15% at 1200 F; stress relieved four hours at 1200 F
3   2370 F solution treated; stress relieved at 1020 F
4   2370 F solution treated
5   2200 F oil quenched; aged 50 hr at 1500 F
6   1920 F air cooled; aged three hours at 1470 F, air cooled; aged 48 hr at 1110 F
7   2250 F oil quenched; aged 50 hr at 1500 F
8   2000 F water quenched; aged 16 hr at 1300 F
9   2100 F water quenched; stress relieved four hours at 1200 F
10   2150 F water quenched; aged 50 hr at 1500 F

TABLE 51

Creep Strengths of Some Austenitic Gas Turbine Steels

No.*	Type	Condition	Stress in 1000 psi for Indicated Creep Rate						Reference
			1200 F		1350 F		1500 F		
			0.1	1.0	0.1	1.0	0.1	1.0% in 1000 hr	
3	19-9DL	1	24.0	31.0	12.0**	15.0**	......	......	(64, 66)
4	CSA	2	20.5	26.0	11.4**a	16.5**a	9.2**b	11.4**b	(64)
5	G. 18B	3	22.4**	31.4**	15.0**	20.0**	......	......	(69)
6	N 158	4	......	......					(66)
7	Discalloy	..	31 **	36 **					(76)
11	S495	5	16.0		15.5**	18.0**	10.0**	14.0**	(66)
11		6					9.6		(77)
12	Timken Alloy	..	19.0	21.0			6.0	7.0	(63)

* for type composition, see Table 47
** based on minimum creep rate in test
(a) 1880 F
(b) 1470 F

Conditions

1   (1200 F) A billet was upset to a disk 19¾ in. in diameter by 3¼ in. thick at a finishing temperature of 1640 F; stress relieved at 1200 F
  (1350 F) 2250 F oil quenched; aged 50 hr at 1350 F

2   A disk, 20½ in. in diameter by 3⅝ in. thick, was forged from 2100 to 1400 F; stress relieved four hours at 1200 F

3   2370 F solution treated

4   Forged; aged 50 hr at 1350 F

5   A forged disk was furnace cooled from 1950 F; aged 20 hr at 1350 F

6   2250 F water quenched; aged 50 hr at 1400 F (1350 F tests) and 1500 F (1500 F tests)

TABLE 52

"Design Data" for Some Austenitic Gas Turbine Steels at 1200 F

No.*	Type	Condition	Stress in 1000 psi for Indicated Percent Total Deformation in										Reference
			100 hr					1000 hr					
			0.1	0.2	0.5	1.0	(Transition)	0.1	0.2	0.5	1.0	(Transition)	
3	19-9DL	1	13.5	20.5	26.0	29.0	39.0	11.5	17.0	22.5	26.0	32.5	(64)
4	CSA	2	12.5	21.0	28.0	30.0	32.0	10.2	17.0	24.0	26.5	26.0	(64)
5	G. 18B	3	....	24.6	30.2	39.?	....	....	17.9	22.4	31.4	....	(69)
7	Discalloy	4	....	....	39	42	46	....	....	34	35	35	(76)
8	R. ex 78	5	....	....	....	....	....	....	17.9	21.8	....	....	(48)
9	R. ex 337A	5	....	....	....	....	....	....	26.9	31.4	....	....	(48)

* for type composition, see Table 47

Conditions

1   A billet was upset to a disk 19¾ in. in diameter by 3¼ in. thick at a finishing temperature of 1640 F; stress relieved at 1200 F
2   A disk, 20½ in. in diameter by 3½ in. thick, was forged from 2100 to 1400 F; stress relieved four hours at 1200 F
3   2370 F solution treated
4   A forged disk was furnace cooled from 1950 F; aged 20 hr at 1850 F
5   Representative of bar material and small disk forgings

[191]

TABLE 53

"Design Data" for Some Austenitic Gas Turbine Steels at 1470 F

No.*	Type	Condition	Stress in 1000 psi for Indicated Percent Total Deformation in										Reference
			100 hr					1000 hr					
			0.1	0.2	0.5	1.0	(Transition)	0.1	0.2	0.5	1.0	(Transition)	
5	G. 18B	1	....	11.2	13.0	14.1	....	8.7	9.4	10.8	11.2	....	(69, 78)
8	R. ex 78	2	....	....	....	....	....	....	4.5	5.6	....	....	(48)
9	R. ex 337A	2	....	....	....	....	....	....	14.6	15.7	....	....	(48)
11	S495	3	10.3†	12.7†	15.2†	16.4†	15.1†	8.3†	10.1†	11.5†	13.1†	11.0†	(66)

* for type composition, see Table 47
† 1500 F

Conditions

1 2370 F solution treated
2 Representative of bar material and small disk forgings
3 2250 F water quenched; aged 50 hr at 1500 F

Section VI – Bibliography

(1) H. Bennek and G. Bandel "Effect of Structure as a Function of Heat Treatment and Alloy Content on the Creep Strength of Steel" Stahl und Eisen, Vol 63 (1943)

(2) H. L. Solberg, G. A. Hawkins and A. A. Potter "Corrosion of Unstressed Steel Specimens and Various Alloys by High-Temperature Steam" Transactions, ASME, Vol 64 (1942)

(3) I. A. Rohrig, R. M. Van Duzer, Jr. and C. H. Fellows "High-Temperature-Steam Corrosion Studies at Detroit" Transactions, ASME, Vol 66 (1944)

(4) Digest of Steels for High Temperature Service, published by the Timken Roller Bearing Company, Canton, Ohio (1946)

(5) H. J. Tapsell "Creep Properties of Steels Utilized in High-Pressure and High-Temperature Superheater and Steam Pipe Practice. Part I: Carbon Steels" Proceedings of the Institution of Mechanical Engineers, Vol 151 (1944)

(6) H. J. Tapsell and R. W. Ridley "Creep Properties of Steels Utilized in High-pressure and High-temperature Superheater and Steam Pipe Practice Part II: 0.5 per cent Molybdenum Steels" Proceedings of the Institution of Mechanical Engineers, Vol 153 (1945)

(7) Technical Bulletin No. 6-D, Properties of Carbon and Alloy Steel Tubing for High Temperature-High Pressure Service, published by the Babcock and Wilcox Tube Company, Beaver Falls, Pennsylvania (1941)

(8) Bulletin No. 26, Technical Data for Refineries, published by the National Tube Company, Pittsburgh, Pennsylvania (1942)

(9) R. W. Emerson "The Fabrication of Carbon-Molybdenum Piping for High-Temperature Service" Proceedings, ASTM, Vol 41 (1941)

(10) A. E. White and S. Crocker "Effect of Grain Size and Structure on Carbon-Molybdenum Steel Pipe" Transactions, ASME, Vol 63 (1941)

(11) S. H. Weaver "The Effect of Carbide Spheroidization upon the Creep Strength of Carbon-Molybdenum Steel" Proceedings, ASTM, Vol 41 (1941)

(12) S. H. Weaver "The Effect of Carbide Spheroidization upon the Rupture Strength and Elongation of Carbon-Molybdenum Steel" Proceedings, ASTM, Vol 46 (1946)

(13) R. F. Miller, W. G. Benz and W. E. Unverzagt "The Creep Strength of 17 Low-Alloy Steels at 1000 F" Proceedings, ASTM, Vol 40 (1940)

(14) H. J. Tapsell, C. A. Bristow and C. H. M. Jenkins "The Properties and Mode of Rupture of a Molybdenum and a Molybdenum-Vanadium Steel, judged from Prolonged Creep Tests to Fracture" Proceedings of the Institution of Mechanical Engineers, Vol 146 (1941)

(15) Private communication from the Shell Development Company, San Francisco, California (June 1947)

(16) A. B. Kinzel and R. W. Moore "Graphite in Low-carbon Steel" Transactions, AIME, Vol 116 (1935)

(17) H. J. Kerr and F. Eberle "Graphitization of Low-Carbon and Low-Carbon-Molybdenum Steels" Graphitization of Steel Piping, published by the ASME (1945)

(18) S. L. Hoyt, R. D. Williams and A. M. Hall "Summary Report on the Joint E.E.I.-A.E.I.C. Investigation of Graphitization of Piping" Welding Research Supplement to the Journal, AWS, Vol 25 (1946)

(19) G. V. Smith, S. H. Brambir and W. G. Benz "Comparative Graphitization of Some Low-Carbon Steels With and Without Molybdenum and Chromium" Transactions, ASME, Vol 68 (1946)

(20) A. B. Wilder and J. R. Tyson "Graphitization of Steel at Elevated Temperatures" Transactions, ASM, Vol 40 (1948)

(21) ASTM Specification A 280-46aT (1946)

(22) A. Aiton "Steam Piping in the Twentieth Century" paper read before the Derby Society of Engineers, England (March 1945)

(23) Rupture Tests on Colmo Creep Resisting Steels, published by Colvilles Limited, Glasgow, Scotland (1947)

(24) Colmo Creep Resisting Steels, published by Colvilles Limited, Glasgow, Scotland

(25) H. M. Wilten and E. S. Dixon "Aging Embrittlement of 4 to 6% Chromium Steels" Proceedings, ASTM, Vol 34, No. II (1934)

(26) H. M. Wilten "Correlation of Failures from Embrittlement of 4 to 6 Per Cent Chromium Steel with the Notched Bar Impact Test" Transactions, ASM, Vol 23 (1935)

(27) W. G. Hildorf, C. L. Clark and A. E. White "Characteristics of 5.0 and 7.0 Per Cent Chromium Steels with Varying Molybdenum and Vanadium Content" Transactions, ASM, Vol 27 (1939)

(28) Digest of Steels for High Temperature Service, published by the Timken Roller Bearing Company, Canton, Ohio (1939)

(29) Technical Bulletin No. 20, A Guide for Users of High Temperature Steels, published by the Timken Roller Bearing Company, Canton, Ohio (1942)

(30) E. C. Wright "Five Per Cent Chromium Steels" Book of Stainless Steels, published by the ASM (1935)

(31) C. L. Clark and J. W. Freeman "Elimination of the Apparent Hot Brittleness of 0.50 Molybdenum Steel" Transactions, ASM, Vol 30 (1942)

(32) C. L. Clark "High Temperature Properties of Steels" Series of Lectures presented before the San Francisco Chapter, ASM (1945)

(33) E. R. Seabloom "Welding of Alloy Steel Piping" Valve World, Vol 43 (1946)

(34) A. E. White, C. L. Clark and C. H. McCollam "Influence of Chromium, Silicon and Aluminum on the Oxidation Resistance of Intermediate Alloy Steels" Transactions, ASM, Vol 27 (1939)

(35) A. M. Borzdyka "Medium Chromium Thermally Stable Steels" Stal, No. 3 (1946)

(36) C. L. Clark "Alloy Steels Intermediate in Chromium" Metal Progress, Vol 50 (1946)

(37) C. T. Evans, Jr. "Wrought Heat Resisting Alloys for Gas Turbine Service" Metal Progress, Vol 48 (1945)

(38) G. A. Homès "Research on the Structural Mechanism of the Mechanical Behavior of Metals at Elevated Temperatures" Revue de Métallurgie, Vol 36 (1939)

(39) J. J. Kanter "Reducing Creep in Alloy Steel Bolting Materials" Steel, Vol 106 (1940)

(40) A. W. Wheeler "A High Temperature Bolting Material" Transactions, ASME, Vol 63 (1941)

(41) C. L. Clark and A. E. White "Creep Characteristics of Metals" Transactions, ASM, Vol 24 (1936)

(42) Resumé of High Temperature Investigations Conducted During 1945, published by the Timken Roller Bearing Company, Canton, Ohio (1946)

(43) Compilation of Available High-Temperature Creep Characteristics of Metals and Alloys, published by the ASME and ASTM (1938)

(44) Creep-Resisting Steels, published by Samuel Fox and Company, Limited, Sheffield, England

(45) Private communication from the Bethlehem Steel Company, Bethlehem, Pennsylvania

(46) R. F. Miller, R. F. Campbell, R. H. Aborn and E. C. Wright "Influence of Heat Treatment on Creep of Carbon-Molybdenum and Chromium-Molybdenum-Silicon Steel" Transactions, ASM, Vol 26 (1938)

(47) N. L. Mochel "Steels for Turbine Rotor Forgings and Their Heat Treatment" Metals and Alloys, Vol 8 (1937)

(48) C. Sykes "Steels for Use at Elevated Temperatures" Journal of the Iron and Steel Institute, Vol 156 (1947)

(49) Special Alloy and Tool Steels, published by Wm. Jessop and Sons, Limited and J. J. Saville and Company, Limited, Sheffield, England (1945)

(50) Data from Pridantsiv, reproduced in F. F. Khimushin (54)

(51) Fox Alloy Steels, published by Samuel Fox and Company, Limited, Sheffield, England (1942)

(52) A. B. Kinzel and R. Franks, The Alloys of Iron and Chromium – Vol II – High Chromium Alloys, published by the McGraw-Hill Book Company (1940)

(53) S. D. Heron, O. E. Harder and M. R. Nestor "Valves and Valve Seat Material Data Sheet" Metal Progress Data Sheet 103 (1946)

(54) F. F. Khimushin, Zharoupornye Stali dlya Aviatsionnykh Dvigatelei, published by Gosudarstvennoe Izdatelstvo Oboronnoi Promyshlennosti, Moscow, U.S.S.R. (1942)

(55) T. W. Merrill "Vanadium Data Sheet – Vanadium Spring Steels" Vancoram Review, Vol 5 (1947)

(56) F. P. Zimmerli "Selecting Spring Materials" Steel, Vol 121 (1947) ; also "Proper Use of Spring Materials" SAE Quarterly Transactions, Vol 2 (1948)

(57) W. Ker-Wilson, discussion of S. G. Hooker (72)

(58) Anonymous "Turbine Discs Use of Pearlitic Steel in Jet Engines" Iron and Steel, Vol 20 (1947)

(59) T. A. Taylor "Recent Developments in Materials for Gas Turbines" Proceedings of the Institution of Mechanical Engineers, Vol 153 (1945)

(60) W. L. Badger "Metallurgical Development of Materials for Turbosuperchargers and Aircraft Gas Turbines" Iron Age, Vol 158 (1946)

(61) D. A. Oliver and G. T. Harris "Ferritic Discs for Gas Turbines" Metallurgia, Vol 34 (1946)

(62) C. H. Smith Jr. "Precision Forging of High Temperature Alloys" Iron Age, Vol 158 (1946)

(63) M. Fleischmann, "16-25-6 Alloy for Gas Turbines" Iron Age, Vol 157 (1946)

(64) J. W. Freeman, E. E. Reynolds and A. E. White "High-Temperature Alloys Developed for Aircraft Turbosuperchargers and Gas Turbines" Symposium on Materials for Gas Turbines, published by the ASTM (1946)

(65) H. Zschokke "The Effect of Cold Working on the Creep Strength" Schweizer Archiv, Vol 12 (1946)

(66) H. C. Cross and W. F. Simmons "Heat-Resisting Metals for Gas-Turbine Parts" Symposium on Materials for Gas Turbines, published by the ASTM (1946)

(67) C. C. Hall "Gas Turbines Use of Steel Under High Temperature Conditions" Iron and Steel, Vol 19 (1946)

(68) Anonymous "Heat and Corrosion Resistant High Temperature Alloys" Product Engineering, Vol 17 (1946)

(69) D. A. Oliver and G. T. Harris "The Development of a High Creep Strength Austenitic Steel for Gas Turbines" paper presented before the West of Scotland Iron and Steel Institute, Glasgow, Scotland (March 14, 1947) ; also Metallurgia, Vol 35 (1947)

(70) W. O. Binder "Alloys for High Temperature Service" Iron Age, Vol 158 (1946)

(71) F. S. Badger, H. C. Cross, C. T. Evans, Jr., R. Franks, R. B. Johnson, N. L. Mochel and G. Mohling "Superalloys for High Temperature Service in Gas Turbines and Jet Engines" Metal Progress, Vol 50 (1946)

(72) S. G. Hooker "Some Aspects of Gas Turbine Development" Transactions of the North-East Coast Institution of Engineers and Shipbuilders, Vol 62 (1946)

(73) E. Epremian "The Development of a Turbosupercharger Bucket Alloy" Transactions, ASM, Vol 39 (1947)

(74) D. A. Oliver and G. T. Harris "Gas Turbines Work on Flash Butt-welded Discs and Shafts" Iron and Steel, Vol 19 (1946)

(75) R. K. Winkleblack "New Heat Resisting Metals for Engines" Automotive and Aviation Industries, Vol 95 (1946)

(76) H. Scott and R. B. Gordon "Precipitation-Hardened Alloys for Gas-Turbine Service" Transactions, ASME, Vol 69 (1947)

(77) J. B. Henry, Jr. "Characteristics of Three High Temperature Alloys" Iron Age, Vol 159 (1947)

(78) D. A. Oliver and G. T. Harris "Gas Turbine Forgings Development of High Creep Strength Austenitic Steels" Iron and Steel, Vol 20 (1947)

SECTION VII

TOOL STEELS

Alloy tool steels are used because of their superiority to carbon tool steels in the following respects: (1)
  (1) greater hardness and strength in large sections
  (2) less distortion during hardening
  (3) higher toughness at the same hardness in small sections
  (4) greater hardness at elevated temperatures
  (5) greater resistance to abrasion at the same hardness
Molybdenum contributes to the attainment of each of the above advantages.

NON-DEFORMING STEELS

Non-deforming steels constitute one of the major categories of tool steels. The outstanding characteristic of these steels is the slight size change during hardening. Little allowance needs to be made for finishing dies to precise dimensions after heat treatment. Furthermore, these steels can be used for dies that cannot be ground after heat treatment. Since other properties (such as good machinability, hardenability or abrasion resistance) may be desired, in addition to small size change, many different types of non-deforming steels are in current use.

Molybdenum is used in most non-deforming steels and in all the recently developed compositions.

As indicated in Table 54, non-deforming steels may be grouped into four major types. These types have various characteristics in common: low size change, high hardness as quenched, good hardenability, and small danger of quench cracking as compared with carbon steels. They vary greatly, however, in machinability, austenitizing temperature, toughness and wear resistance. In general, with the notable exception of Steel 3A, these steels do not have red hardness properties which would make them useful for hot working applications.

Historically, Type 1 is the oldest. As typified by Steel 1E, these compositions are the well known oil hardening non-deforming steels.

[195]

TABLE 54

Typical Compositions and Heat Treatment Temperatures of Non-Deforming Tool Steels

Type	%C	%Mn	%Si	%Co	%Cr	%Mo	%Ni	%V	%W	Normalizing air cool from F	Annealing cool slowly from F	typical resultant Brinell hardness	Hardening quench in	Hardening from F
1A	0.60	0.40	0.25		1.25	0.35				1525 to 1575	1450 to 1500	197	oil	1475 to 1525
1B	0.70	0.50	0.25		1.00	0.35	1.5			1525 to 1575	1450 to 1500	197	oil	1475 to 1525
1C	0.70	0.80	0.25		1.00	0.35				1525 to 1575	1450 to 1500	197	oil	1475 to 1525
1D	0.75	0.85	0.25			0.80				1550 to 1600	1450 to 1450	197	oil	1400 to 1450
1E	0.90	1.60	0.25		0.35*	0.25		0.25*		1500 to 1550	1375 to 1425	197	oil	1400 to 1450
1F	1.00	0.35	0.25		1.20	0.30				1600 to 1650	1400 to 1450	197	oil	1600 to 1650
1G	1.20	0.25	0.25		0.50	0.25		0.25*	1.7	1650 to 1700	1450 to 1500	200	oil	1575 to 1625
2A	0.70	2.00	0.30		1.00	1.35				not rec †	1325 to 1375	225	air	1525 to 1575
2B	1.00	2.00	0.25		2.00	1.00				not rec †	1375 to 1425**	241	air	1550 to 1600
2C	1.00	3.00	0.25		1.00	1.00				not rec †	1400 and 1850***	241	air	1450 to 1500
3A	0.40	0.35	1.10	3.5	5.00	1.35		0.45		not rec †	1575 to 1625	210	air	1825 to 1875
3B	1.00	0.50	0.25		5.00	1.10		0.50*		not rec †	1625 to 1575	217	air	1750 to 1800
4A	1.00	0.30	0.25		12.00	0.80	1.0*	0.50*		not rec †	1600 to 1650	217	air	1800 to 1850
4B	1.40	0.30	0.25		12.00	0.80		0.50*		not rec †	1600 to 1650	229	air	1800 to 1850
4C	1.50	0.30	0.25		12.00	0.80		0.50*		not rec †	1600 to 1650	229	air	1800 to 1850
4D	2.25	0.30	0.25		12.00	0.80		0.50*		not rec †	1600 to 1650	235	air	1800 to 1850

*optional

**for minimum hardness (229 Brinell maximum), heat to 1600 F, cool at 20 F per hour to 400 F, reheat to 1825 F, hold four hours per inch of section and air cool

***heat to 1400 F, cool at 20 F per hour to 1000 F, reheat to 1850 F and cool at 20 F per hour

†normalizing is generally not recommended for these compositions

In addition to their relatively low cost as compared with that of the other non-deforming grades, the Type 1 steels have the advantage of considerably better machinability. Moreover, these steels can be quenched from low temperatures, thereby minimizing scaling and other heat treating problems. Their hardenability is appreciably greater than that of carbon tool steels (Figure 130), but it is lower than that of the other types of non-deforming steels. Their resistance to breakage in service is intermediate between that of Types 3 and 4, while their wear resistance is the lowest of any of the non-deforming steels.

Type 2 comprises three steels recently developed to give a combination of better hardenability and abrasion resistance than Type 1 steels, combined with a lower austenitizing temperature and greater ease of processing than Type 3 and Type 4 steels. The lower austenitizing temperature means less decarburization and scaling during heat treatment. As an example of the hardenability of these steels, Steel 2A will harden to Rockwell C 60 in an eight inch round on air cooling (4).

The steels in Type 3 have better abrasion resistance than those in the first two groups but have the disadvantages of poorer machinability and much higher austenitizing temperatures. However, in the period since the introduction of these steels, Steel 3B in particular has gained much popularity as a happy compromise between Types 1 and 4.

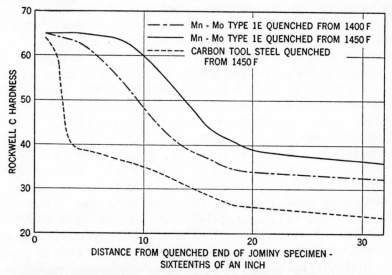

FIG 130 – Comparative Hardenability of Manganese-Molybdenum Non-Deforming Steel Type 1E and 1% C Tool Steel. Standard Jominy specimens but normalizing prior to testing omitted. Each curve represents the average of a band. For type composition of Type 1E, see Table 54 (2, 3)

Type 4 steels have by far the highest abrasion resistance of the non-deforming steels. Their hardenability is so high that, in any normally encountered size, they will harden through. They have the disadvantage of requiring a high austenitizing temperature and of being difficult to machine. As a result of their high carbon and chromium contents, these steels have a tendency to develop a banded structure through carbide segregation which leads to directional properties with respect to toughness and size change (5).

Table 54 also indicates the heat treatment temperatures of these non-deforming steels. The usual precautions should be taken against decarburization in annealing. Type 1 steels are generally not likely to decarburize during hardening. Type 2 steels only occasionally require special precautions against decarburization during hardening. Because of the high austenitizing temperatures required, Types 3 and 4 are subject to decarburization. These steels, therefore, are best heated for hardening in a controlled atmosphere furnace or pack hardened using either a neutral or a carbonaceous medium. Excessive heating temperatures above those recommended for hardening or excessive holding times should be avoided for all types since they will cause the retention of too much austenite with resultant low hardness and possible large size changes. Consequently, it is often advantageous to lower the austenitizing temperature somewhat when larger sizes (which require longer soaking times) are hardened. The air hardening steels in this table may on occasion be oil quenched but this practice entails greater size change.

The non-deforming steels are normally tempered to a hardness of Rockwell C 58 to 62. Figure 131 shows tempering temperature – hardness curves for a typical steel of each of the four types. It will be noted that the curves are similar at the lower tempering temperatures which are most used. At higher tempering temperatures, Types 3 and 4 show pronounced secondary hardening, the amount of which increases with the austenitizing temperature.

Subzero treatments have been applied to some of these steels, particularly Type 3B and Type 4C. As air cooled from 1800 F, Type 3B will retain over 30% austenite, while Type 4C will retain over 20% (9). Since much of this austenite is transformed to martensite by cooling to − 120 F immediately after hardening, higher-than-normal hardnesses of Rockwell C 67 to 68 may thus be obtained. Some of this added hardness is retained after low temperature tempers. Although the size change is greater than in specimens not so treated (10), the higher hardness may be advantageous in some applications.

The unnotched Izod impact – tempering temperature curves in the lower half of Figure 131 indicate the best tempering temperatures for optimum toughness. While there is no quantitative relationship between any impact test and actual shock in service, it is reported that dies tempered at the toughness peaks generally give the best performance provided the corresponding hardness is adequate.

In the consideration of these curves as an indication of the relative toughness of the four types of non-deforming steels, it must be remembered that there are differences in toughness among

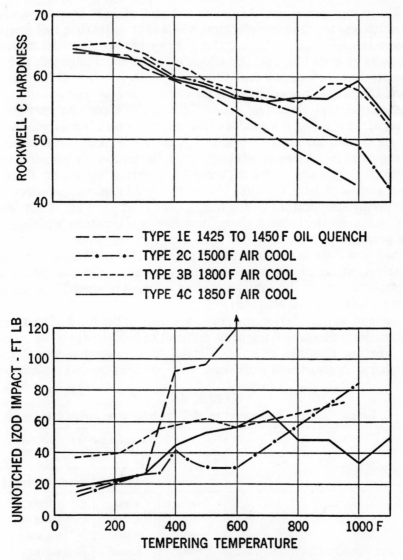

— — — — TYPE 1E 1425 TO 1450 F OIL QUENCH
— • — • — TYPE 2C 1500 F AIR COOL
- - - - - - TYPE 3B 1800 F AIR COOL
———— TYPE 4C 1850 F AIR COOL

FIG 131 – Effect of Tempering Temperature on the Hardness and Unnotched Izod Impact of Four Representative Non-Deforming Tool Steels. For type compositions, see Table 54 (3, 6, 7, 8)

the steels of each type. In general, the higher carbon steels within each type are less tough at a given hardness than the lower carbon steels; for example, Steel 4D is not as tough as Steel 4C. Furthermore, these impact tests were made on longitudinal samples. It is well known that the relative transverse toughness is less in a steel with pronounced structural banding than in a more homogenous steel. In most dies, transverse toughness is as important a factor in service life as longitudinal toughness.

The comparative size change as a result of heat treatment will be much less for the non-deforming steels than for carbon tool steels. There are differences among the various types of non-deforming steels as indicated by Table 55 which gives length change values for one steel of each of the four types. As hardened, the oil hardened Steel 1E changes the most, Steels 2B and 3B are intermediate and the high carbon high chromium Steel 4C changes the least. As tempered, Steel 4C still shows the smallest change, but Steel 3B is largest and Steels 1E and 2B are intermediate. A certain control of the length change may be exerted by adjustments in the tempering temperature although, obviously, the tempering temperature cannot be chosen on the basis of length change alone. Figure 132 shows the effect of tempering temperature on the length change of Steel 1E. A marked expansion accompanies a sharp increase in magnetism within the temperature range 425 to 450 F at which the decomposition of retained austenite is accelerated. There are also differences among the steels of each type; moreover, many factors other than nominal composition affect the actual size change found in specific tools and dies hardened in the shop (5).

Some of the non-deforming steels are used in the form of castings for intricate dies which might be difficult to produce from bar stock or forgings. Castings of Steels 4B and 4C give good service for a number of types of cold work dies. They are heat treated essentially

TABLE 55
Length Change Characteristics of Non-Deforming Steels (11)

Type*	Austenitized five minutes at F**	Average Change in Length Referred to Original Annealed Condition (in. per in.)	
		as–hardened	as–tempered at 375 F
1E...	1425	0.0015	0.00055
2B...	1600	0.0010	0.0005
3B...	1750	0.00115	0.00085
4C...	1825	0.00055	0.00025

* for type composition, see Table 54
** 1E oil quenched; other steels cooled in a water cooled tube at a rate approximately comparable to that of a ¾ in. round bar, air cooled

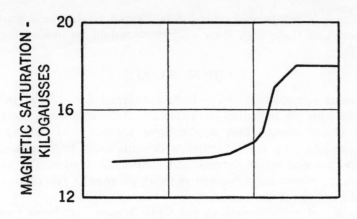

OIL QUENCHED FROM 1425 F

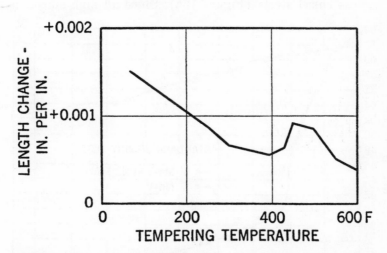

FIG 132 – Effect of Tempering Temperature on the Length Change and Magnetic Saturation of Type 1E. For type composition, see Table 54 (11)

the same as indicated in Table 54, but a tempering temperature of about 1000 F is generally used. A double temper with intermediate cooling to room temperature is often recommended to give the best toughness by insuring complete decomposition of the retained austenite and tempering of the resultant martensite.

The selection of the proper type of non-deforming steel depends on economic considerations which must take into account the intended life of the die, ease of processing, required toughness and wear resistance. For example, steels of Type 1 are preferred for cut plastic molds because of the large amount of machining involved.

But, for long run thread rolling dies, Type 4 steels would generally be chosen as their high wear resistance would be needed for long die life.

CHISEL STEELS

Various compositions have been developed for chisels, punches and the like, as indicated in Table 56. Although these steels are called chisel steels, their applications include coal cutting bits, spring collets, long slender punches, beading tools, spike mauls, boilermaker's tools, screw drivers and cold shear blades. The silicon-manganese steels have become popular as shanks for carbide and tipped high speed steel tools.

The use of molybdenum in the Type 1 steels produces excellent hardenability (Figure 133). At equivalent hardness, the steels containing molybdenum will tend to be tougher than the plain silicon-manganese chisel steels (Figure 134). Since all high silicon steels

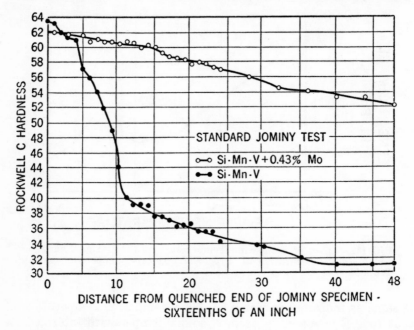

FIG 133 – Effect of Molybdenum on the Hardenability of a Silicon-Manganese-Vanadium Chisel Steel (1)

	Analyses						End-Quenched from F
	%C	%Mn	%Si	%Cr	%Mo	%V	
Si-Mn-V............	0.55	0.67	2.47	0.33	....	0.29	1650
Si-Mn-V+Mo........	0.56	0.85	2.06	0.24	0.43	0.25	1625

TABLE 56

Typical Compositions and Heat Treatment Temperatures of Chisel Steels†

Type	%C	%Mn	%Si	%Cr	%Cu	%Mo	%V	%W	Normalizing air cool from F	Annealing cool slowly from F	typical resultant Brinell hardness	Hardening quench in	Hardening from F
1A	0.50	0.40	1.00	....	....	0.50	0.25*	....	1625 to 1675	1400 to 1450	217	water / oil	1625 to 1675 / 1600 to 1650**
1B	0.50	0.90	1.50	....	....	0.40	0.25*	....	1625 to 1675	1400 to 1450	217	water / oil	1550 to 1600 / 1625 to 1675**
1C	0.50	0.90	1.85	....	....	1.30	0.35	....	1625 to 1675	1450 to 1500	...	water / oil	1525 to 1575 / 1600 to 1650
1D	0.60	0.75	1.90	0.30*	....	0.35	0.30*	....	1625 to 1675	1425 to 1475	217	water / oil	1550 to 1600 / 1625 to 1675***
1E	0.50	0.90	2.00	....	....	2.00	0.25	....	1625 to 1675	1450 to 1500	...	water / oil	1625 to 1675 / 1625 to 1675
1F	0.50	1.00	2.00	....	....	0.60	0.50	....	1625 to 1675	1400 to 1450	...	water / oil	1575 to 1625 / 1625 to 1675**
1G	0.55	0.80	2.30	....	....	0.50	0.25	....	1625 to 1675	1400 to 1450	...	water / oil	1550 to 1600 / 1600 to 1650**
2	0.50	....	....	1.50	....	0.50	0.25	2.50	not rec***	1425 to 1475	207	oil / air	1650 to 1800 / 1750 to 1850
3A	0.33	0.40	0.65	0.75	0.75	0.75	....	....	....	1500 to 1550	180	water / oil	1500 to 1650 / 1600 to 1800
3B	0.33	0.70	0.60	0.80	0.45	0.45	0.15*	....	....	....	...	water	1550 to 1650
3C	0.35	0.70	0.25	0.75	....	0.45	....	....	....	1500 to 1550	180	water / oil	1500 to 1650 / 1600 to 1800

*optional
**except for chisel shanks, generally oil quenched only in relatively small sections
***normalizing is generally not recommended for this composition
†in the case of pneumatic chisels and similar tools, the entire tool is often oil quenched and tempered at 800 to 1000 F; then the point is heated to a suitable temperature and water quenched with a subsequent low temperature temper optional

[203]

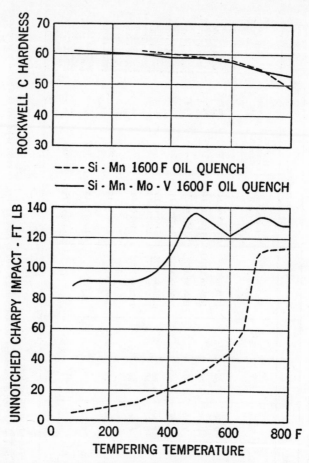

FIG 134 – Comparative Toughness of Silicon-Manganese and Silicon-Manganese-Molybdenum-Vanadium Chisel Steels (12)

	Analyses				
	%C	%Mn	%Si	%Mo	%V
Si–Mn..........................	0.63	0.78	1.95	....	....
Si–Mn–Mo–V.................	0.55	0.80	2.30	0.50	0.25

are susceptible to decarburization, suitable precautions should be taken with Type 1 steels either to prevent decarburization during heat treatment or to remove it after treatment. Type 2 has similar characteristics but a greater resistance to softening on heating, so that it is sometimes used for "semi-hot work" applications. Type 3 steels are known as non-tempering chisel steels, since they do not require tempering after hardening. These steels are primarily for use in the field, where accurate temperature control is not available. They do not have as good wear resistance as Type 1 and Type 2 steels but they are easier to heat treat.

MISCELLANEOUS LOW ALLOY TOOL STEELS

Table 57 gives the compositions and heat treatment temperatures of miscellaneous low alloy tool steels containing molybdenum. The Type 1 steels were developed primarily for taps but are also used for other fine edged cutting tools, such as small broaches and reamers, as well as for gages and lathe centers. Type 2 is used for clicker dies to cut leather, rubber and fabrics. The main application of the Type 3 steels is for carburized plastic molding dies. The low as-annealed hardness of Steel 3A makes it suitable for molds to be formed by cold hubbing while Steel 3B is for cut molds. The steels in Type 4 are cast compositions designed particularly for dies to be flame hardened. Type 5, also a casting, is used for heavy duty forming rolls. Many types of wood saws are made of Type 6.

GRAPHITIC STEELS

These steels are characterized by the presence of free graphite. It is reported that the graphite imparts free machining properties in the annealed condition and improves the wear resistance as heat treated, because of its lubricating properties. Table 58 shows typical compositions and heat treatments for four steels of this class.

The normalizing and annealing treatments cause about 0.3 to 0.7% carbon to change from the carbide form to free graphite, which is not dissolved on subsequent heat treatment. The molybdenum content of Type 1A makes it oil hardening, with all its attendant advantages as compared to the basic silicon graphitic steel, which is water hardening. Furthermore, the molybdenum tends to improve the toughness at any given hardness (Figure 135). Steels 1A and 1B are used for applications such as punches and dies for cold working and shaping steel, brass and aluminum. Type 2 has non-deforming properties if oil quenched, but hardness values four to five points Rockwell C higher are obtained by water quenching. Typical applications include bar and tube drawing dies, coining dies, air hammer pistons and slitting rolls. Type 3 shows less size change than Types 1 and 2, combined with a better resistance to softening on tempering.

DIE BLOCKS

Although die blocks are used at moderately elevated temperatures, they are normally not considered as true hot work steels; moreover,

TABLE 57

Typical Compositions and Heat Treatment Temperatures of Miscellaneous Low Alloy Tool Steels

Type	Compositions							Normalizing	Annealing		Hardening		Tempering	
	%C	%Mn	%Si	%Cr	%Mo	%Ni	% Other	air cool from F	cool slowly from F	typical resultant Brinell hardness	quench in	from F	F	approximate resultant Rockwell hardness
1A	1.20	0.30	0.25	1.40	0.45	....	......	1575 to 1625	1425 to 1475	205	oil	1550 to 1600	350	C 62
1B	1.25	0.85	0.25	0.50	0.50	....	0.25 V*	1575 to 1625	1425 to 1475	197	oil	1500 to 1550	350	C 62
2	0.55	0.60	0.20	0.70	0.35	....	......	......	1400 to 1450	160	oil	1550 to 1600	500	C 54
3A	0.06	0.40	0.20	1.35	0.20	0.55	......	1650 to 1700	1475 to 1525	105	oil	1525 to 1575 (a)	400	C 62**
3B	0.30	0.75	0.50	0.80	0.25	....	......	......	......	210	oil	1500 to 1550 (b)	400	C 60**
4A	0.45	1.00	0.40	1.00	0.30	....	0.90 Cu	......	......	235	....	(c)	....	......
4B	0.50	1.15	....	1.20	0.40	....	0.10 V	......	......	229	....	(c)	....	......
5	0.60	0.70	....	1.00	0.40	0.45	0.10 V	......	1475 to 1525	229	air	1575 to 1625	600	C 40
6	0.75	0.30	0.30	0.15	0.15	0.70	......	......	......	....	oil	(d)	(d)	C 50

*optional
**case hardness
(a) after carburizing at 1650 F, this steel is cooled to room temperature, then reheated as indicated for hardening
(b) after carburizing at 1600 F, this steel may be oil quenched from the carburizing temperature or may be cooled to the indicated temperature before quenching. The latter treatment gives the least size change
(c) working surfaces flame hardened
(d) saw manufacturers generally use specially controlled practices to ensure straightness of the finished product

TABLE 58

Typical Compositions and Heat Treatment Temperatures of Graphitic Tool Steels

Type	Compositions							Normalizing	Annealing		Hardening	
	%C	%Mn	%Si	%Cr	%Mo	%Ni	%W	air cool from F	cool slowly from F	typical resultant Brinell hardness	quench in	from F
1A..........	1.50	0.30	0.80	....	0.25	....	....	1575 to 1625	1450 to 1500	210	oil	1475 to 1525
1B..........	1.30	1.00	1.40	0.25	0.25	....	....	1550 to 1600	1450 to 1500	210	oil	1475 to 1525
2..........	1.50	0.30	0.65	....	0.50	....	2.80	1675 to 1725	1400 to 1450	248	water*	1450 to 1550
3..........	1.50	1.25	1.00	0.50	0.50	1.75	....	1675 to 1725	1475 to 1525	248	air	1625 to 1675**

* Irregular sections and tools under one inch in diameter are oil quenched from the high side of the temperature range

** some retained austenite will be present as-hardened. Therefore, this steel is frequently reheated to 1550 F and air cooled to increase the amount of martensite and thus the wear resistance. Tools under ½ in. rd are given a single hardening treatment by air cooling from 1450 F

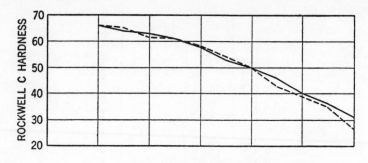

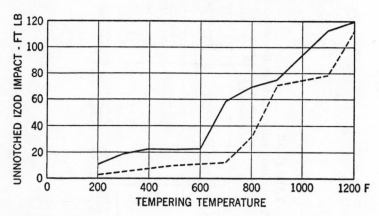

FIG 135 – Comparative Toughness of Silicon and Silicon-Molybdenum Graphitic Steels (13)

	Compositions			
	%C	%Mn	%Si	%Mo
Si..	1.50	0.40*	0.90	....
Si–Mo.....................................	1.50	0.40*	0.80	0.25

*max

their compositions differ appreciably from those of the more highly alloyed hot work steels to be considered next. Molybdenum steels have been specified for many years for die blocks as they have successfully met rigid requirements.

Typical compositions and heat treatment temperatures for die blocks are given in Table 59. Because of the size of die blocks and the necessity of avoiding distortion in heat treatment, suitable precautions must be taken to ensure uniform heating and quenching. The tempering temperature should be over about 600 F and usually is 1000 to 1150 F. At least one hour at temperature per inch of

TABLE 59

Typical Compositions and Heat Treatment Temperatures of Die Block Steels

Type	Compositions								Normalizing air cool from F	Annealing cool slowly from F	Hardening quench in	Hardening from F*
	%C	%Mn	%Si	%Cr	%Cu	%Mo	%Ni	%V				
1	0.55	0.65	0.25	0.65	....	0.30	1.50	0.10**	1575 to 1625	1400 to 1450	oil	1500 to 1600
2	0.55	0.55	0.25	0.80	1.75	0.35	1.50	......	1600 to 1650	1425 to 1475	oil	1575 to 1625
3	0.50	0.75	0.25	1.00	....	0.35	0.95	......	1575 to 1625	1425 to 1475	oil	1550 to 1600
4	0.60	0.70	0.25	1.15	....	0.50	....	0.15	1625 to 1675	1400 to 1450	oil	1500 to 1575
5	0.55	0.60	0.80	1.00	....	0.80	1.50	0.10**	1675 to 1725	1400 to 1450	oil air blast	† 1575 to 1700

*the high side of the temperature range should be used for larger die blocks
**optional
†some producers recommend 1475 to 1575 F while others recommend 1650 to 1700 F

thickness is recommended. Improved properties are stated to result from a double temper (14) or longer tempering times (15). Table 60 gives a general guide to the selection of the proper hardness as a function of the die block size and depth of impression.

Die blocks may be heat treated before or after machining. If the final hardness is to be under about 400 Brinell, the die blocks are usually machined after heat treatment to eliminate the need of compensation for warpage and dimensional changes during heat treatment. If a higher hardness is desired, the block is generally machined before heat treatment. Type 2 with its high copper content is an

TABLE 60
Die Block Hardness Selection for Chromium-Molybdenum-Nickel Steel
Die Blocks (16)

Sclero-scope Hardness	Approximate Brinell Hardness	Applications
67 to 70*	495 to 514	The maximum cross section of the height by the length or width is recommended at 10 x 8 in. This degree of hardness is for use on very shallow impressions not over 1/8 in. deep and is primarily used for forgings of the flat tableware type requiring extremely close tolerances.
63 to 67*	461 to 495	The maximum cross section of the height by the length or width is recommended at 12 x 10 in. This degree of hardness is for the use of very shallow impressions not over 1/4 in. deep and is primarily used for small forgings with very close tolerances.
60 to 63*	435 to 461	The maximum cross section of the height by the length or width is recommended at 14 x 12 in. This hardness is for relatively shallow impressions similar to the recommendations given for 56 to 60 Scleroscope and where, in addition, very close tolerances are required.
56 to 60	410 to 435	For use in dies with shallow impressions up to approximately 3/8 in. average depth for small tools such as wrenches and pliers, flat pieces such as ring gears, small brass and copper forgings, small automobile connecting rods and similar parts of a generally regular and flat design. It is recommended that the maximum cross section be not over 10 x 16 in. and the length not over 16 in. On a block of this hardness, the shank is tempered to a lesser degree of hardness to prevent breakage of the shank.
52 to 55	375 to 401	For use in dies with relatively shallow impressions up to about one inch average depth, for the general run of average forgings which do not contain deep locks or intricate designs. It is recommended that the cross sectional area of the height and width of the block be a maximum of 100 sq in. and the length not over 30 in.
48 to 51	341 to 363	For use in dies with average impressions up to approximately three inches deep for the general run of forgings. The greater toughness in this hardness of block permits the use of more intricate design of forgings, deeper locks and large heavy forgings. It is recommended for use on blocks whose cross sectional area of the height and width has a maximum of 100 sq in. when not over six feet in length. On shorter blocks where the length is not over three feet, a maximum cross section of the height and width is recommended as 14 x 27 in.
45 to 47	321 to 335	For use in dies with deep impressions and intricate shapes. This hardness of block has greater toughness and durability than the harder grades of blocks but has not the wearing qualities or the resistance to the abrasive action of hot metal flow in the die impressions. Heat checking of the impression is minimized due to the lower hardness of this block. The size of this hardness of block is limited only by the capacity of the hammer and the size obtainable from the die block maker.
40 to 45**	285 to 321	This hardness of block is particularly adapted for the production of large heavy sections, for blocking impressions where the forging is blocked in a separate set of dies on relatively large and bulky pieces, and for the use of flat or roller dies in drop hammers.

* to obtain these hardnesses, the die is generally heat treated after the impression is machined in the block
** this hardness is usually obtained by air cooling and tempering

exception to this generalization since it is readily machinable at hardnesses as high as 477 Brinell (14).

If special requirements such as resistance to severe washing exist, inserts may be used, particularly in dies for small forgings. The proper steel for these inserts will depend upon design and working conditions but will usually be one of the hot work or high speed steels (pp 214-220).

HOT WORK STEELS

Hot work steels may be divided into three main classes (see Table 61) depending upon whether the dominant alloying element is chromium, molybdenum* or tungsten.

Some hot work applications do not require steels of the type to be described. For example, in zinc and lead die casting dies, where the temperatures encountered are low, nitrided nitriding steels** are often used, as are chromium-molybdenum steels similar to Steel 3B in Table 57. For zinc die casting dies, however, the latter steel is not carburized but is oil quenched and tempered to 225 to 325 Brinell. Similar chromium-molybdenum steels with free machining additions of silver or lead are advantageous for dies that require a large amount of machining. Large mandrel bars for hot fabricating steel tubing may be made from steels with about 0.25 to 0.40% carbon, 0.60 to 1.20% chromium, 0.20 to 0.60% molybdenum and 1.75 to 3.00% nickel, oil quenched or air cooled from 1550 F and tempered at 400 to 1100 F. For piercing points, a steel with about 0.35% carbon, 2.5% chromium, 0.5% molybdenum and 3.5% nickel is used satisfactorily.

Table 61 also shows typical heat treatment temperatures for the most widely used hot work steels containing molybdenum. Decarburization or carburization during heat treatment should be avoided since either will increase the susceptibility to heat checking during service. Precautions against decarburization should be taken especially with Steels 1D, 1E, 1F, 1G and all Type 3 steels. Protective surface coatings, or controlled atmosphere furnaces, or pack hardening in neutral media are effective in preventing decarburization and carburization. The tempering temperature should always be higher than the expected service temperature. Consequently the tempering temperature is generally at least 900 F and usually 1000 to 1200 F. Figure 136 shows tempering temperature – hardness curves for four representative steels. Double tempering is sometimes

---

* One molybdenum base steel of considerable interest is not included in Table 61 as it is still in the development state. This steel, which contains about 0.15 to 0.35% carbon and 3% molybdenum, is hardened to about Rockwell C 20 to 40 by cooling from 1750 to 1950 F in water, oil or air and tempering at 900 to 1300 F. It has shown considerable promise for certain applications that require a high degree of resistance to heat checking.
** Such as the G and G Modified compositions of Table 14 (p 95).

TABLE 61

Typical Compositions and Heat Treatment Temperatures of Hot Work Steels

Type	Compositions								Annealing**		Hardening		
	%C	%Mn	%Si	%Cr	%Mo	%Ni	%V	%W	cool slowly from F	typical resultant Brinell hardness	preheat F	quench in	from F
1A	0.65	0.80	....	3.75	0.70	....	0.55	....	1500 to 1550	212	1375 to 1425	oil, air	1750 to 1900†
1B	0.95	0.25	0.25	3.75	0.50	....	0.50*	....	1500 to 1550	217	1375 to 1425	air	1725 to 1775
1C	0.55	0.30	0.40	3.90	0.45	....	0.90*	....	1525 to 1575	212	1375 to 1425	air	1625 to 1675
1D	0.35	0.25	0.90	5.00	1.60	....	0.25*	1.25	1575 to 1625	210	1375 to 1425	oil, air	1850 to 1950†
1E	0.40	0.35	1.10	5.00	1.85	....	0.45*‡	....	1575 to 1625	210	1375 to 1425	oil, air	1800 to 1900†
1F	0.35	0.35	0.90	5.00	2.25	....	....	....	1575 to 1625	...	1375 to 1425	oil, air	1825 to 1875
1G	0.50	1.25	0.30	7.00	0.75	1.50	....	....	1300 to 1350	248	1475 to 1525	air	1775 to 1825
2A	0.45	....	....	1.50	0.50	....	0.25	2.25	1425 to 1475	207	....	oil	1650 to 1750
2B	0.85	0.25	1.20	5.00	0.50	....	....	5.00	1350 to 1400	...	1100 to 1150	air	1750 to 1850
2C	0.35	0.25	0.25	4.00	2.10	2.50	....	14.00	1575 to 1625	279	1475 to 1525	oil, air	1850 to 2250†
3A	0.20	....	....	3.25	4.25	....	0.75*	1.10	1525 to 1575	...	....	oil	2010 to 2100
3B	0.30	0.30	1.10	2.60	4.80	....	1.00	1.80	1525 to 1575	...	....	oil	2010 to 2100
3C	0.85	....	....	4.75	5.25	....	0.60	....	1500 to 1550	...	1475 to 1525	air	2175 to 2225
3D	0.35	0.25	0.25	3.50	6.25	....	0.75	1.00	1525 to 1575	229	1475 to 1525	oil, air	2050 to 2250†
3E	0.60	0.30	0.30	3.20	8.30	....	1.55	....	1550 to 1600	...	1575 to 1625	oil, air	2150 to 2200

* optional
** normalizing is generally not recommended for these compositions
† low side of temperature range for oil quenching, high side for air cooling
‡ the vanadium content is sometimes increased to 1%, especially for die casting dies; the austenitizing temperature is often somewhat higher in such cases than for the lower vanadium or the vanadium-free compositions

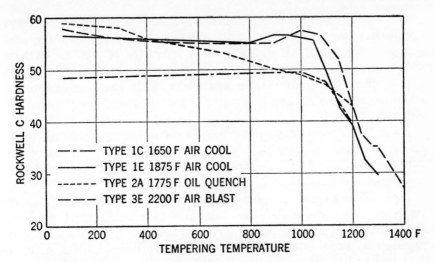

FIG 136 – Effect of Tempering Temperature on the Hardness of Four Representative Hot Work Steels. For type compositions, see Table 61 (7, 17, 18, 19)

recommended for the higher alloy types to increase toughness. Long tempering times are required for die casting dies. Three to six hours is the minimum time while 24 to 30 hours are frequently utilized for large die casting dies.* Die casting dies are often gas nitrided after complete heat treatment and grinding to produce a very hard wear resistant surface (21) which will resist erosion and adhesion of the material being cast.

Steels 1A, 1B and 1C have good toughness and heat check resistance but lower red hardness and wear resistance at operating temperatures than the higher chromium steels, Steels 2B, 2C or the other high tungsten hot work steels, or Type 3 steels. They are not as shock resistant as the low tungsten Steel 2A but are more resistant to softening at elevated temperatures. Typical applications are billet shears, bolt trimmer dies, dies with sharp corners, flying shears, gripper dies for bolts and rivets, heading dies for automatic machines, swaging dies and upsetters.

Steels 1D and 1E are the most widely used general purpose hot work steels because of their good toughness and red hardness. They are preferred to high tungsten hot work steels where shock is involved or where it is necessary to water cool the dies in service. Steel 1D is more wear resistant than Steel 1E but is more susceptible to heat checking. Both steels are used for extrusion dies, forging dies for aluminum and brass, gripper dies, heading dies, inserts for forging dies and upsetters, mandrels, punches, piercing

---

* The hardness after such prolonged tempers will be lower than that found after short tempers. "Master tempering curves" can be prepared that will indicate the relationship between tempering temperature, tempering time and hardness (20).

[213]

points and shear blades. As a casting, Steel 1D has likewise found application for general hot work purposes including heading and gripper dies. Steel 1E (at a Brinell hardness of 400 to 444) is outstanding for aluminum and magnesium die casting dies, cores, ejector pins, plungers, sleeves and slides. It is also economical for long run zinc die casting dies and for inserts and cores for zinc die casting.

Steel 1F is recommended for high production applications, especially on abrasive material, and is widely applied as an insert for forging dies. Steel 1G is a special purpose steel for flying shears and billet shears operating at high temperatures.

Steel 2A is harder at room temperature than most of the higher tungsten types but it does not maintain this hardness at working temperatures. This steel is useful for applications involving considerable shock, such as heading dies for square headed bolts, gripper dies in hand fed machines, tools with deep grooves, and hot shear blades with notched edges. Steel 2B is used for long run aluminum and magnesium die casting dies. Steel 2C has the highest hot working range of any of the tungsten hot work steels (1). Adequate preheating before service is advisable for all hot work tools but is especially necessary for this grade as it has low toughness at temperatures below about 1000 F. Steel 2C is suitable for applications involving high temperatures and high wear resistance but not requiring high shock resistance.

Type 3 steels with their excellent hot hardness properties are comparable to the high tungsten hot work steels. It has been reported that Steel 3D, for example, has better physical properties and is especially resistant to heat checking as compared with high tungsten hot work steels at the same hardness (1).

Molybdenum high speed steels may be used for hot work purposes. These steels are discussed in the next portion of this section. Since hot work dies generally do not require as high hardnesses as cutting tools, they may be tempered at higher temperatures, or lower carbon modifications may be applied.

HIGH SPEED STEELS*

The essential red hardness of high speed steels requires the presence of either molybdenum or tungsten or both. The use of molybdenum for this purpose is as old as that of tungsten. However, during the first years of this century when high speed steels were being developed, molybdenum was both rare and expensive. Moreover, the molybdenum steels were erratic in performance due to the

---

* Small percentages of molybdenum up to about 1% are commonly added to tungsten high speed steels — particularly the cobalt or high vanadium types. These steels are not discussed here.

formation of a soft skin during heating in the crude hardening equipment then available. Therefore, for many years attention was devoted predominantly to the tungsten types. The first modern molybdenum high speed steel (5 in Table 62) was introduced in 1932 after molybdenum had become economically competitive with tungsten and after well controlled hardening equipment was available. A second molybdenum high speed steel (4 in Table 62) was developed almost concurrently. Since then, a number of additional molybdenum high speed steels has gained commercial acceptance.

Representative compositions of five molybdenum high speed steels are given in Table 62. Steels 3, 4 and 5 are considered general purpose steels suitable for the majority of high speed steel applications. Cobalt in amounts from 5 to 12% is sometimes added to the molybdenum high speed steels to obtain better performance on hard materials at high speeds. Typical of these is Steel 1, although cobalt may be added to the other types as well. The high vanadium Steel 2 is also a special purpose steel, adapted particularly for cutting abrasive materials.

The processing and heat treatment are essentially the same for molybdenum as for tungsten high speed steels except that the temperatures are lower for the former. Table 63 shows the usual heat treatment temperatures for molybdenum high speed steels. Salt baths or controlled atmosphere furnaces are excellent for heating all types of high speed steels for hardening.

Steels with high molybdenum contents, like steels with high cobalt contents, are more susceptible to decarburization in oxidizing atmospheres at high temperatures than the 18% tungsten – 4% chromium – 1% vanadium type. This tendency is noticeable in Steels 1, 4 and 5; but, if suitable salt baths or controlled atmosphere furnaces are used, there is no opportunity for decarburization to occur. When these steels are heated in direct fired or semi-muffle furnaces, however, they should be protected by special paints, borax, or boric acid.

The usual tempering temperatures are indicated in Table 63. Higher temperatures than those given may be used for punches and dies where lower hardnesses are desirable. Double tempering (with intermediate cooling to room temperature) is often advocated to increase toughness.

Special treatments may be used for molybdenum as well as for tungsten high speed steels. Significant amounts of bainite seem to improve the continuous cutting efficiency of molybdenum high speed steel even more than that of the 18% tungsten – 4% chromium – 1% vanadium high speed steel (Table 64). Pack hardening to improve the abrasion resistance of punches and dies may be done with the same practice as is used for tungsten high speed steels. Surface hard-

TABLE 62
Representative Compositions of Molybdenum High Speed Steels

No.	Type*	%C	%Co	%Cr	%Mo	%V	%W
1	5-4-4-2+8	0.80	7.8	4.0	4.2	1.6	5.5
2	5-5-4-4	1.30	...	4.5	4.5	4.0	5.5
3	6-6-4-2	0.80	...	4.2	5.0	2.0	6.5
4	0-8-4-2	0.85	...	4.0	8.0	2.0	...
5	1-9-4-1	0.80	...	8.8	8.5	1.2	1.5

* type represents approximately the %W−%Mo−%Cr−%V+%Co

TABLE 63
Heat Treatment Temperatures of Molybdenum High Speed Steels

No.*	Annealing		Hardening			
	furnace coo from F	typical resultant Brinell hardness	preheat F	high heat** F	temper F	typical Rockwell C hardness after 1050 F temper
1	1600 to 1650	248	1500 to 1550	2225 to 2275	1025 to 1075	66
2	1575 to 1625	248	1450 to 1600	2200 to 2250	1025 to 1075	66
3	1550 to 1600	235	1500 to 1550	2220 to 2270	1025 to 1075	65
4	1500 to 1550	229	1500 to 1550	2200 to 2250	1000 to 1075	65
5	1525 to 1575	229	1500 to 1550	2200 to 2250	1000 to 1075	65

* for type composition, see Table 62
** temperatures should be lowered by about 25 F if salt baths are used for heating

TABLE 64

Effect of Primary and Secondary Bainite on the Cutting Efficiency
of Molybdenum and Tungsten High Speed Steels (22)

Structure	Actual Cutting Efficiency of Molybdenum High Speed Steel*		Comparative Cutting Efficiency of Molybdenum High Speed Steel* Based on 18–4–1 as 100%	
	continuous cutting	interrupted cutting	continuous cutting	interrupted cutting
Conventional (a)...................	119	138	100	182
Primary Bainite (b).................	213	83	129	95
Secondary Bainite (c)...............	178	105	149	118
Primary and Secondary Bainite (d)....	307	127	200	147

*a slight modification of Steel 3 in Table 62 with about 0.8% C, 4% Cr, 4.1% Mo, 1.5% V, 5.5% W
(a) molybdenum steel austenitized at 2225 F, tungsten steel at 2350 F; both oil quenched to room temperature and tempered at 1050 F for 2+2 hr
(b) molybdenum steel austenitized at 2225 F, tungsten steel at 2350 F; both quenched into bath at 460 F and held for seven hours, then tempered at 1050 F for 4+2 hr
(c) molybdenum steel austenitized at 2225 F, tungsten steel at 2350 F; both oil quenched to room temperature, tempered at 1050 F for four hours, cooled to 460 F and held seven hours, then air cooled to room temperature
(d) molybdenum steel austenitized at 2225 F, quenched into bath at 460 F and held seven hours, tempered at 1050 F for six hours, cooled to 460 F and held six hours, retempered at 1050 F for two hours, cooled to 460 F and held for four hours, then air cooled to room temperature. Tungsten steel austenitized at 2350 F, quenched into bath at 460 F and held for seven hours, tempered at 1050 F for six hours, cooled to 460 F and held for six hours, then air cooled to room temperature

ening of heat treated high speed steel tools by nitriding in molten cyanide baths has been found beneficial for parts such as taps and drills. The nitriding practice is the same for molybdenum as for tungsten high speed steels although the molybdenum types appear to nitride more readily (1). Other superficial treatments, such as chromium plating and oxide coatings, have been applied to a lesser extent.

One of the advantages of molybdenum high speed steels is their lower specific gravity as compared with the tungsten types (see Table 65). As tool steel is purchased by weight, this means, for

TABLE 65

Specific Gravity Values of Molybdenum High Speed Steels

No.*	Type	Specific Gravity	Percentage Saving in Weight as Compared to 18–4–1**
1........................	5–4–4–2+8	8.15	6
2........................	5–5–4–4	7.98	8
3........................	6–5–4–2	8.14	6
4........................	0–8–4–2	7.88	9
5........................	1–9–4–1	8.00	8

*for type composition, see Table 62
**$\frac{\text{sp gr of 18–4–1} - \text{sp gr of Mo high speed steel}}{\text{sp gr of 18–4–1}} \times 100$ where specific gravity of 18–4–1 =8.68

example, that 9% more tools are available from molybdenum high speed steel 4 than from 18% tungsten – 4% chromium – 1% vanadium high speed steel.

Since the molybdenum high speed steels are noted for their high toughness as compared with tungsten high speed steels, they are used to exceptional advantage in applications requiring increased shock resistance such as saw blades, punches and dies. The true toughness can be determined only in actual service but an indication is given by the comparison in Figure 137 of the unnotched Izod impact values and in Figure 138 of the deflection in bend tests of molybdenum steel 3 and the 18% tungsten – 4% chromium – 1% vanadium type. A striking example, more closely related to actual cutting operations, is shown by the data in Table 64. With a conven-

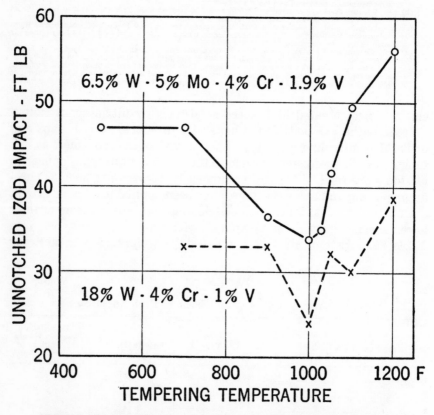

FIG 137 – Comparative Unnotched Izod Impact of Molybdenum and Tungsten High Speed Steels. The molybdenum steel was preheated at 1500 F, transferred to a high heat furnace at 2250 F for 2½ min, oil quenched and tempered at the indicated temperatures for two hours. The tungsten steel was preheated at 1500 F, transferred to a high heat furnace at 2350 F for 2½ min, oil quenched and tempered at the indicated temperatures for two hours (23, 24)

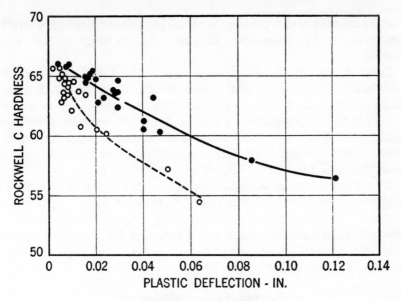

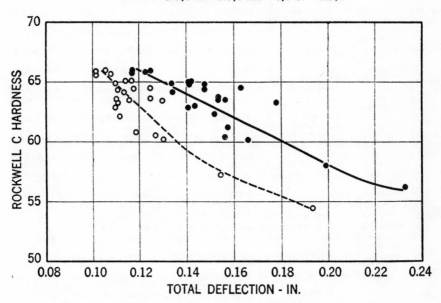

FIG 138 – Comparative Total and Plastic Deflection of Molybdenum and Tungsten High Speed Steels at Equivalent Hardnesses. Molybdenum steel austenitized at 2225 F and tungsten steel at 2350 F to give identical grain size values. Both steels oil quenched and tempered at or above the maximum secondary hardness peak. Bend test samples 0.140 x 0.500 x 2 in. (25)

tional heat treatment, the molybdenum high speed steel gave an 82% longer tool life in interrupted cutting than the tungsten high speed steel.

Several large automobile companies in the U.S.A. have adopted molybdenum high speed steel 3 as a standard. As the result of long plant experience, it has been concluded that this steel is at least equal to the 18% tungsten – 4% chromium – 1% vanadium type as a general purpose high speed steel. Furthermore, molybdenum high speed steels account for a large majority of the tonnage used for twist drills and hack saw blades.

There has been considerable interest in cast high speed steel tools. Since the steel is not hot worked, it is possible to use compositions that are not readily forgeable but that have high cutting ability. For example, high abrasion resistance is reported for the following composition: 0.5 to 0.9% carbon, 1% boron, 8% cobalt, 4% chromium, 8% molybdenum and 2% vanadium.

Section VII – Bibliography

(1) J. P. Gill, R. S. Rose, G. A. Roberts, H. G. Johnstin and R. B. George, Tool Steels, published by the ASM (1944)

(2) S. M. DePoy "Hardenability of Common Toolsteels" Metal Progress Data Sheet 80 (1946)

(3) Deward Oil Hardening Die Steel, published by the Allegheny Ludlum Steel Corporation, Pittsburgh, Pennsylvania (1946)

(4) Carpenter Matched Tool Steel Manual, published by the Carpenter Steel Company, Reading, Pennsylvania (1946)

(5) H. Scott and T. H. Gray "Dimensional Changes on Hardening High Chromium Tool Steels" Transactions, ASM, Vol 29 (1941)

(6) Airloy Air Hardening Die Steel, published by the Allegheny Ludlum Steel Corporation, Pittsburgh, Pennsylvania (1947)

(7) Tool Steels, published by the Universal-Cyclops Steel Corporation, Bridgeville, Pennsylvania.

(8) Ontario Air Hardening Die Steel, published by the Allegheny Ludlum Steel Corporation, Pittsburgh, Pennsylvania (1947)

(9) O. Zmeskal and M. Cohen "The Tempering of Two High-Carbon High-Chromium Steels" Transactions, ASM, Vol 31 (1943)

(10) L. E. Gippert and G. M. Butler, Jr. "Changes in Size and Toughness of High Carbon-High Chromium Steels Due to Subzero Treatments" Transactions, ASM, Vol 39 (1947)

(11) G. M. Butler, Jr. "Study of Dimensional and Other Changes in Various Die Steels due to Heat Treatment" Transactions, ASM, Vol 30 (1942)

(12) Bethlehem Tool Steels, published by the Bethlehem Steel Company, Bethlehem, Pennsylvania (1937)

(13) Timken Graphitic Steels, published by the Timken Roller Bearing Company, Canton, Ohio

(14) Hot Work Die Steels, published by A. Finkl & Sons Company, Chicago, Illinois (1946)

(15) B. Thomas "Die Block Heat Treatment" Metallurgia, Vol 25 (1942)

(16) W. Naujoks and D. C. Fabel, Forging Handbook, published by the ASM (1939)

(17) LaBelle 89 Hot Work Steel, published by the Crucible Steel Company of America, New York City, New York (1945)

(18) Carpenter No. 883 Hot Work Tool Steel, published by the Carpenter Steel Company, Reading, Pennsylvania

(19) Bethlehem Hot Work 8 Tool Steel, published by the Bethlehem Steel Company, Bethlehem, Pennsylvania (1942)

(20) G. A. Roberts, A. H. Grobe and C. F. Moersch, Jr. "The Tempering of High Alloy Tool Steels" Transactions, ASM, Vol 39 (1947)

(21) Committee on Die Castings, Aluminum and Magnesium Division, AFA "Aluminum Alloy Die Casting" American Foundryman, Vol 9 (1946)

(22) C. K. Baer and P. Payson "Bainitic Hardening of High Speed Steel" Transactions, ASM, Vol 39 (1947)

(23) L-XX High Speed Steel, published by the Allegheny Ludlum Steel Corporation, Pittsburgh, Pennsylvania (1947)

(24) DBL-2 High Speed Steel, published by the Allegheny Ludlum Steel Corporation, Pittsburgh, Pennsylvania (1946)

(25) A. H. Grobe and G. A. Roberts "The Bend Test for Hardened High Speed Steel" Transactions, ASM, Vol 40 (1948)

SECTION VIII

STEEL CASTINGS

Steel castings may be divided into the same classifications as wrought steel. Alloy engineering castings, high alloy corrosion resistant castings as well as castings for service at low and elevated temperatures are discussed here. Tool steel castings are covered in Section VII and nonferrous castings in Section X.

ALLOY ENGINEERING CASTINGS

In addition to the points discussed in Section IV, the foundryman is particularly interested in the following advantages of molybdenum:

(1) Molybdenum is the only common alloying element contributing strongly to hardenability that is not lost by oxidation in foundry melting practice. Hence, when added hardenability is required, molybdenum offers certain specific benefits:

A. accurate control of the molybdenum content and, therefore, improved control of hardenability
B. high recovery of molybdenum from both additions and scrap (particularly important in foundries because of the high percentage necessarily remelted in the form of gates, risers and other return scrap)
C. no molybdenum oxide inclusions.

(2) Since a carbon content of under 0.20% is desired in many castings, there are definite economic and technical advantages in the fact that the standard forms in which molybdenum is added contain little or no carbon (pp 49, 50).

(3) Because molybdenum reduces or eliminates temper brittleness (as described at length in Section I, pp 4-9), liquid quenching after tempering, which is often practiced to avoid temper brittleness, is usually unnecessary. Such quenching is particularly undesirable when treating castings having complicated shapes.

(4) Molybdenum and copper are the only two common alloying elements that decrease the tendency toward the type of intergranular fracture apparently caused by the precipitation of aluminum nitride at the primary austenite grain boundaries (1, 2).

(5) Unlike manganese and chromium, molybdenum appears to have no significant effect on sensitivity to quench-cracking, despite its marked effect on hardenability (3).

The flexibility of the foundry process permits the ready adjustment of composition to meet special requirements. Thus, although many of the standard wrought engineering steels have their counterparts in castings, a variety of other compositions is also used.

The mechanical properties of castings are generally evaluated on the basis of tests made on test coupons (cast integrally with the castings or separately), which are heat treated with the casting. The properties discussed in this section are those of such test pieces unless otherwise stated.

In many respects, the properties of castings are similar to those of the comparable wrought steels. Virtually the same hardness – tensile strength correlation can be used (Figure 44, p 59). There is, however, a tendency for castings to show a slightly higher hardness than wrought steels for a given tensile strength.

The yield point – tensile strength ratio varies with the tensile strength in approximately the same manner as has been indicated for wrought steels (Figure 45, p 59). In other words, the more fully hardened the steel, the higher the ratio for any given tensile strength. Therefore, tensile tests on quenched and tempered coupons of alloy steels with the commonly used carbon contents will give results approximating the ratios for tempered martensite unless the hardenability of the steel is so low as to produce incomplete hardening. Steels tempered at low temperatures may show lower yield points than would be expected from Figure 45. The ratios of normalized and tempered test bars of alloy steels will approach the dotted line at the bottom, because of incomplete hardening, although highly alloyed steels which harden fully in the coupon size on normalizing will naturally give ratios close to the normal expectancy of tempered martensite.

So far as is known, all the principles of endurance behavior which apply to wrought steels (pp 60, 61, 70, 71) are equally relevant to cast steels. The endurance limit – tensile strength ratio for cast steels is generally given as about 40 to 50%.

For all practical purposes, cast steels may be said to have the same hardenability as wrought steels of the same composition and grain size (4, 5). Therefore, any of the hardenability data in Section IV is applicable to cast steels as well, provided segregation is not severe. Cast steels may, however, have slightly higher hardenability than the corresponding wrought steels because of their normally higher silicon and possibly higher manganese contents (6). Hardenability data cannot be precisely correlated with the mechanical properties of small coupons (7), but they are particularly valuable when the mechanical property requirements apply to the casting rather than to the coupon. The greatest practical application of hardenability data in this field is in connection with castings to be quenched and tempered.

As with wrought steels, more complete hardening produces better mechanical properties. A minimum of 80% martensite as-quenched is suggested (Figure 139) in the SAE recommended practice for

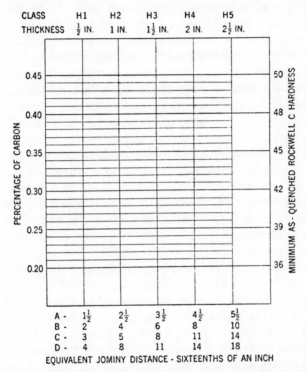

FIG 139 – Relationship between Critical Section Thickness, Degree of Hardenability Required, Hardenability, Carbon Content and Minimum As-Quenched Hardness of Steel Castings. The thickness values at the top apply to the thickness of the casting or of the most highly stressed section. The equivalent Jominy distances at the bottom correspond to the following four degrees of hardenability:

A – for desired quench hardness to a depth of ⅛ of critical section thickness—agitated water quench
B – for desired quench hardness at a depth of ¼ of critical section thickness—agitated water quench
C – for desired quench hardness at center of critical section thickness—agitated water quench
D – for desired quench hardness at center of critical section thickness—agitated oil quench

The minimum carbon content (established by the foundry) then determines the minimum as-quenched hardness necessary at this distance from the quenched end of the Jominy test specimen to obtain the optimum mechanical properties after tempering. The as-quenched hardness values correspond to approximately 80% martensite. The values in this diagram were obtained from plate sections; for rounds, see Figure 71, p 88 (8)

[223]

automotive steel castings to obtain the optimum properties after tempering. In general, the best mechanical properties seem to be coincident with the minimum hardenability that will produce the maximum hardening for any particular cooling rate. With further increases in the hardenability, some deterioration in properties is observed, possibly associated with the presence of retained austenite in the areas of maximum segregation, which is subsequently transformed to undesirable constituents during tempering (9).

The degree of hardenability required depends largely upon the type of stresses to which the part will be subjected in service. The SAE takes this factor into consideration by giving for each thickness four degrees of hardenability, corresponding to full hardening with an agitated water or oil quench, as well as to hardening to $\frac{1}{8}$ and $\frac{1}{4}$ of the critical section thickness (Figure 139).

Practically any desired degree of hardenability can be obtained by the selection of a suitable combination of alloying elements and carbon content. Figures 140 and 141 show representative Jominy hardenability curves for several cast steels with about 0.30% carbon but widely varying hardenability, while Figure 142 indicates the effect of carbon content on the hardenability of a single alloy base.

The cross section hardness of quenched and tempered castings can be determined rather accurately from the results of tempered Jominy test specimens (Figure 143). For the usual casting compositions with medium to high hardenability, however, the tempered hardness is a fairly direct function of the quenched hardness. Therefore, the hardness as-tempered can be predicted from the hardness at the appropriate position on an as-quenched Jominy test specimen. Figure 144 shows a chart applicable to cast steels with calculated D_I values from 3.00 to 6.00. As the D_I decreases below 3.00, the tempered hardness for a given as-quenched hardness and tempering temperature also decreases (12).

Increasing the carbon content increases the strength and decreases the ductility of cast as well as wrought steels, provided the thermal treatment is kept the same. The effect of carbon within the usual limits of about 0.20 to 0.40% is illustrated in Figure 145. Generally, it is preferable to use as low a carbon content as is compatible with the required strength and desired tempering temperature. The low carbon minimizes cracking in trimming, welding and quenching, but increases casting difficulties.*

In general, the machinability of alloy steel castings is similar to

---

* Higher carbon contents have been specified in an unusual series of hypereutectoid steels used by a large automobile company. For example, crankshafts are made of a composition containing about 1.5% carbon, 0.7% manganese, 1.0% silicon, 0.2% chromium, 0.8% copper and 0.2% molybdenum, heat treated to about 250 Brinell by the following treatment: 1650 F for one hour; air cool to black; 1400 F for 1½ hours; furnace cool to 1100 F; then air cool. Here, the high carbon content not only improves casting properties but also forms, during the heat treatment, secondary graphite which reduces wear.

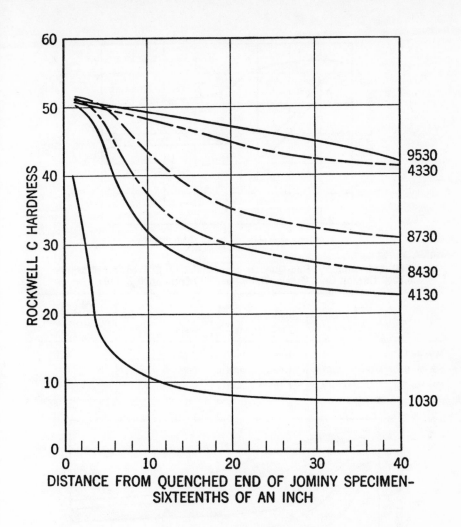

FIG 140 – Jominy End-Quench Hardenability Curves for Various 0.30% Carbon Cast Steels. Curves for alloy steels based on normal expectancy bands in original reference. McQuaid-Ehn grain size: 5 to 9 (6)

	Compositions					
	%C	%Mn	%Si	%Cr	%Mo	%Ni
1030	0.27 to 0.33	0.55 to 0.80	0.40 to 0.60	....	....	....
4130	0.27 to 0.33	0.55 to 0.90	0.40 to 0.60	0.50 to 0.80	0.20 to 0.30	....
4330	0.27 to 0.33	0.55 to 0.90	0.40 to 0.60	0.50 to 0.80	0.25 to 0.35	1.40 to 2.00
8430	0.27 to 0.33	1.30 to 1.60	0.40 to 0.60		0.30 to 0.40	....
8730	0.27 to 0.33	0.70 to 0.90	0.40 to 0.60	0.40 to 0.60	0.25 to 0.35	0.40 to 0.70
9530	0.27 to 0.33	1.30 to 1.60	0.40 to 0.60	0.40 to 0.60	0.30 to 0.40	0.40 to 0.70

Note: curve for 9530 corrected on basis of information from the Steel Founders' Society of America

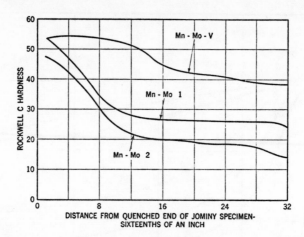

FIG 141 – Jominy End-Quench Hardenability Curves for Various
0.30% Carbon Cast Steels, End-Quenched from 1600 F (10)

	Analyses					McQuaid-Ehn Grain Size
	%C	%Mn	%Si	%Mo	%V	
Mn–Mo 1...........	0.31	1.04	0.37	0.40	....	8
Mn–Mo 2...........	0.28	1.00	0.38	0.24	....	8
Mn–Mo–V..........	0.32	1.50	0.48	0.53	0.13	8

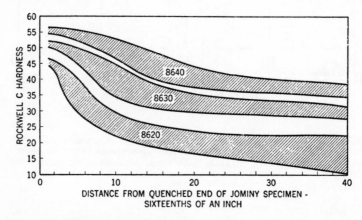

FIG 142 – Effect of Carbon Content on the Hardenability of Cast
Steel. McQuaid-Ehn grain size: 5 to 9 (6)

	Compositions					
	%C	%Mn	%Si	%Cr	%Mo	%Ni
8620	0.17 to 0.23	0.70 to 0.90	0.40 to 0.60	0.40 to 0.60	0.10 to 0.20	0.40 to 0.70
8630	0.27 to 0.33	0.70 to 0.90	0.40 to 0.60	0.40 to 0.60	0.10 to 0.20	0.40 to 0.70
8640	0.37 to 0.43	0.70 to 0.90	0.40 to 0.60	0.40 to 0.60	0.10 to 0.20	0.40 to 0.70

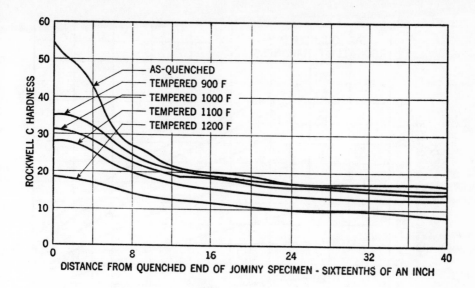

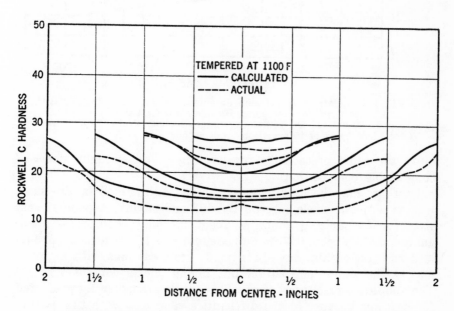

FIG 143 – Correlation of Tempered End-Quench Hardenability Test with Experimentally Determined Cross Section Hardness of Manganese-Molybdenum Cast Steel. Heat analysis: 0.35% C, 1.08% Mn, 0.35% Si, 0.033% P, 0.024% S, 0.16% Mo. End-quenched from 1575 F. Note: the factors used for calculation differ slightly from those shown in Figure 71, p 88 (11)

that of the equivalent wrought steels. The optimum microstructures are affected by carbon and alloy content in the same way for castings as for wrought steels (see Table 27, p 123). Alloy steel castings re-

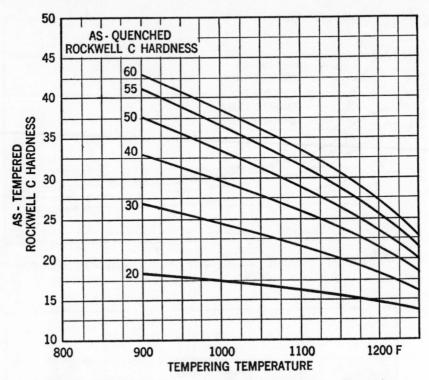

FIG 144 – Relationship between As-Quenched Hardness, Tempering Temperature and As-Tempered Hardness for Cast Steels with 3.00 to 6.00 Calculated D₁. Tempering time: one hour. Note: figure corrected on basis of information from author (12)

quire the same precautions for welding as do wrought steels of comparable composition.

Castings may be carburized, cyanided or nitrided in the same way as wrought steels (see pp 105-108 and 93-96). A popular cast steel for carburizing contains about 0.15% carbon, 0.7% manganese, 0.3% silicon, 0.25% molybdenum and 1.75% nickel. Carburized rock bit cutters have been made from castings with approximately the same composition but higher nickel content (3.5%). The aluminum-free types of nitriding steels are generally preferred for castings because of the difficulties connected with the casting of high aluminum steels. One composition used for castings to be nitrided contains about 0.18% carbon, 0.5% manganese, 0.4% silicon, 2.5% chromium, 0.4% molybdenum and 0.2% vanadium.

Factors Affecting the Ductility of Castings

Because there is no mechanical working, the ductility and toughness of cast steel are especially sensitive to the quantity and distribution of non-metallic inclusions, particularly sulphides. Grain boundary sulphide inclusions (often called Type II or eutectic type grain

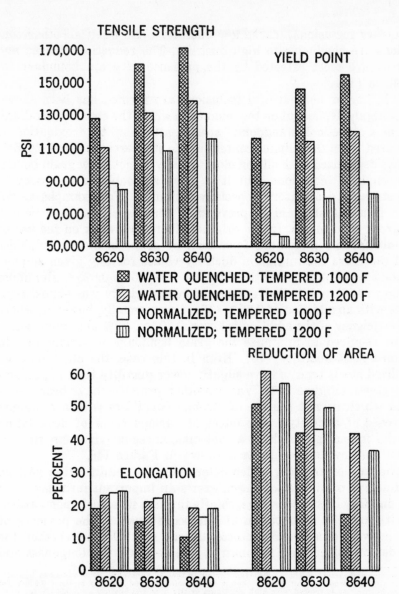

FIG 145 – Effect of Carbon Content and Thermal Treatment on the Mechanical Properties of Cast Steel. McQuaid-Ehn grain size: 5 to 8 (13)

	Compositions					
	%C	%Mn	%Si	%Cr	%Mo	%Ni
8620	0.17 to 0.23	0.70 to 0.90	0.40 to 0.60	0.40 to 0.60	0.10 to 0.20	0.40 to 0.70
8630	0.27 to 0.33	0.70 to 0.90	0.40 to 0.60	0.40 to 0.60	0.10 to 0.20	0.40 to 0.70
8640	0.37 to 0.43	0.70 to 0.90	0.40 to 0.60	0.40 to 0.60	0.10 to 0.20	0.40 to 0.70

boundary inclusions) cause low ductility even when all other conditions are conducive to high ductility. The reduction of area and impact are most affected by the presence of grain boundary inclusions (14).

Whether or not harmful inclusions are formed has been shown to be highly dependent on the manner in which the steel is deoxidized. From a practical standpoint, special attention to deoxidation is required when the sulphur content of the steel exceeds about 0.025%. Steels deoxidized with silicon alone usually do not show grain boundary sulphide inclusions. But it is often advisable or necessary to use stronger deoxidizers, especially aluminum. For example, aluminum is a valuable aid in preventing pinholes in castings poured in green sand molds. In the original laboratory work on the use of aluminum, the maximum formation of grain boundary sulphides and therefore the minimum ductility values for any given sulphur content were obtained with additions of 0.015 to 0.025% aluminum (Figure 146), while the recovery of good ductility was almost complete with an addition of 0.05% (15). Commercially, however, where the efficiency of the addition is lower, 0.10 to 0.20% aluminum seems to be required to minimize the grain boundary inclusions and to restore good ductility (16). Even in this case, the aluminum deoxidized steels tend to have slightly lower ductility than aluminum-free steels (Figure 147). Various other practices have been developed which permit the use of strong deoxidizers with a minimum decrease of ductility.* The effect of various types of deoxidation on the impact strength of a cast manganese-molybdenum steel at room and low temperatures is shown in Figure 148.

The rate of freezing which determines the solidification pattern and degree of alloy segregation exerts an important influence upon the ductility of steel castings, chiefly through its effect upon hardenability and the distribution of microconstituents. The presence of any network of a second microconstituent, regardless of whether it is harder or softer than the matrix, will decrease the toughness and

* Titanium and zirconium show a behavior similar to that of aluminum. Some work has indicated that the maximum sulphur content that is permissible for good ductility is about 0.040% for experimental steels treated with high aluminum or titanium and slightly over 0.050% for steels treated with zirconium (18). Another method that has given good ductility in commercial heats supplements a high aluminum addition of 0.125 to 0.175% with an addition of calcium-silicon (19). Calcium additions of 0.05 to 0.10% used in conjunction with 0.10 to 0.20% aluminum, titanium or zirconium produce inclusions of the so-called peritectic type. The ductility of steel with peritectic type inclusions approaches closely that of silicon deoxidized steel (18). Satisfactory properties have been reported for a practice involving oxidation of the steel followed by finishing with 0.10 to 0.20% calcium and a moderately high aluminum addition of 0.05 to 0.10%. Zirconium was not quite as effective as calcium (20). Another method of obtaining sound castings with relatively high ductility is to deoxidize with silicon and a small amount of a strong deoxidizer. The effective addition that will promote soundness without causing the formation of grain boundary inclusions varies with the furnace practice and composition of the steel but may be limited to about 0.025% maximum aluminum, titanium or zirconium. Up to 0.10% calcium or 0.15% vanadium is also used for this treatment (18). Neither calcium nor vanadium will produce the deleterious grain boundary type inclusions when used alone (15). Where the concentration of the deoxidizer is critical, thorough diffusion is essential. Otherwise, segregation of the deoxidizer may cause local formation of harmful inclusions. Preference is sometimes given to more dilute deoxidizers (as calcium-manganese-silicon rather than calcium-silicon) for greater assurance of uniformity. Selenium has been shown to have some virtue in spheroidizing the grain boundary sulphide inclusions (21).

[230]

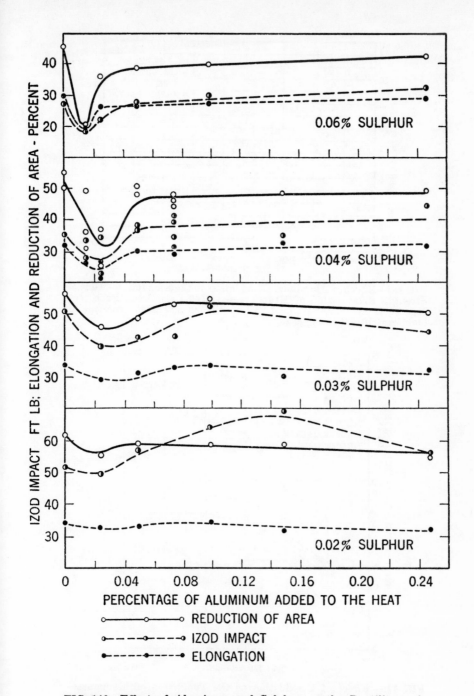

FIG 146 – Effect of Aluminum and Sulphur on the Ductility and Toughness of Laboratory Steel Castings Containing about 0.28% C, 0.7% Mn, 0.3% Si. Test coupons air cooled from 1650 F and tempered two hours at 750 F. Note: higher amounts of aluminum are required in commercial practice (15)

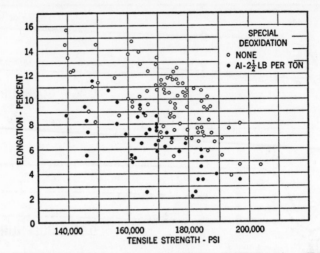

FIG 147 – Effect of Aluminum Deoxidation on the Elongation – Tensile Strength Relationship of Heat Treated 4140 Cast Steel. Each test represents an individual heat. All specimens machined from metal mold centrifugal castings (17)

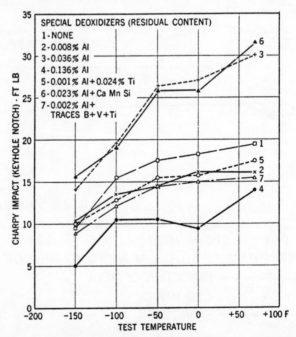

FIG 148 – Effect of Deoxidation on the Toughness of Manganese-Molybdenum Cast Steel. All the steels were deoxidized by adding ferrosilicon and ferromanganese in like quantities. The heats were then tapped and special deoxidizers added to the ladle. The residual amounts of these deoxidizers are indicated in the figure. Approximate composition: 0.3% C, 1.4% Mn, 0.3% Mo. Heat treatment: air cooled from 1650 F, water quenched from 1575 F, tempered at 1275 F (22)

[232]

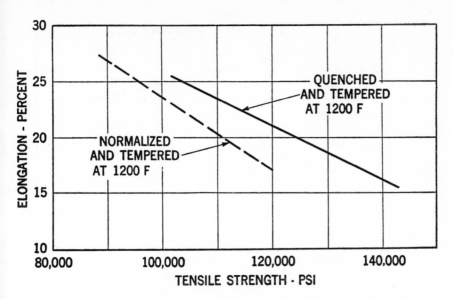

FIG 149 – Effect of Heat Treatment on the Elongation – Tensile Strength Relationship of Commercial Heats of Low Alloy Cast Steels. McQuaid-Ehn grain size: 5 to 8. Coupons heat treated as indicated. Cooperative study by 30 steel foundries (13)

| | Compositions Investigated | | | | | |
	%C	%Mn	%Si	%Cr	%Mo	%Ni
1330	0.27 to 0.33	1.35 to 1.70	0.40 to 0.60	....	....	....
8030	0.27 to 0.33	1.00 to 1.30	0.40 to 0.60	....	0.10 to 0.20	....
8430	0.27 to 0.33	1.30 to 1.60	0.40 to 0.60	....	0.30 to 0.40	....
8630	0.27 to 0.33	0.70 to 0.90	0.40 to 0.60	0.40 to 0.60	0.10 to 0.20	0.40 to 0.70
8730	0.27 to 0.33	0.70 to 0.90	0.40 to 0.60	0.40 to 0.60	0.25 to 0.35	0.40 to 0.70
9430	0.27 to 0.33	1.00 to 1.30	0.40 to 0.60	0.20 to 0.40	0.08 to 0.15	0.40 to 0.70
9530	0.27 to 0.33	1.30 to 1.60	0.40 to 0.60	0.40 to 0.60	0.30 to 0.40	0.40 to 0.70

ductility of the casting (23).

Although the ductility and toughness of steel castings will vary inversely with the tensile strength, narrow bands cannot be drawn because of the aforementioned factors that affect the relationship. However, Figures 149, 150 and 151, based on a recent, large scale, cooperative study, indicate roughly the relation between tensile strength and the elongation, reduction of area and impact strength of normalized and tempered as well as quenched and tempered coupons of low alloy cast steels. The superior properties obtained by water quenching as compared with normalizing are evident.

Alloy engineering steel castings are generally normalized and tempered or quenched and tempered. In recent years, the latter treatment has steadily gained popularity (6). A preliminary normalizing or "homogenizing" treatment at about 1650 to 1850 F followed by air cooling is frequently used, especially for large cast-

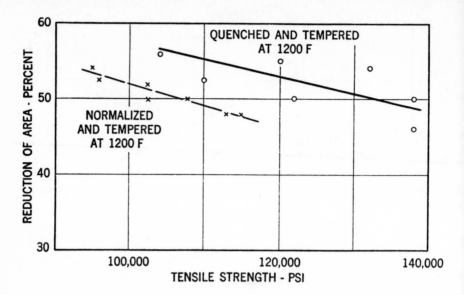

FIG 150 – Effect of Heat Treatment on the Reduction of Area – Tensile Strength Relationship of Commercial Heats of Low Alloy Cast Steels. McQuaid-Ehn grain size: 5 to 8. Coupons heat treated as indicated. Cooperative study by 30 steel foundries (13)

	Compositions Investigated					
	%C	%Mn	%Si	%Cr	%Mo	%Ni
1330	0.27 to 0.33	1.35 to 1.70	0.40 to 0.60	. . . .	. . . .	. . . .
8030	0.27 to 0.33	1.00 to 1.30	0.40 to 0.60	. . . .	0.10 to 0.20	. . . .
8430	0.27 to 0.33	1.30 to 1.60	0.40 to 0.60	. . . .	0.30 to 0.40	. . . .
8630	0.27 to 0.33	0.70 to 0.90	0.40 to 0.60	0.40 to 0.60	0.10 to 0.20	. . . .
8730	0.27 to 0.33	0.70 to 0.90	0.40 to 0.60	0.40 to 0.60	0.25 to 0.35	0.40 to 0.70
9430	0.27 to 0.33	1.00 to 1.30	0.40 to 0.60	0.20 to 0.40	0.08 to 0.15	0.40 to 0.70
9530	0.27 to 0.33	1.30 to 1.60	0.40 to 0.60	0.40 to 0.60	0.30 to 0.40	0.40 to 0.70

ings.* The usual temperature for a single normalizing is about 1550 to 1700 F. Otherwise, the castings are heated 25 to 50 F over the Ac3 temperature and cooled in air or quenched in water or oil, depending upon the composition of the casting and the desired hardness. Differential quenching is common. The approximate tempering temperature for any desired hardness can be estimated from Figure 43 (p 57) although specific tests will be needed to determine the actual temperature required. Compositions with high molybdenum contents will need somewhat higher tempering temper-

* In a recent investigation the effects of homogenizing for various times at 1650 to 2250 F were studied. No significant change was observed in the austenitic (fracture) grain size, hardenability, impact at room and subatmospheric temperatures, susceptibility to temper brittleness, tensile properties, and microstructure as quenched and tempered. As the homogenizing temperature was increased, there was a gradual diffusion of the macroscopic dendritic pattern and, with the higher temperatures, a reduction in the heterogeneity of the as-homogenized microstructure. It was concluded that no benefits are gained by homogenizing relatively low alloy steels. With higher alloy steels, however, a prolonged high temperature treatment (such as 12 hr at 2250 F) will minimize the incidence of quenching cracks and improve the uniformity of the microstructure as-homogenized (24).

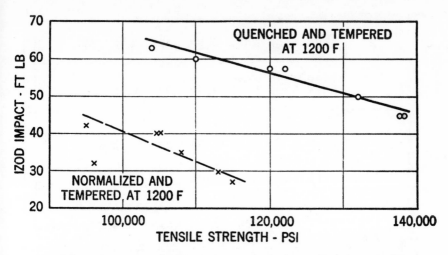

FIG 151 – Effect of Heat Treatment on the Impact – Tensile Strength
Relationship of Commercial Heats of Low Alloy Cast Steels. McQuaid-
Ehn grain size: 5 to 8. Coupons heat treated as indicated. Cooperative
study by 30 steel foundries (13)

	Compositions Investigated					
	%C	%Mn	%Si	%Cr	%Mo	%Ni
1330	0.27 to 0.33	1.35 to 1.70	0.40 to 0.60	....	....	....
8030	0.27 to 0.33	1.00 to 1.30	0.40 to 0.60	....	0.10 to 0.20	....
8480	0.27 to 0.33	1.30 to 1.60	0.40 to 0.60	....	0.30 to 0.40	....
8630	0.27 to 0.33	0.70 to 0.90	0.40 to 0.60	0.40 to 0.60	0.10 to 0.20	0.40 to 0.70
8730	0.27 to 0.33	0.70 to 0.90	0.40 to 0.60	0.40 to 0.60	0.25 to 0.35	0.40 to 0.70
9430	0.27 to 0.33	1.00 to 1.30	0.40 to 0.60	0.20 to 0.40	0.08 to 0.15	0.40 to 0.70
9530	0.27 to 0.33	1.30 to 1.60	0.40 to 0.60	0.40 to 0.60	0.30 to 0.40	0.40 to 0.70

atures than indicated by these curves. If the steel contains a high
percentage of copper, precipitation hardening at tempering temperatures of about 900 F is likely (see, for example, (25)). Except
for applications that require high hardness, the usual tempering
temperatures are about 1000 to 1250 F.

It is often helpful to know the possible chemical compositions and
thermal treatments that will produce a desired tensile strength in a
test coupon. Typical tensile properties for some of the common low
alloy steels, normalized and tempered as well as quenched and
tempered, are reproduced in Tables 66 and 67, arranged in order
of increasing tensile strength.

It seems fairly clear from Tables 66 and 67 that there is a wide
degree of interchangeability among the compositions listed. Therefore, unless special conditions such as abrasion or corrosion or requirements for high impact at low temperatures or high strength
at elevated temperatures are involved, economic considerations and
ease of processing will dictate the final choice among the steels of
suitable hardenability characteristics.

TABLE 66

Typical Tensile Properties of Normalized and Tempered Alloy Cast Steels Containing Molybdenum

Type	Tensile Strength 1000 psi	Yield Point 1000 psi	Elongation percent*	Reduction of Area percent	BHN	%C	%Mn	%Cr	%Cu	%Mo	%Ni	air cooled from F	tempered at F	Ref
C-Mo..........	74	52	29.5	54.4	137	0.20	0.71	....	....	0.48	....	1650	1200	(26)
Cu-Mo.........	74	59	32.0	61.0	....	0.22	0.71	....	1.28	0.19	....	1700 & 1600	1200	(26)
C-Mo..........	78	48	30.0	56.2	168	0.25	0.70	....	....	0.56	....	....	1250	(27)
Cr-Mo.........	78	46	29.5	58.7	156	0.32	0.79	0.83	....	0.32	....	1650	1200	(26)
Cr-Mo.........	80	56	26.0	57.0	184	0.19	0.90	0.60	....	0.70	....	1750	1300	(26)
C-Mo..........	80	50	27.0	51.0	....	0.27	0.66	....	....	0.50	....	....	1250	(27)
Mn-Mo.........	82	59	27.0	55.0	165	0.20	1.11	....	....	0.33	....	....	1250	(27)
C-Mo..........	82	52	23.5	46.5	....	0.30	0.71	....	....	0.58	....	....	1250	(27)
Mn-Mo.........	88	58	28.0	63.0	179	0.28	1.25	....	....	0.84	....	1650	1275	(26)
C-Mo-Ni.......	84	62	28.0	54.5	156	0.29	0.76	....	....	0.52	0.52	1700	1200	(28)
Cr-Mo-Ni......	84	58	27	60	....	0.21	0.76	0.52	....	0.20	....	1650	1200	(28)
Cr-Mo-Ni......	85	54	29.2	51.6	170	0.24	0.99	0.45	....	0.28	0.45	1650	1275	(26)
Mn-Mo.........	86	57	26.5	50.3	163	0.30	1.20	....	....	0.27	....	1650	1200	(26)
Mn-Mo.........	87	62	25.5	51.7	172	0.24	1.32	....	....	0.39	....	....	1250	(27)
Cu-Mo.........	87	69	23.0	50.0	....	0.27	0.58	....	1.21	0.20	....	1600	1225	(26)
Cr-Mo.........	88	59	29.0	58.6	168	0.31	0.69	0.57	....	0.22	....	1650	1250	(26)
Mo-Ni.........	88	55	25.0	48.6	....	0.22	0.72	....	....	0.26	1.50	1750	1100	(26)
Cr-Mo.........	89	63	22.5	59.4	....	0.12	0.64	2.52	....	0.45	....	1650	1250	(26)
Cr-Mo.........	89	60	24.0	48.0	....	0.88	0.80	0.85	....	0.88	....	....	1200	(27)
Mn-Mo.........	90	60	24.0	50.0	....	0.34	1.35	....	....	0.82	....	....	1250	(26)
Cu-Mn-Mo......	90	69	25	54	183	0.29	1.02	....	0.95	0.13	....	1650	1200	(26)
Mo-Ni.........	90	60	29.0	46.5	....	0.31	0.95	....	....	0.27	1.29	....	1200	(26)
Cr-Mo.........	91	58	23.8	51.2	192	0.30	0.98	1.05	....	0.34	....	1650	1200	(26)
Mo-Ni.........	91	61	24.8	54.5	....	0.32	0.70	....	....	0.32	1.85	1700	1275	(29)
Cu-Mn-Mo......	91	67	25.0	59.5	187	0.22	1.07	....	1.05	0.31	....	1650	1250	(26)
Mn-Mo-Ni......	91	62	29.0	54.8	....	0.25	1.22	....	....	0.44	1.18	1600	1150	(26)
Mn-Mo-Ni......	92	62	27.5	48.0	....	0.85	1.02	....	....	0.28	1.81	....	1200	(26)
Mo-Ni.........	92	69	25.5	63	187	0.22	0.66	....	....	0.44	....	1750	1200	(26)
Cr-Mo-Ni......	92	66	22.5	44.9	179	0.24	0.75	0.71	....	0.19	0.56	1750	1275	(26)
Mn-Mo.........	92	65	25.2	52.5	187	0.30	1.25	....	....	0.35	....	....	1250	(27)
Cu-Mo.........	93	64	22.5	50.0	....	0.32	0.80	....	0.95	0.22	....	1550	1100	(26)
Mn-Mo-Ni......	93	64	27.0	49.0	....	0.81	1.10	....	....	0.22	1.40	....	1200	(26)

TABLE 66 — (Continued)

Type	Tensile Strength 1000 psi	Yield Point 1000 psi	Elongation percent*	Reduction of Area percent	BHN	%C	%Mn	%Cr	%Cu	%Mo	%Ni	air cooled from F	tempered at F	Ref
Cr-Mo	93	60	27.0	50.8	..	0.28	0.67	0.32	..	0.51	..	1650	1200	26
Mn-Mo	94	65	24.1	49.5	192	0.32	1.15	..	..	0.34	..	..	1250	27
Cr-Mo-Ni	94	64	25	52	..	0.21	0.76	0.52	..	0.20	0.52	1650	1000	28
Mn-Mo	94	69	23.5	52.5	192	0.31	1.63	..	..	0.35	..	1700	1200	26
Mn-Mo	94	75	25.0	47.5	197	0.31	1.50	..	..	0.22	..	1650	1300	26
Mo-Ni	95	67	26.5	53.5	196	0.24	0.65	..	..	0.40	1.62	..	1200	26
Mn-Mo	95	77	25.5	56.0	196	0.24	1.42	..	..	0.88	..	1700 & 1550	1150	26
Cr-Mo	95	65	22.8	53.0	202	0.34	0.89	1.01	..	0.38	..	1650	1200	26
Mn-Mo	96	71	21.5	42.9	187	0.35	1.12	..	..	0.49	..	1725	1275	26
Mn-Mo	96	71	24.0	56.0	183	0.29	1.89	..	..	0.41	..	1700	1200	26
Mn-Mo	96	68	23.8	49.5	..	0.36	1.33	..	..	0.35	..	..	1250	26
Mn-Mo	96	75	22.8	55.7	195	0.28	1.46	..	..	0.36	..	1700 & 1600	1225	26
Mn-Mo	97	70	26	54	..	0.29	1.30	..	..	0.38	..	1650	1200	28
Cr-Mn-Mo-Ni	97	70	24	54	..	0.30	1.11	0.48	..	0.12	0.67	1650	1250	28
Cr-Mo-Ni	97	65	24.5	48.9	..	0.35	0.78	0.59	..	0.20	0.64	1650	1250	28
Cr-Mn-Mo	97	73	25.0	49.0	..	0.26	1.25	0.51	..	0.47	..	1700	1200	26
Mo-Ni	97	75	23.5	48.7	212	0.30	0.70	..	..	0.40	1.62	1700	1200	28
Mn-Mo	98	70	23.0	49.0	208	0.40	1.60	..	..	0.35	..	..	1250	28
Mn-Mo	99	71	24.0	55.0	204	0.40	1.29	..	..	0.27	..	1800 & 1550	1200	28
Mn-Mo	99	72	20.5	53.2	207	0.31	1.02	..	..	0.50	..	1700	1200	27
Mn-Mo	99	75	21.0	43.4	207	0.31	1.50	..	..	0.22	..	1650	1200	26
Mn-Mo	100	80	26.0	40.0	200	0.25	1.50	..	..	0.88	..	..	1200	28
Mn-Mo	100	70	24.0	50.0	..	0.35	1.75	..	..	0.30	..	1650	1200	26
Cr-Mo-Ni	101	75	20.8	38.8	212	0.31	0.70	0.34	..	0.16	0.56	1700	1200	26
Cr-Mn-Mo-Ni	102	71	22	51	..	0.26	1.07	0.39	..	0.15	0.52	1650	1000	28
Mn-Mo	102	67	24	50	..	0.33	1.18	..	..	0.14	..	1650	1100	28
Mn-Mo	103	73	21.5	37.3	207	0.33	1.25	0.15	..	0.23	0.19	1600	1250	27
Cr-Mn-Mo	103	75	22.0	50.0	200	0.28	1.33	0.78	..	0.32	..	1650	1250	26
Cu-Mo	104	79	22.0	41.0	217	0.26	0.73	..	0.88	0.86	..	1500	1000	27
Mo-Ni	104	81	21.0	46.5	..	0.35	0.98	..	..	0.26	1.92	..	1200	26
Cu-Mn-Mo	105	71	22.0	46.2	202	0.22	1.07	..	1.05	0.31	..	1750 & 1650	1100	26
Mo-Ni	105	75	22.8	42.1	207	0.30	0.80	..	..	0.26	3.70	1650	1200	26

[237]

TABLE 66 — (Continued)

Type	Tensile Strength 1000 psi	Yield Point 1000 psi	Elongation percent*	Reduction of Area percent	BHN	%C	%Mn	%Cr	%Cu	%Mo	%Ni	air cooled from F	tempered at F	Ref
Cr-Mn-Mo	106	77	23.0	52.0	207	0.34	1.19	0.96	.....	0.34	.....	1600	1300	(27)
Cr-Mo	106	74	18.2	39.4	223	0.37	0.96	0.92	.....	0.87	.....	1650	1200	(26)
Mn-Mo	106	74	24	46	.....	0.29	1.30	.....	.....	0.38	.....	1650	1000	(28)
Mn-Mo	107	81	22.0	52.6	237	0.31	1.02	.....	.....	0.50	.....	1700	1100	(27)
Cr-Mo-Ni	108	82	20.5	49.1	223	0.29	0.92	0.61	.....	0.25	0.77	1600	1250	(26)
Cr-Mn-Mo	108	83	19.5	41.5	.....	0.32	1.54	0.51	.....	0.30	.....	1575	1300	(26)
Cr-Mn-Mo	108	78	20.0	41.8	.....	0.30	1.41	0.45	.....	0.30	.....	1575	1300	(26)
Mn-Mo	109	70	21	42	.....	0.33	1.18	.....	.....	0.14	.....	1650	1000	(28)
Cr-Mo-Ni	109	87	21	44.5	.....	0.29	0.95	0.55	.....	0.17	0.62	1650	1200	(28)
Cr-Mn-Mo	110	81	23.0	55.8	238	0.34	1.50	0.65	.....	0.35	.....	1650	1250	(27)
Cr-Mn-Mo	111	79	19.5	46.7	222	0.38	1.30	0.80	.....	0.33	.....	1650	1250	(27)
Cr-Mo-Ni	111	85	20.0	43.5	217	0.31	0.77	0.75	.....	0.32	1.76	1800 & 1550	1250	(26)
Cr-Mo-Ni	112	84	19.0	44.6	.....	0.28	0.55	0.77	.....	0.35	2.11	.....	1150	(27)
Cr-Mo-Ni	112	85	20.0	41.5	.....	0.43	0.76	0.85	.....	0.27	0.51	1650	1250	(26)
Cr-Mo	112	82	17.0	45.8	.....	0.30	0.70	1.35	0.25	0.46	0.55	1650	1200	(26)
Cr-Mn-Mo-Ni	112	86	19	49	.....	0.32	1.47	0.60	.....	0.35	.....	1650	.....	(28)
Cr-Mo-Ni	114	80	19.5	44.9	235	0.38	0.75	0.71	.....	0.28	2.06	1600	1200	(26)
Cr-Mo-Ni	115	93	17.5	40.8	241	0.33	0.81	0.91	.....	0.33	0.28	1600	1100	(26)
Cr-Mn-Mo	116	90	20.0	45.8	.....	0.38	1.61	0.67	.....	0.30	.....	1600	1250	(26)
Cr-Mo-Ni	116	93	20.0	48.0	235	0.38	0.72	0.74	.....	0.32	1.91	1800 & 1550	1250	(26)
Mn-Mo	116	90	17.5	36.3	.....	0.38	1.43	.....	.....	0.47	.....	1600	1260	(26)
Cr-Mo-Ni	117	92	15.5	37.5	.....	0.32	0.81	0.59	.....	0.27	1.39	.....	1150	(27)
Cr-Mo-Ni	118	94	17.0	38.5	.....	0.34	0.71	0.56	.....	0.24	1.63	.....	1150	(27)
Cr-Mn-Mo	118	96	17.5	35.4	228	0.40	1.17	0.70	.....	0.20	.....	1800 & 1550	1200	(26)
Cr-Mo-Ni	118	90	17	40	.....	0.43	0.77	0.57	.....	0.18	0.69	1650	1200	(28)
Cr-Mo	118	94	18.2	46.4	255	0.35	0.84	0.85	.....	0.34	0.02	1650	1100	(26)
Cr-Mn-Mo-Ni	118	88	21.8	49.4	258	0.33	1.35	0.60	.....	0.35	1.15	1650	1250	(27)
Cr-Mo-Ni	118	90	17.0	40.0	.....	0.35	0.86	0.68	.....	0.25	1.39	.....	1150	(27)
Cr-Mn-Mo-Ni	119	91	19.5	42.7	269	0.42	1.48	0.60	.....	0.39	1.26	1650	1250	(27)
Cr-Mo-Ni	120	94	15.5	36.5	.....	0.31	0.80	0.61	.....	0.28	1.47	.....	1150	(27)
Cr-Mo-Ni	120	93	16.5	36.0	.....	0.35	0.80	0.55	.....	0.24	1.42	.....	1150	(27)
Mn-Mo	120	93	18.0	45.4	280	0.35	1.70	.....	.....	0.35	.....	1650	1000	(29)

TABLE 66 — (Continued)

Type	Tensile Strength 1000 psi	Yield Point 1000 psi	Elongation percent*	Reduction of Area percent	BHN	Analyses %C	%Mn	%Cr	%Cu	%Mo	%Ni	Treatment air cooled from F	tempered at F	Ref
Cr-Mo-Ni........	120	89	19	41	....	0.29	0.95	0.55	....	0.17	0.62	1650	1000	(28)
Cr-Mo-Ni........	120	92	17	38	....	0.32	0.80	0.50	....	0.29	0.60	1650	1200	(28)
Cr-Mo-Ni........	120	94	17.0	40.0	....	0.35	0.78	0.59	....	0.21	1.44	....	1150	(27)
Cu-Mo...........	121	92	18.0	38.0	....	0.20	0.66	....	1.60	0.30	....	1650	950	(26)
Cr-Mo-Ni........	123	88	17.5	37.0	228	0.36	0.77	0.94	....	0.32	1.87	1700	1200	(26)
Cr-Mn-Mo........	123	87	15.7	28.5	254	0.42	1.28	0.94	....	0.40	....	1650	1250	(27)
Cr-Mo-Ni........	124	92	16.0	35.5	....	0.44	0.67	0.60	....	0.22	1.89	....	1150	(27)
Cr-Mo-Ni........	131	101	16.5	46.5	....	0.35	0.95	0.68	....	0.39	1.96	....	1150	(27)
Cr-Mo-Ni........	132	105	14.0	29.0	241	0.31	0.71	1.71	....	0.39	3.15	1725 & 1525	1150	(26)
Cr-Mo-Ni........	134	107	15.5	36.5	262	0.38	0.63	0.63	....	0.61	2.44	1800 & 1550	1200	(26)
Mn-Mo...........	134	101	15.2	44.0	292	0.35	1.70	....	....	0.35	....	1650	700	(29)
Cr-Mo-Ni........	136	107	15	41	....	0.31	0.87	0.63	....	0.35	0.79	1650	1000	(28)
Cr-Mo-Ni........	148	111	17	39.0	269	0.31	0.76	1.30	....	0.51	3.15	1800 & 1550	1200	(26)
Cr-Mn-Mo-Ni.....	145	117	18	42	....	0.31	1.89	0.62	....	0.41	0.64	1650	1000	(28)
Cr-Mn-Mo........	154	110	16.4	37.7	348	0.34	1.50	0.65	....	0.35	....	1650	1000	(27)
Cr-Mn-Mo-Ni.....	164	119	13.5	31.2	364	0.28	1.56	0.68	....	0.36	1.18	1650	1000	(27)
Cr-Mn-Mo........	166	132	12.0	34.8	360	0.34	1.50	0.65	....	0.35	....	1650	700	(27)
Cr-Mn-Mo-Ni.....	168	131	14.2	34.9	373	0.33	1.85	0.60	....	0.36	1.15	1650	1000	(27)
Cr-Mn-Mo-Ni.....	175	149	11.5	32.8	364	0.28	1.86	0.68	....	0.36	1.18	1650	700	(29)
Cr-Mn-Mo-Ni.....	176	142	18.5	36.6	387	0.34	1.58	0.71	....	0.32	1.22	1650	1000	(27)
Cr-Mn-Mo-Ni.....	177	146	14.5	36.2	402	0.42	1.48	0.60	....	0.39	1.26	1650	1000	(27)
Cr-Mn-Mo-Ni.....	195	151	10.5	31.2	402	0.33	1.85	0.60	....	0.35	1.15	1650	700	(27)
Cr-Mn-Mo-Ni.....	205	167	10.0	31.5	430	0.42	1.48	0.60	....	0.39	1.26	1650	700	(29)

* in 2 in. on a 0.505 in. diameter specimen
Note: Properties obtained from coupons about one inch in section, but some were as small as ⅜ in. and a few as large as 1¼ in.

TABLE 67

Typical Tensile Properties of Quenched and Tempered Alloy Cast Steels Containing Molybdenum

Type	Tensile Strength 1000 psi	Yield Point 1000 psi	Elongation percent*	Reduction of Area percent	BHN	%C	%Mn	%Cr	%Cu	%Mo	%Ni	quenched In	quenched from F	tempered at F	Ref
Mn-Mo	87	62	27.5	62.5	187	0.28	1.29	....	....	0.30	....	water	1500	1300	(27)
Mn-Mo	96	64	25.0	57.8	196	0.34	1.10	0.34	....	0.18	0.56	water	1600	1200	(26)
Cr-Mo-Ni	97	73	27	59.5	212	0.31	0.70	....	....	0.16	....	water	1600	1275	(26)
Mn-Mo	99	79	24.0	56.0	202	0.34	1.10	....	....	0.18	....	water	1700	1200	(26)
Mn-Mo	100	84	23.5	57.0	212	0.28	1.29	....	....	0.30	....	water	1500	1200	(27)
Mn-Mo	102	76	25.8	58.6	228	0.33	1.60	....	....	0.35	....	oil	1575	1250	(26)
Mo-Ni	102	89	22.5	48.6	225	0.30	0.70	....	....	0.40	1.62	oil	1600	1200	(26)
C-Mo	102	88	22.0	47.0	217	0.35	0.75	....	....	0.17	....	water	1650	1200	(26)
C-Mo	105	83	20.0	45.8	....	0.28	0.76	0.62	....	0.34	....	oil	1550	1250	(26)
C-Mo	105	77	20.0	42.0	217	0.39	0.85	....	....	0.14	....	water	1650	1200	(26)
Mn-Mo	105	80	22.5	56.0	214	0.30	1.15	....	....	0.28	....	water	1600	1200	(26)
Mn-Mo	106	82	19.0	43.4	223	0.35	1.22	....	....	0.34	....	water	1500	1200	(26)
Cr-Mo-Ni	106	85	21.2	39.9	....	0.32	0.98	0.38	....	0.17	0.52	oil	1550	1200	(26)
Mo-Ni	106	90	22.0	46.5	235	0.30	0.70	....	....	0.40	1.62	water	1550	1200	(26)
Cr-Mo	107	86	19.8	44.7	235	0.28	0.82	0.92	....	0.34	....	water	1475	1200	(26)
Cr-Mo-Ni	108	92	23	63	....	0.20	0.78	0.60	....	0.16	0.60	water	1575	1200	(28)
Cr-Mo	108	78	20.5	42.8	248	0.35	0.85	0.75	....	0.45	....	oil	....	....	(26)
Mn-Mo	108	82	20.0	42	217	0.35	1.57	....	....	0.24	....	oil	1650	1200	(26)
Cr-Mo	108	84	21.2	51.9	223	0.30	0.98	1.05	....	0.34	....	water	1475	1200	(29)
Cr-Mo-Ni	108	84	22	50.3	241	0.24	0.99	0.45	....	0.28	0.45	water	1575	1200	(26)
C-Mo	111	92	17.5	46.5	228	0.20	0.71	....	....	0.48	....	water	1625	1100	(26)
Cr-Mn-Mo	112	89	18.0	38	235	0.32	0.82	0.51	....	0.18	0.63	water	1625	1175	(26)
Cr-Mo	112	94	18.0	50.0	230	0.30	0.80	0.80	....	0.20	....	water	1550	1250	(26)
Mn-Mo	112	81	18.0	36.6	223	0.39	1.05	0.08	....	0.30	0.13	oil	1600	1300	(26)
Cu-Mn-Mo	113	100	20	55	241	0.34	1.04	....	0.72	0.31	....	water	1500	1200	(26)
Cr-Mn-Mo	114	94	23.0	56.1	256	0.34	1.50	0.65	....	0.35	....	oil	1575	1250	(27)
Mn-Mo	114	94	22	52	....	0.33	1.28	....	....	0.17	....	water	1575	1200	(28)
Cr-Mo-Ni	114	93	21.0	61.1	241	0.32	0.87	2.67	0.10	0.45	0.87	water	1675	1200	(26)
Mn-Mo	115	99	18.0	37.0	241	0.35	1.50	....	....	0.26	....	water	1650	1200	(26)
Mn-Mo	115	90	20.0	48.0	227	0.30	1.25	....	....	0.30	....	water	....	1250	(26)
Mn-Mo	115	97	18.7	34.1	....	0.26	1.35	....	....	0.30	....	oil	1600	1250	(26)
Cr-Mo	116	97	18.3	43.3	251	0.35	0.91	1.00	....	0.37	....	water	1475	1200	(26)

[240]

TABLE 67—(Continued)

Type	Tensile Strength 1000 psi	Yield Point 1000 psi	Elongation percent*	Reduction of Area percent	BHN	%C	%Mn	%Cr	%Cu	%Mo	%Ni	quenched in	from F	tempered at F	Ref
Cr-Mo-Ni	116	96	19.0	43.4	....	0.28	0.99	0.74	....	0.27	0.63	water	1550	1175	(26)
Mn-Mo	116	101	19.5	46.6	255	0.36	1.26	....	....	0.20	....	water	1575	1150	(26)
Cr-Mo-Ni	116	100	18.4	36.5	....	0.30	0.94	0.47	....	0.29	0.52	water	1600	1175	(26)
Cr-Mn-Mo	118	90	17.5	42.0	248	0.32	1.37	0.75	....	0.32	....	oil	1600	1250	(27)
Cr-Mo	118	101	14.5	45.7	255	0.28	0.79	0.89	....	0.35	....	water	1475	1100	(26)
Mn-Mo-Ni	118	100	19.0	55.0	....	0.30	1.16	....	....	0.31	0.74	water	1600	1150	(26)
Cr-Mo-Ni	118	99	20.0	48.4	269	0.24	0.99	0.45	....	0.28	0.45	water	1575	1100	(26)
Cr-Mn-Mo-Ni	119	92	22.0	45.7	262	0.28	1.56	0.68	....	0.36	1.18	oil	1550	1250	(27)
Mn-Mo	121	95	17.0	35.6	241	0.41	1.17	....	....	0.32	....	oil	1700	1200	(26)
C-Mo	121	103	18.0	40.8	255	0.38	0.72	....	....	0.26	....	oil	1600	1200	(26)
Mn-Mo	122	97	13.0	32.7	251	0.33	1.25	0.15	....	0.23	0.19	water	1600	1100	(26)
Cr-Mo-Ni	122	105	20	58.3	269	0.31	0.70	0.34	....	0.16	0.56	water	1600	1100	(26)
Mn-Mo	123	102	19	45	....	0.33	1.20	....	....	0.29	....	water	1575	1200	(28)
Cr-Mn-Mo-Ni	123	103	21	55	241	0.34	1.04	0.44	....	0.12	0.64	water	1575	1200	(28)
Cr-Mo-Ni	123	97	20.5	45.0	....	0.37	0.78	0.78	....	0.27	2.05	oil	1550	1250	(26)
Mn-Mo	125	111	16.5	41.8	255	0.38	1.43	....	....	0.20	....	water	1575	1150	(26)
Cr-Mo-Ni	125	111	20	53	....	0.28	0.88	0.69	....	0.23	0.87	water	1575	1200	(28)
Cr-Mn-Mo-Ni	125	94	19.2	36.4	269	0.42	1.48	0.60	....	0.39	1.26	oil	1550	1250	(27)
Cr-Mn-Mo-Ni	125	98	19.5	45.7	269	0.34	1.58	0.71	....	0.32	1.22	oil	1550	1250	(27)
Cr-Mo-Ni	126	118	20.0	41.0	248	0.36	0.75	0.75	....	0.30	2.02	oil	1550	1250	(26)
Cr-Mo-Ni	128	110	15.9	37.9	261	0.29	0.94	0.67	....	0.24	0.62	water	1550	1150	(26)
Cr-Mo	128	111	15.3	45.9	277	0.32	0.79	0.83	....	0.32	1.70	water	1475	1000	(26)
Mo-Ni	128	104	16.4	43.2	277	0.28	0.70	0.12	0.17	0.38	0.60	oil	1570	1000	(30)
Cr-Mo-Ni	128	115	17	55	....	0.20	0.78	0.60	....	0.16	....	water	1575	1000	(28)
Cr-Mn-Mo-Ni	133	118	19	....	....	0.32	1.47	0.60	0.25	0.35	0.55	water	1575	1200	(28)
Cr-Mo-Ni	133	116	14.0	38.1	285	0.33	0.81	0.91	....	0.33	0.28	water	1500	1100	(26)
Mo-Ni	133	108	12.6	31.0	269	0.29	0.78	0.12	0.15	0.32	1.21	oil	1570	1000	(30)
Mn-Mo	134	117	17.5	48.0	302	0.28	1.29	....	....	0.30	....	water	1500	1050	(27)
Cr-Mo-Ni	137	125	16	50	285	0.31	0.70	0.34	....	0.16	0.56	water	1600	1000	(26)
Mn-Mo	138	116	14	48	302	0.30	1.35	....	....	0.35	....	water	1650	900	(29)
Cr-Mo-Ni	140	125	14.0	35.0	....	0.33	0.76	0.50	....	0.38	0.59	water	1640	1200	(26)
Cr-Mo-Ni	140	126	18	50	....	0.30	0.70	0.53	....	0.28	0.52	water	1575	1200	(28)

TABLE 67—(Continued)

Type	Tensile Strength 1000 psi	Yield Point 1000 psi	Elongation percent*	Reduction of Area percent	BHN	Analyses						Treatment			Ref
						%C	%Mn	%Cr	%Cu	%Mo	%Ni	quenched in	quenched from F	tempered at F	
C-Mo.........	141	125	12	31	269	0.38	0.94	.....	.....	0.30	.....	oil	1600	1200	(26)
Mo-Ni.........	144	127	16.0	38.2	310	0.30	0.70	.....	.....	0.40	1.62	oil	1600	1000	(26)
Mn-Mo.........	145	123	15.5	36.5	280	0.30	1.25	.....	.....	0.30	.....	water	.....	1000	(26)
Mn-Mo.........	145	120	14.5	37.5	280	0.30	1.15	.....	.....	0.28	.....	water	1600	1000	(26)
Cr-Mo.........	145	134	12.7	33.3	321	0.37	0.96	0.92	.....	0.37	.....	water	1475	1100	(26)
Cr-Mo-Ni.........	146	130	19	43	..	0.43	0.77	0.57	.....	0.18	0.69	water	1575	1200	(28)
Cr-Mo-Ni.........	147	132	12.5	34.5	..	0.32	0.81	0.59	.....	0.27	1.39	water	1650	1150	(27)
Cr-Mo.........	148	136	12.2	30.5	316	0.34	0.84	0.98	.....	0.39	.....	water	1475	1100	(26)
Cr-Mo-Ni.........	148	135	12.0	34.0	..	0.31	0.80	0.61	.....	0.28	1.47	water	1650	1150	(27)
Cr-Mo-Ni.........	148	136	12.0	31.0	..	0.35	0.86	0.68	.....	0.25	1.39	water	1650	1150	(28)
Cr-Mo-Ni.........	150	135	12.5	36.4	363	0.24	0.99	0.45	.....	0.28	0.45	water	1575	900	(26)
Cr-Mo-Ni.........	150	135	12.0	32.0	..	0.30	0.85	0.55	.....	0.27	1.68	water	1650	1150	(27)
Cr-Mo-Ni.........	150	135	13.0	35.0	..	0.32	0.78	0.58	.....	0.23	1.42	water	1650	1150	(27)
Cr-Mo-Ni.........	150	136	13.5	35.0	..	0.34	0.71	0.56	.....	0.24	1.63	water	1650	1150	(27)
Cr-Mo-Ni.........	151	138	13.5	35.5	..	0.35	0.78	0.59	.....	0.21	1.44	water	1650	1150	(27)
Mn-Mo.........	151	137	15	38	..	0.29	1.30	.....	.....	0.38	.....	water	1575	1000	(28)
Cr-Mo-Ni.........	151	138	14	38	..	0.28	0.83	0.69	.....	0.23	0.87	water	1575	1000	(28)
Cr-Mo-Ni.........	152	139	11.0	26.0	..	0.35	0.80	0.55	.....	0.24	1.42	water	1650	1150	(27)
Cr-Mn-Mo-Ni.........	152	139	15	38	..	0.30	1.11	0.48	.....	0.12	0.67	water	1575	1000	(28)
Cr-Mn-Mo-Ni.........	155	139	11.0	28.0	..	0.44	0.67	0.60	.....	0.22	1.39	water	1650	1150	(27)
Mn-Mo.........	156	136	12	40	363	0.30	1.35	.....	.....	0.35	2.44	water	1650	600	(29)
Cr-Mo-Ni.........	158	143	10.5	27.6	321	0.38	0.63	0.63	.....	0.61	.....	oil	1550	1150	(26)
Mn-Mo.........	163	146	13	31	..	0.33	1.28	.....	.....	0.17	.....	water	1575	1000	(28)
Cr-Mn-Mo-Ni.........	167	156	12	31	..	0.32	1.47	0.60	0.25	0.35	0.55	water	1575	1000	(28)
C-Mo.........	168	151	7.5	24.4	375	0.33	0.72	.....	.....	0.26	.....	oil	1600	800	(26)
Mn-Mo.........	168	152	15.3	42.6	374	0.35	1.70	.....	.....	0.35	.....	oil	1575	1000	(29)
Cr-Mo-Ni.........	168	156	14	43.5	..	0.30	0.70	0.53	.....	0.28	0.52	water	1575	1000	(28)
Mo-Ni.........	173	162	12.0	24.8	365	0.30	0.70	.....	.....	0.40	1.62	water	1550	800	(26)
Cr-Mn-Mo-Ni.........	182	172	12.7	33.3	402	0.28	1.56	0.68	.....	0.36	1.18	oil	1550	1000	(27)
Cr-Mn-Mo.........	185	171	13.3	36.3	406	0.34	1.50	0.65	.....	0.35	.....	oil	1575	1000	(27)
Cr-Mn-Mo-Ni.........	188	171	12.5	32.0	414	0.33	1.35	0.60	.....	0.35	1.15	oil	1575	1000	(27)
Cr-Mn-Mo-Ni.........	193	169	10.7	25.3	418	0.42	1.48	0.60	.....	0.39	1.26	oil	1550	1000	(27)
Cr-Mn-Mo-Ni.........	196	171	11.0	24.1	418	0.34	1.58	0.71	.....	0.32	1.22	oil	1550	1000	(27)

* in 2 in. on a 0.505 in. diameter specimen

Note: Properties obtained from coupons about one inch in section but some were as small as ⅞ in. and a few as large as 1¾ in.

Wear Resistance

Molybdenum alloy steel castings have found extensive use in the mining industry for such applications as ball mill liners, dipper teeth and grinding balls, where the steel is required to resist the erosive attack of materials varying in hardness from that of talc and calcite to pyrites and quartz. There is little evidence that any of the alloying elements added to steel improves its wear resistance except by altering the microstructure and therefore hardness of the steel (unless corrosion is an important factor). In general, the wear resistance of steel improves with higher hardness and with increasing carbon content, at least up to the eutectoid percentage. The ideal microstructure is a mixture of martensite and austenite, or low temperature bainite and austenite. The presence of carbides (unless intergranular) is beneficial if the impact requirements of the part will permit their presence (31).

There are many applications where, either by reason of the cost of the alloying elements necessary to provide this structure or because the conditions of impact are such that the wear resistant parts would break in service, a microstructure of softer constituents such as fine pearlite proves advisable (31). For example, some types of ball mill liners are so heavy in cross section that it is impractical to add sufficient alloy for the production of a martensitic-austenitic structure. Such liners are therefore made from a high carbon alloy steel of a type that will produce a relatively hard type of pearlite. Pearlite of this type may, in general, be expected to wear from 15 to 35% faster than a mixture of martensite and austenite. It will, however, have much better wear resistance than the softer types of unalloyed pearlite and will also generally be substantially more wear resistant than austenitic manganese steel. Table 68 gives suggested compositions for different applications.

HIGH ALLOY CORROSION RESISTANT STEEL CASTINGS

Molybdenum is added to high alloy corrosion resistant steel castings to improve their corrosion resistance. Although amounts up to 3% have been used in various high chromium steels, the two most prominent classes of corrosion resistant castings containing molybdenum are the chromium-nickel and the iron-silicon types.

Chromium-Molybdenum-Nickel Steel Castings

The "18-8" type with molybdenum is the most popular of the molybdenum containing chromium-nickel corrosion resistant steel casting grades. Molybdenum produces a notable improvement in the corrosion resistance of the 18-8, so this composition is satisfactory in many applications where the 18-8 without molybdenum does not have adequate corrosion resistance. The molybdenum modification is

TABLE 68

Compositions and Applications of Wear Resistant Steel Castings

%C	%Mn	%Cr	%Cu	%Mo	%Ni	Treatment	Applications	Ref
0.40	0.70	1.10	....	0.25	....	air cool from 1700 F, temper at 1050 to 1250 F	car wheels, caterpillar track treads, couplers for mine cars, crusher frames, knuckles for mine cars, track rollers	(32)
0.50	1.35	1.10	....	0.40	....	air cool or oil quench from about 1650 F, temper at 700 to 1300 F	crusher rolls, drilling and excavating equipment	(27)
0.55	0.70	1.10	....	0.35	....	air cool from 1700 F, temper at 1050 to 1250 F	ball mill low discharge grates, lift pans and scoop lips, dipper teeth, elevator buckets, mine car wheels	(32)
0.85	0.80	2.10	....	0.35	....	air cool from 1750 to 1800 F, temper at 700 to 1100 F	ball mill liners	
0.65	0.80	2.25	....	0.40	....	quench from 1800 F into salt bath at 600 F, hold six hours, air cool	general purpose wear resistant castings	
0.95	1.10	2.75	....	0.45	....	as cast (sand cool) or air cool from 1750 to 1800 F, temper at 800 to 900 or 1200 to 1250 F	ball mill liners, pump liners, sand and gravel pump runners, tires for muckingmachines,wear plates	(32)
0.50	0.60	3.00	....	0.50	....	air cool from 1750 F, temper at 1050 to 1250 F	jaw crusher plates, roll shells, wearing plates in coarse ore bins	(32)
0.80	0.80	1.00	0.30	0.25	....	air quench to 650 F from chill molds	grinding balls for mild or moderate impact	
1.10	0.80	1.50	0.30	0.25	....	air quench to 1025 F from molds	grinding balls for severe impact	
0.40	0.70	0.70	....	0.35	1.25	differentially harden to Brinell 330 to 370 on cutting edge	clamshell bucket lips	(33)
0.30	0.75	0.75	....	0.25	2.00	differentially harden	impact hammers, power shovel and scarifier teeth, sprockets	(27)
0.45	0.75	0.75	....	0.30	2.00	double normalize and temper to Brinell 225 to 250	ball joints, impellers, levers, pump casings	(27)

particularly widely used in the manufacture of paper pulp where sulphurous acid and sulphite liquors are encountered.

Castings of this grade generally contain about 18 to 21% chromium, 9 to 12% nickel and 2 to 3% molybdenum. The standard compositions of the Alloy Casting Institute (34) for these steels are:

Designation	%C max	%Mn max	%Si max	%P max	%S max	%Cr	%Ni	%Mo
CF-8M	0.08	1.50	1.50	0.04	0.04	18 to 21	9 to 12	2.0 to 3.0
CF-12M	0.12	1.50	1.50	0.04	0.04	18 to 21	9 to 12	2.0 to 3.0

It will be noted that the nickel is lower than that normally used for wrought material. As indicated by Figure 90 (p 128), delta ferrite will be present along with austenite in the castings. Since ease of hot working is not a problem and since castings are seldom stress relieved at temperatures where the ferrite would transform to the brittle sigma phase, delta ferrite is not objectionable as it is in most wrought material. On the contrary, the presence of delta ferrite in castings for room temperature service is desirable as it decreases the susceptibility to intergranular corrosion (p 130) since the carbides precipitate in the discontinuous pools of delta ferrite before they precipitate in the grain boundaries.*

Castings are generally softened by rapid cooling from a high temperature before they are placed in service. In this condition, the steel has the optimum corrosion resistance since all the carbides are in solution (except in the center of large castings where the cooling rate may not be fast enough to prevent the carbides from precipitating during cooling (36)). The minimum temperature from which the steel should be quenched for maximum corrosion resistance will vary with the molybdenum content as indicated in Figure 152. It is often desirable to use somewhat higher temperatures where the rate of carbide solution is faster (36).

The tensile strength of this grade is usually somewhat higher than that of cast 18-8 without molybdenum but the other mechanical properties are similar. Cast coupons, rapidly cooled from around 2050 F, will show about 75,000 to 90,000 psi tensile strength, 40,000 to 50,000 psi "yield point", 40 to 50% elongation and 50 to 65% reduction of area.

Apart from resistance to intergranular corrosion, castings of 18-8 with molybdenum have about the same corrosion resistance as the wrought material (Table 30, pp 135-138).

While the 18-8 with molybdenum is the most popular of the chromium-molybdenum-nickel series, an addition of about 3% molybdenum is often made to other standard chromium-nickel compositions. These include the 15% chromium – 35% nickel, 20% chromium – 25% nickel, 25% chromium – 12% nickel and 25% chromium – 20% nickel types. The effect of the molybdenum is basically the same in these steels as in the 18-8 with molybdenum.

A number of special purpose, high alloy casting compositions, usually containing chromium, nickel, copper, and molybdenum, are used for applications where the more common types are not suffi-

---

* While columbium can be added to wrought 18-8 with molybdenum to prevent the susceptibility to intergranular corrosion of a substantially austenitic composition, this practice appears unsatisfactory for castings of the above compositions (35). The addition of the ferrite-former columbium to the normally partially ferritic castings produces a very large amount of ferrite, which seems to be the reason for the substantial decrease in general (not intergranular) corrosion observed after sensitizing at 1200 F (35).

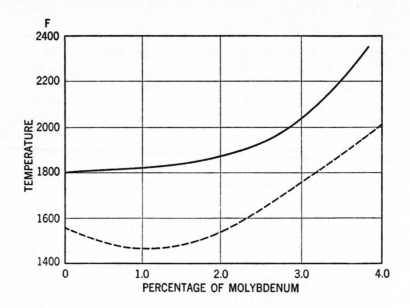

FIG 152 – Relation between Corrosion in Boiling 65% Nitric Acid, Molybdenum Content of "18-8" with Molybdenum and Temperature from which Samples Were Quenched. Samples above the dotted line had an average corrosion rate corresponding to 0.0025 in. penetration per month as determined by 48 hour tests. Samples below the dotted line had higher corrosion rates. The corrosion rate was constant with time above the solid line but increased with time below it. Base composition: 0.09% C, 0.80% Mn, 1.00% Si, 19% Cr, 0.06% N, 9% Ni. Samples held at temperature 30 minutes before water quenching (37)

ciently resistant. Typical compositions generally made as castings are listed in Table 69. In addition, many of the compositions in Table 34 (p 142) are furnished as castings as well as in the wrought condition. The corrosion resistance of these steels is higher than that of the 18-8 with molybdenum but will vary with the specific

TABLE 69

Typical Compositions of Special Purpose Cast Corrosion Resistant Steels

%C	%Si	%Cr	%Ni	%Cu	%Mo
0.15	...	10.0	20.0	4.0	4.0
0.08	0.6	12.0	28.5	3.5	3.5*
0.05	...	15.3	35.4	2.0	3.5
0.06	...	19.0	23.5	1.8	2.5
0.06	1.0	19.0	22.0	1.0	3.0
0.06	1.0	20.0	30.0	4.0	3.0
0.15	1.2	24.0	20.0	3.5	2.0

* 0.5% Sb also present

composition. Except for lower ductility and toughness, the physical and mechanical properties will be similar to those of cast 18-8 with molybdenum. Other even higher alloy casting compositions with better corrosion resistance in some media are discussed in Section X (pp 332-334). One of the large uses of these special compositions is for pumps, pipes and fittings for handling acid and other highly corrosive solutions.

Iron-Molybdenum-Silicon Castings

The addition of molybdenum to a 14% silicon iron markedly increases its resistance to hydrochloric acid (38) (Figure 153). The usual chemical limits are about 0.5 to 0.85% carbon, 3.5 to 4.0% molybdenum and 14.0 to 16.0% silicon; 1% nickel is sometimes present. This material is not malleable and therefore is produced in cast

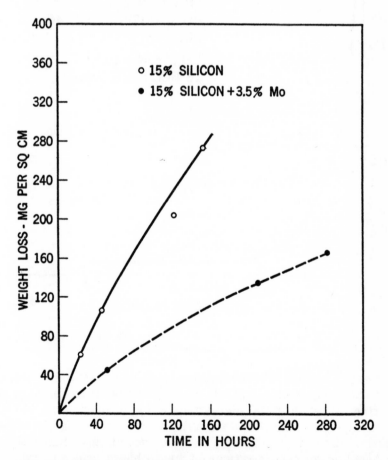

FIG 153 – Effect of Molybdenum on the Rate of Corrosion of 15% Silicon Iron in Boiling 70% Hydrochloric Acid (39)

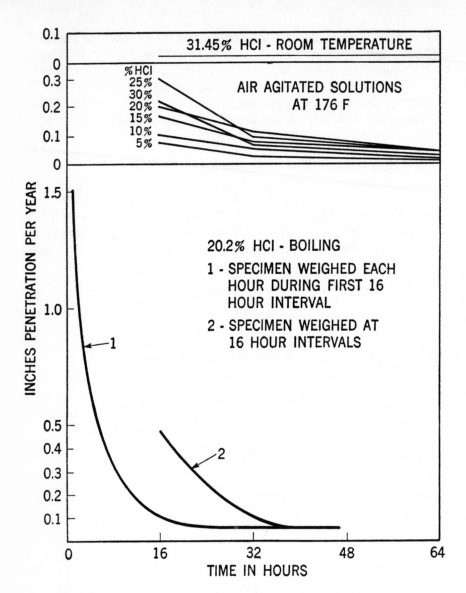

FIG 154 – Rate of Corrosion of 14% Silicon – 4% Molybdenum – 1%
Nickel Iron in Various Hydrochloric Acid Solutions (40)

form only. Castings must be finished by grinding. Its high hardness
(approximately Rockwell C 52) confers resistance to abrasion and
scouring. After an initial high attack in hydrochloric acid, the corrosion rate gradually decreases until it becomes negligible after a
period of time (Figure 154). The major use of this composition is
for handling all concentrations of hydrochloric acid and its com-
pounds at temperatures up to boiling. It is equally resistant to almost

all other commercial acids. Applications include pumps, valves, pipe fittings, heat exchangers and condensers.

STEEL CASTINGS FOR ELEVATED TEMPERATURE USE

Steel castings for elevated temperature use are in general similar in composition to wrought steels for equivalent service, although the carbon content is normally somewhat higher. The elevated temperature characteristics are comparable, so the properties given in Section VI can be applied to castings as well as to wrought steels. The ASME codes for power boilers and unfired pressure vessels (Appendix E) specify the same maximum working stresses for wrought and cast steels of corresponding compositions, although they provide for a "casting quality factor" as indicated in Footnote 7. An interesting measure of the value of molybdenum for elevated temperature service is the fact that 11 of the 13 alloy steel casting compositions listed contain molybdenum.

The most usual molybdenum contents for carbon-molybdenum steel castings are 0.5 and 1.0% (for elevated temperature properties, see pp 11, 145-150; Appendix E). These castings are used for many applications such as steam line valves and fittings, steam turbine casings and some oil refinery fittings. Cast carbon-molybdenum steel reportedly shows a somewhat greater resistance to graphitization than wrought carbon-molybdenum steel (41), but the possibility of graphitization (p 151) should still be considered, especially when high aluminum additions are made (42).

A composition with about 0.25% carbon, 0.6% manganese, 0.5% chromium and 0.5% molybdenum has been proposed (42, 43) for use with the comparable low chromium-molybdenum steel piping (p 151) where graphitization may be encountered in carbon or carbon-molybdenum steels. The creep strength at 900 F is apparently somewhat increased by the chromium addition (44). Some graphitization has been observed in this steel after 10,000 hours at 1025 F (44, 45). One valve company has advocated the use of a chromium-molybdenum-nickel steel containing about 0.25% carbon, 0.6% manganese, 0.5% chromium, 0.4% molybdenum and 0.9% nickel* (46). Another valve company has suggested a modification of the 0.5% chromium-0.5% molybdenum steel by the addition of titanium and vanadium (44).

The most popular casting compositions of the chromium-molybdenum series with up to 9% chromium are the 2% chromium – 0.5% molybdenum, the 2.25% chromium – 1.0% molybdenum, the 5% chromium – 0.5% molybdenum and the 9% chromium – 1.0% molybdenum types (for elevated temperature properties, see pp 152-161; Appen-

---

* For maximum allowable working stresses, see Appendix E.

dix E). The castings are usually normalized and tempered rather than annealed. Applications include valves, pipe fittings, valve trim, oil pump castings, return bends and flanges, particularly for oil refinery service.

Although castings of the "18-8" type with molybdenum for room temperature applications often contain delta ferrite, castings for elevated temperature use should be balanced to produce a fully austenitic structure and thus avoid any possible formation in service of the weak but brittle sigma phase from the delta ferrite (p 127). As indicated by Figure 90 through 93 (pp 128-131), this would mean that castings with 18% chromium would have about 14% nickel and 2% molybdenum, or, with 16% chromium, about 13% nickel and 3% molybdenum. Since nitrogen is a potent austenite former, the nitrogen content of border-line castings may be increased from the usual 0.05 to 0.06% up to 0.10 to 0.15% (for example, by the use of high nitrogen ferrochromium) as a safeguard against the presence of delta ferrite. If there is a possibility of intergranular corrosion (pp 129, 130) in service, the castings are sometimes softened by rapid cooling from approximately 1850 F and then heated at 1550 F long enough to precipitate and agglomerate the carbides. In this way, selective precipitation along the grain boundaries is avoided (for high temperature properties, see pp 11, 163-165).

Castings of the 19-9WMo composition (Table 47, p 182) are used for gas turbine casings (47).

There has been some industrial use of molybdenum in heat resistant castings of the 25% chromium – 12% nickel type. The basic composition is border-line and may be either completely austenitic or partly ferritic, depending upon the balance of chromium and nickel as well as on the carbon and nitrogen contents.*

Substantially austenitic alloys have much better load carrying capacity at elevated temperatures than partly ferritic alloys. Furthermore, any delta ferrite present will transform to sigma on holding at intermediate temperatures (particularly at about 1600 F) and thus lead to a loss of room temperature ductility. Both types of structures will be embrittled by precipitation in about the same temperature range, although this effect seems to be more marked at 1400 F than at 1600 F (48). The amount of this precipitation increases with the nitrogen and carbon contents; the latter is usually about 0.25 to 0.50% or substantially higher than in the 18-8 type with molybdenum. Since structure has such a pronounced influence on the properties of this steel, the effect of molybdenum additions on the analysis balance must be considered. The ferrite forming

---

* For alloys with about 0.07 to 0.09% nitrogen, the ratio of $\dfrac{\%Cr - 16\% \ C}{\%Ni}$ should not exceed about 1.7 if the alloy is to be substantially austenitic (48).

TABLE 70

Effect of Variation in Structure on the Properties of Castings of the
25% Chromium – 12% Nickel – 1% Molybdenum Type (49)

No.	Analyses							Structure	As-Cast Properties	
	%C	%Mn	%Si	%Cr	%Ni	%Mo	%N		Tensile Strength psi	Elongation percent*
1	0.31	0.48	0.55	27.1	10.8	1.05	0.16	partly ferritic	92,500	22.5
2	0.37	0.47	0.58	25.4	12.0	1.01	0.19	subst. austenitic	92,500	19.5

No.	Room Temperature Properties after Aging 24 hr at 1400 F, Furnace Cool		Stress–Strain–Rupture Tests at 1400 F 20,000 psi		
	Tensile Strength psi	Elongation percent*	Life, hours	Rate, percent per hour	Elongation percent*
1	95,750	20.8	11.6	1.01	16.0
2	102,400	8.3	25.4	0.04	1.5

No.	Creep Characteristics at 1800 F			
	Limiting Creep Strength for Minimum Creep Rate of 0.0001% per hour psi	Creep Tests with Stress of 2,000 psi		
		Duration, hours	Rate, percent per hour	Elongation percent**
1	830	290	0.0118	3.8
2	2,200	1,115	0.000055	0.12

No.	Room Temperature Properties after Creep Test		
	Tensile Strength psi	Elongation percent*	Permeability H = 24
1	74,500	7.0	2.125
2	80,500	3.0	1.003

*in 2 in. on a 0.505 in. diameter specimen
**in 4 in. on a 0.505 in. diameter specimen

effect of molybdenum in this composition has been stated to be about
four times as great as that of chromium (48). A partially ferritic
and a substantially austenitic steel of the 25-12 type with 1% molybdenum are compared in Table 70. The higher strength of the substantially austenitic steel at elevated temperatures will be noted.

It has been claimed that the addition of about 2% molybdenum
with about the same amount of either columbium or titanium greatly
improves the creep strength at 1800 F of steels of the 15% chromium
– 35% nickel type (50).

STEEL CASTINGS FOR LOW TEMPERATURE USE

The principles governing the low temperature behavior of steel castings are the same as those for wrought steel (pp 114-122). The best low temperature impact properties are obtained by quenching and tempering when this is practicable. Normalizing and tempering gives lower values while annealing or normalizing gives the lowest impact values (Figure 155). For maximum toughness, steels to be used in the quenched and tempered condition should have sufficient hardenability for full hardening as the presence of ferrite, pearlite or bainite is deleterious. Bainite formed at low temperatures appears to be less injurious than that formed at higher temperatures (Figure 156). Figures 3 and 6 (pp 5, 8) show the pronounced lowering of the low temperature impact properties that can be caused by temper brittleness. Therefore, molybdenum steels are advantageous for low temperature service: 1) because their good hardenability aids in securing the fully hardened condition preferred for maximum toughness and 2) because they are relatively immune to temper brittleness. Comparative impact properties of several medium carbon alloy steel

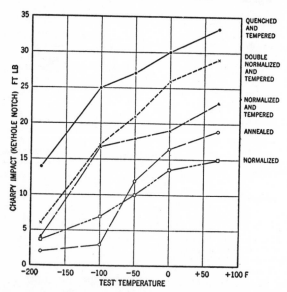

FIG 155 – Effect of Heat Treatment on the Low Temperature Impact Properties of 4630 Cast Steel (22, 51)

Analysis: 0.30% C, 0.68% Mn, 0.39% Si, 0.025% P, 0.042% S, 0.20% Cr, 0.28% Mo, 1.66% Ni

Deoxidation: deoxidized with aluminum to give a residual aluminum content of about 0.02 to 0.04%

Thermal Treatment:
Quenched and Tempered: air cooled from 1650 F, water quenched from 1550 F, tempered at 1275 F
Double Normalized and Tempered: air cooled from 1650 F, air cooled from 1550 F, tempered at 1275 F
Normalized and Tempered: air cooled from 1650 F, tempered at 1275 F
Normalized: air cooled from 1650 F
Annealed: furnace cooled from 1650 F

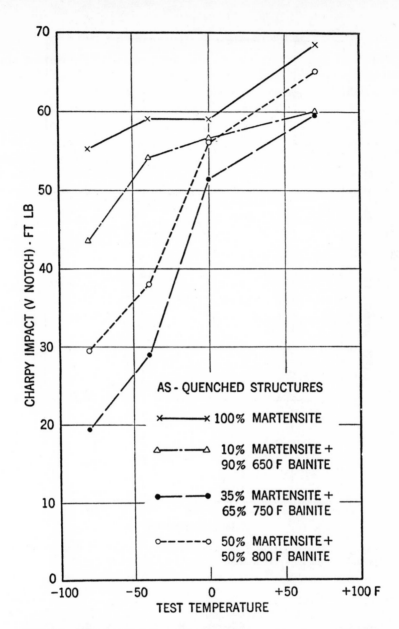

FIG 156 – Effect of Bainite on the Low Temperature Impact Properties of a Cast Chromium-Manganese-Molybdenum Steel (52)

Analysis: 0.28% C, 2.14% Mn, 0.65% Cr, 0.49% Mo
Thermal Treatment: (over-size Charpy specimens)
    100% **Martensite:** water quenched from 1700 F*
     50% **Martensite + 50% 800 F Bainite:** austenitized at 1700 F,
        cooled to 800 F, held 10,000 sec and air cooled*
     35% **Martensite + 65% 750 F Bainite:** austenitized at 1700 F,
        cooled to 750 F, held 1,000 sec and air cooled*
     10% **Martensite + 90% 650 F Bainite:** austenitized at 1700 F,
        cooled to 650 F, held 1,000 sec and air cooled*
*all specimens subsequently tempered at 1200 to 1250 F and water quenched to give Brinell hardness 240 to 248

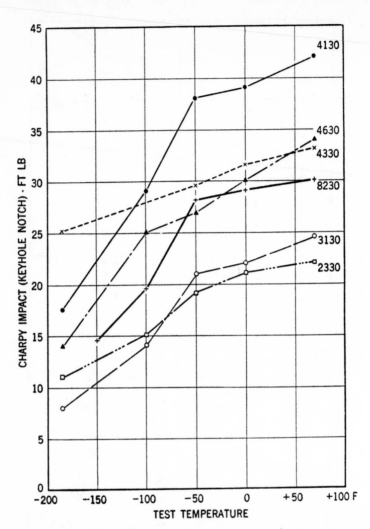

FIG 157 – Comparative Low Temperature Impact Properties of
Quenched and Tempered, Medium Carbon, Cast Alloy Steels (22, 51)

	Analyses							
	%C	%Mn	%Si	%P	%S	%Cr	%Mo	%Ni
2330..................	0.26	0.62	0.31	0.029	0.026	0.10	....	3.36
3130..................	0.26	0.73	0.43	0.030	0.042	0.69	....	1.10
4130..................	0.30	0.71	0.29	0.022	0.019	0.82	0.22	0.03
4330..................	0.26	0.59	0.44	0.032	0.023	0.62	0.30	1.82
4630..................	0.30	0.68	0.39	0.025	0.042	0.20	0.28	1.66
8230..................	0.33	1.38	0.58	0.023	0.031	....	0.28	....

Deoxidation: deoxidized with aluminum to give a residual aluminum content of about 0.02 to 0.04%
Thermal Treatment: air cooled from 1650 F, water quenched from 1550 F, tempered at 1275 F

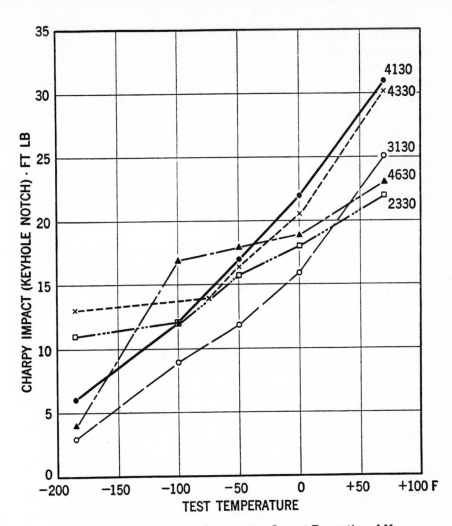

FIG 158 – Comparative Low Temperature Impact Properties of Normalized and Tempered, Medium Carbon, Cast Alloy Steels (22, 51)

	Analyses							
	%C	%Mn	%Si	%P	%S	%Cr	%Mo	%Ni
2330....................	0.26	0.62	0.31	0.029	0.026	0.10	....	3.36
3130....................	0.26	0.73	0.43	0.030	0.042	0.69	....	1.10
4130....................	0.30	0.71	0.29	0.022	0.019	0.82	0.22	0.03
4330....................	0.26	0.59	0.44	0.032	0.023	0.62	0.30	1.82
4630....................	0.30	0.68	0.39	0.025	0.042	0.20	0.28	1.65

Deoxidation: deoxidized with aluminum to give a residual aluminum content of about 0.02 to 0.04%
Thermal Treatment: air cooled from 1650 F, tempered at 1275 F, except for 2330 which was tempered at 1250 F

compositions are reproduced in Figure 157 for quenched and tempered and in Figure 158 for normalized and tempered specimens. For low temperature service where high strength is not necessary and where quenching is not feasible, low carbon molybdenum-nickel steels come into consideration. With molybdenum present, less nickel is required than in simple nickel steels. It has been concluded, for example, that good impact properties (Charpy keyhole notch) can be secured at temperatures as low as − 200 F with properly deoxidized, normalized and tempered steel castings containing a maximum of 0.15% carbon and either 3.75% nickel or a combination of 2.75% nickel and approximately 0.3% molybdenum (53).

Section VIII − Bibliography

(1) C. H. Lorig "Causes and Prevention of Intergranular Fracture in Cast Steel" AIME, Electric Furnace Steel Conference, Vol 3 (1945)

(2) C. H. Lorig and A. R. Elsea "Occurrence of Intergranular Fracture in Cast Steels" Transactions, AFA, Vol 55 (1947)

(3) M. C. Udy and M. K. Barnett "A Laboratory Study of Quench Cracking in Cast Alloy Steels" Transactions, ASM, Vol 38 (1947)

(4) J. B. Caine "Hardenability of Some Cast Steels" Transactions, AFA, Vol 52 (1944)

(5) K. L. Clark and J. H. Richards "Hardenability and the Steel Casting" Transactions, AFA, Vol 52 (1944)

(6) "Hardenability of Cast Steels" Steel Casting Report No. 2, published by the Steel Founders' Society of America

(7) H. A. Schwartz "Hardenability and Interchangeability of Cast Steels" Iron Age, Vol 154 (1944)

(8) SAE Handbook, published by the SAE (1947)

(9) C. R. Wilks, H. S. Avery and E. Cook "Relation of Quenching Rate and Hardenability to the Mechanical Properties of Several Heat Treated Cast Alloy Steels" Transactions, ASM, Vol 38 (1947)

(10) F. Kiper "Hardenability of Some Cast Steels" Metals and Alloys, Vol 19 (1944)

(11) E. J. Wellauer "Use of the End-Quench Test for Cast Steel" Metals and Alloys, Vol 19 (1944)

(12) E. J. Wellauer "Hardenability Test for Quenched and Tempered Steel" Iron Age, Vol 158 (1946)

(13) "Mechanical Properties of Low Alloy Cast Steels" Steel Casting Report No. 1, published by the Steel Founders' Society of America

(14) H. T. Protheroe "The Influence of Melting Conditions on the Physical Properties of Steel Castings" Journal of the Iron and Steel Institute, Vol CL, No. 2 (1944)

(15) C. E. Sims and F. B. Dahle "Effect of Aluminum on the Properties of Medium Carbon Cast Steel" Transactions, AFA, Vol 46 (1938)

(16) Discussion of C. E. Sims and F. B. Dahle (15)

(17) S. F. Carter and C. K. Donoho "Acid Electric Steel for Castings" Transactions of the Electrochemical Society, Vol 91 (1947)

(18) W. Crafts, J. J. Egan and W. D. Forgeng "Formation of Inclusions in Steel Castings" Transactions, AIME, Vol 140 (1940)

(19) F. Grotts, discussion of C. E. Sims and F. B. Dahle (15)

(20) A. P. Gagnebin "The Effect of Deoxidation Treatments on the Ductility of Cast Steels" Transactions, AFA, Vol 46 (1938)

(21) A. P. Gagnebin "Influence of Selenium on Sulphide Inclusions and Ductility of Cast Steel" Transactions, AFA, Vol 55 (1947)

(22) "Low-Temperature Impact Properties of Cast Steels − 2" Steel Casting Report No. 5, published by the Steel Founders' Society of America

(23) G. A. Timmons "Factors Affecting the Ductility of Cast Steel" Transactions, AFA, Vol 51 (1943)

(24) J. G. Kura and P. C. Rosenthal "Homogenization Heat Treatments for Cast Steel" Transactions, AFA, Vol 54 (1946)

(25) H. F. Taylor, H. R. Bishop and R. C. Wayne "Copper and the Steel Casting — An Alloy for Postwar Consideration" Transactions, AFA, Vol 54 (1946)

(26) Data obtained mainly from foundries

(27) Steel Castings Handbook, published by the Steel Founders' Society of America (1941)

(28) M. F. Hawkes "Mechanical Properties of Cast Low Alloy Steels" Transactions, ASM, Vol 39 (1947)

(29) Cast Metals Handbook, published by the AFA (1944)

(30) W. J. Crook "Weldable High Strength Steel Castings" Metal Progress, Vol 50 (1946)

(31) T. E. Norman and C. M. Loeb, Jr. "Wear Tests on Grinding Balls" AIME TP 2319; Metals Technology, Vol 15 (1948)

(32) T. E. Norman "Wear Resistant Steel Castings for the Mining Industry" Metallurgia, Vol 33 (1945)

(33) "14-Ton Lifting Bucket Made Resistant to Wear and Impact" Nickel Steel Topics, Vol 16 (1947)

(34) Standard Designations and Chemical Composition Ranges for Heat and Corrosion Resistant Castings, issued by the Alloy Casting Institute (1947)

(35) E. A. Schoefer "Cast Alloys Stabilized with Columbium or Titanium" Alloy Casting Bulletin No. 10, published by the Alloy Casting Institute (1947)

(36) "Effect of Heat Treatment on Corrosion Resistance – Part Two" Alloy Casting Bulletin No. 7, published by the Alloy Casting Institute (1946)

(37) "Effect of Heat Treatment on Corrosion Resistance – Part One" Alloy Casting Bulletin No. 6, published by the Alloy Casting Institute (1946)

(38) K. I. Vashchenko "Antichlor" Trudy Tsentra Laboratoriya, Zavoda "Bol'chevik" (1940) as abstracted in Khimischeski Referatnyi Zhurnal, Vol 4 (1941)

(39) J. E. Hurst "High-Si Acid-Resisting Cast Iron" Foundry Trade Journal, Vol 71 (1943)

(40) "Durichlor" Bulletin 400 A, published by the Duriron Company, Dayton, Ohio (1935)

(41) H. J. Kerr and F. Eberle "Graphitization of Low-Carbon and Low-Carbon-Molybdenum Steels" Graphitization of Steel Piping, published by the ASME (1945)

(42) J. J. Kanter "Studies on Susceptibility of Casting Steels to Graphitization" Transactions, ASME, Vol 68 (1946)

(43) J. J. Kanter "Improved Steels for High Pressure Temperature Power Piping" Valve World, Vol 42 (1945)

(44) V. T. Malcolm and S. Low "The Welding of High-Temperature, High-Pressure Steel Valves" Welding Journal, Vol 26 (1947)

(45) Discussion of J. J. Kanter (42)

(46) A. J. Smith, J. Urban and J. W. Bolton "Graphitization in Some Cast Steels" Welding Research Supplement to the Journal, AWS, Vol 25 (1946)

(47) H. A. Knight "Super Alloys for High Temperature Service" Materials and Methods, Vol 23 (1946)

(48) J. T. Gow and O. E. Harder "Balancing the Composition of Cast 25% Chromium – 12% Nickel Type Alloys" Transactions, ASM, Vol 30 (1942)

(49) H. S. Avery, E. Cook and J. A. Fellows "Engineering Properties of Heat-Resistant Alloys" Transactions, AIME, Vol 150 (1942)

(50) H. M. German, discussion of H. S. Avery and N. A. Matthews "Cast Heat Resistant Alloys of the 16% Chromium – 35% Nickel Type" Transactions, ASM, Vol 38 (1947)

(51) "Low Temperature Impact Properties of Cast Steels – 1" Steel Casting Report No. 4, published by the Steel Founders' Society of America

(52) P. C. Rosenthal and G. K. Manning "Heat Treatment of Heavy Cast Steel Sections" Foundry, Vol 74 (1946) ; also Steel, Vol 119 (1946)

(53) T. N. Armstrong and A. P. Gagnebin "Impact Properties of Some Low Alloy Nickel Steels at Temperatures Down to – 200 Degrees Fahr." Transactions, ASM, Vol 28 (1940)

SECTION IX

CAST IRON

Cast irons are conventionally divided into three groups: gray, white and malleable, which will be discussed in this order.

GRAY IRON

The extensive use of molybdenum in gray cast iron is adequate testimony to the economical advantages of its positive action in bringing about the following benefits:

(1) marked improvement in strength
(2) improved toughness
(3) greater uniformity
(4) decreased section sensitivity
(5) higher strength at elevated temperatures
(6) higher hardenability of heat treated iron

Molybdenum gives desirable improvements in the properties of all classes of gray cast iron. As it is not a graphitizing element, it does not require "balancing" of the composition to improve properties. While no change in melting practice is necessary, the better the base iron, the more pronounced are the advantages of the molybdenum addition. From a practical viewpoint, molybdenum causes foundrymen no trouble. It is easily added in the ladle and the usual additions are so small that the metal is not cooled appreciably.

Properties

The British Research Committee on High-Duty Cast Irons for General Engineering Purposes concluded in their Third Report that molybdenum had the most pronounced effect on tensile strength, for a given percentage addition, of all the alloying elements and combinations covered (1). The improvement is proportional to the molybdenum content, at least for amounts up to 1%. Combinations of copper and molybdenum (1.16 to 1.63% copper with 0.53 to 0.75% molybdenum) and molybdenum and nickel (0.53 to 0.76% molybdenum with 0.79 to 1.68% nickel) were next most effective, while chromium-copper, chromium-nickel, copper, copper-nickel, and nickel were considerably less effective for a given percentage of alloy. Their results (Figure 159) are interesting as an indication of the strengthening effect of molybdenum under carefully controlled conditions; although the properties of these irons are not

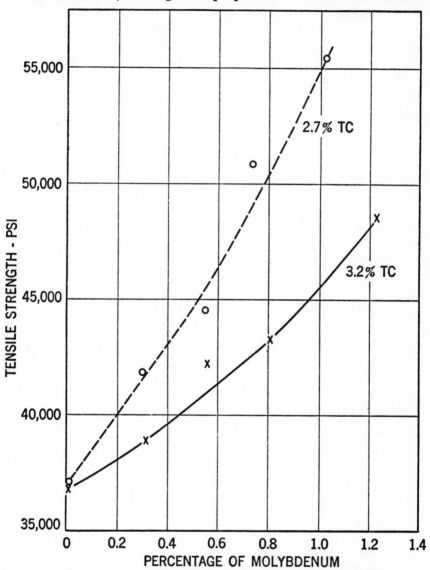

FIG 159 – Effect of Molybdenum on the Tensile Strength of Two Gray Cast Irons, as Reported by the British Research Committee on High-Duty Cast Irons for General Engineering Purposes. Approximate compositions of base irons: 3.2% TC, 1.0% CC, 1.5% Si, 0.7% Mn, 0.4% P, 0.05% S; and 2.7% TC, 0.7% CC, 2.4% Si, 0.6% Mn, 0.13% P, 0.04% S. 0.798 in. diameter specimens were machined from the broken halves of 1.2 in. diameter transverse strength specimens (1)

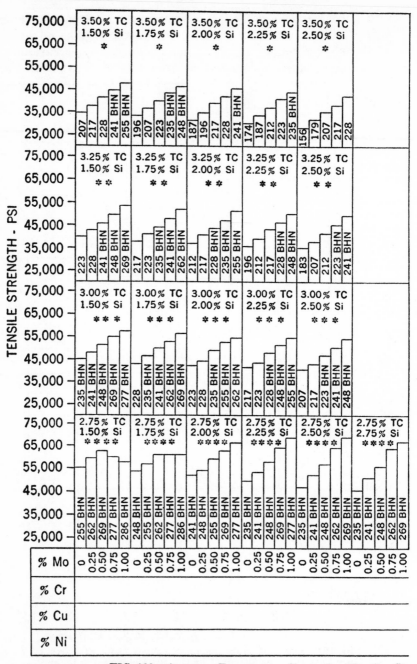

FIG 160 – Average Expectancy Chart for Tensile Strength

* The cupola is used almost exclusively as the melting unit for cast irons with this carbon content. A very small proportion of the tonnage in this group is inoculated

** Cupola melting is generally considered satisfactory for these irons, although other types of melting furnaces can be used successfully. A sizeable amount of the iron in this group is inoculated

*** Irons with this carbon content may be melted in either the cupola, electric or air

3.50% TC | **3.50% TC** | **3.50% TC** | **3.50% TC** | **3.50% TC**
1.50% Si / * : 207, 241 BHN, 235 BHN, 255 BHN, 241 BHN, 255 BHN
1.75% Si / * : 196, 235 BHN, 228 BHN, 248 BHN, 235 BHN, 248 BHN
2.00% Si / * : 187, 228, 223 BHN, 241 BHN, 228, 241 BHN
2.25% Si / * : 174, 223, 217, 235 BHN, 223, 235 BHN
2.50% Si / * : 156, 217, 212, 228, 217, 228 BHN

3.25% TC | **3.25% TC** | **3.25% TC** | **3.25% TC** | **3.25% TC**
1.50% Si / * * : 223, 225 BHN, 248 BHN, 269 BHN, 248 BHN, 269 BHN
1.75% Si / * * : 217, 248 BHN, 241 BHN, 262 BHN, 241 BHN, 262 BHN
2.00% Si / * * : 212, 241 BHN, 235 BHN, 255 BHN, 235 BHN, 255 BHN
2.25% Si / * * : 196, 235 BHN, 228 BHN, 248 BHN, 228 BHN, 248 BHN
2.50% Si / * * : 183, 228 BHN, 223 BHN, 241 BHN, 223 BHN, 241 BHN

3.00% TC | **3.00% TC** | **3.00% TC** | **3.00% TC** | **3.00% TC**
1.50% Si / * * * : 235 BHN, 262 BHN, 255 BHN, 277 BHN, 255 BHN, 286 BHN
1.75% Si / * * * : 228, 255 BHN, 248 BHN, 269 BHN, 248 BHN, 277 BHN
2.00% Si / * * * : 223, 248 BHN, 241 BHN, 262 BHN, 241 BHN, 269 BHN
2.25% Si / * * * : 217, 241 BHN, 235 BHN, 255 BHN, 235 BHN, 262 BHN
2.50% Si / * * * : 207, 235 BHN, 228 BHN, 248 BHN, 228 BHN, 255 BHN

2.75% TC | **2.75% TC** | **2.75% TC** | **2.75% TC** | **2.75% TC** | **2.75% TC**
1.50% Si / * * * * : 255 BHN, 277 BHN, 269 BHN, 286 BHN, 277 BHN, 293 BHN
1.75% Si / * * * * : 248 BHN, 269 BHN, 262 BHN, 286 BHN, 269 BHN, 286 BHN
2.00% Si / * * * * : 241 BHN, 262 BHN, 255 BHN, 277 BHN, 262 BHN, 277 BHN
2.25% Si / * * * * : 235 BHN, 262 BHN, 255 BHN, 277 BHN, 255 BHN, 277 BHN
2.50% Si / * * * * : 235 BHN, 262 BHN, 255 BHN, 277 BHN, 255 BHN, 274 BHN
2.75% Si / * * * * : 235 BHN, 255 BHN, 248 BHN, 269 BHN, 255 BHN, 269 BHN

TENSILE STRENGTH - PSI (75,000 / 65,000 / 55,000 / 45,000 / 35,000 / 25,000)

% Mo	0	0.50	0.50	0.75	0.40	0.75
% Cr					0.25	0.35
% Cu			1.00			
% Ni		0.50	0.75			

and Brinell Hardness of Gray Cast Iron (1.2 in. diameter section)

furnace, but the most uniform results are obtained with the electric or cupola-electric duplex process. Inoculation is the general practice for these irons

**** Irons in this group are generally melted in the electric or air furnace and only rarely in the cupola, except in connection with an electric furnace for duplexing. Inoculation is considered a necessary part of the procedure in making satisfactory low carbon, high strength iron typical of commercial practice. This increase in strength may be attributed to a direct solid solution effect in the ferrite and to a retardation of the transformation of the austenite. Other things being equal, the lower the total carbon of a gray iron, the better are the mechanical properties to be obtained from carefully chosen alloy combinations (1) (for example, see Figure 11, p 16 and Figure 159). As an aid in the determination of the approximate composition needed for a specific tensile strength, Figure 160 gives the normally expected tensile strength in a 1.2 in. diameter section for various combinations of carbon, silicon, chromium, copper, molybdenum and nickel.

The transverse strength (modulus of rupture*) increases with increasing tensile strength. The ratio of the transverse strength to the tensile strength, however, decreases progressively as the tensile strength of the iron increases (3). Additions of molybdenum have a pronounced favorable influence on the transverse strength which increases proportionally to the molybdenum content (Figure 161). The total deflection values show a general tendency to increase with increasing molybdenum (Figure 161). In some irons the deflection reaches a maximum and then decreases with higher molybdenum contents, but up to 1% molybdenum at least the deflection is generally higher than in unalloyed irons. This contrasts with the behavior of the copper, copper-nickel, nickel and some of the chromium-nickel irons studied by the Research Committee on High-Duty Cast Irons for General Engineering Purposes (1).

The hardness of cast iron is determined primarily by its microstructure. There is usually no direct relationship between this factor and other mechanical properties (4) although high strength irons tend to have higher hardnesses than low strength irons** (note, for example, the normally expected hardnesses indicated in Figure 160). Generally, the rate of increase of hardness with increasing molybdenum is less than the rate of increase of tensile strength (see Figure 11, p 16). In many cases, molybdenum has

---

* The transverse strength is usually reported as the ultimate load in pounds, but sometimes (particularly outside the U.S.A.) the results are converted to "modulus of rupture" values. The following formulas (2) are convenient for this purpose:

$$\text{Modulus of rupture} = \frac{2.546 \times LS}{D^3} \text{ (for round bars)}$$

$$\text{Modulus of rupture} = \frac{3\,LS}{2\,BH^2} \text{ (for rectangular bars)}$$

where L = span
S = ultimate load
D = diameter of bar
B = width of bar
H = height of bar

** A statistical analysis was made of the relationship between Brinell hardness and the tensile strength of 1553 specimens of varying sizes (5). The equation that best fit the data was

$$\text{Tensile strength in psi} = 1.82(BHN)^{1.85}$$

The standard deviation for all values was 17.70% with a correlation coefficient of 0.782. The best straight line equation

$$\text{Tensile strength in 1000 psi} = 0.38\,BHN - 44.6$$

fit quite well for irons in class 25 and above but the standard error was 23.5% and the calculated tensile strengths were much too low in the lower range.

been found to raise the hardness less per unit of increased tensile strength than other alloying elements (Figure 162).

Many types of impact tests, such as single blow tests on a notched or unnotched bar*, repeated impact and drop impact tests, have been tried for cast iron but none has as yet gained universal acceptance (see, for example, 8, 9). The area under the stress-strain diagram of a transverse test is often considered a reliable indication of toughness. Evaluated on this basis, molybdenum improves the

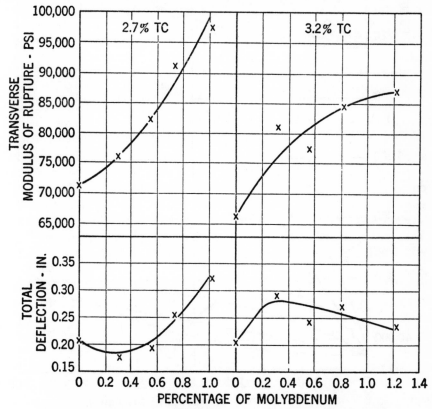

FIG 161 – Effect of Molybdenum on the Transverse Strength (Modulus of Rupture) and Total Deflection of Two Gray Cast Irons, as Reported by the British Research Committee on High-Duty Cast Irons for General Engineering Purposes. Approximate compositions of base irons: 3.2% TC, 1.0% CC, 1.5% Si. 0.7% Mn, 0.4% P, 0.05% S; and 2.7% TC, 0.7% CC, 2.4% Si, 0.6% Mn, 0.13% P, 0.04% S. 1.2 in. diameter test bars, machined to 1.13 in.; 18 in. between supports (1)

---

* It is of interest that the former British standard specification covering a single blow impact test on notched test pieces has been superseded by a specification (7) prescribing an unnotched specimen, 0.798 in. in diameter x 3 in. long, broken in a 120 ft lb Izod type machine. The foreword to this latter specification states "For cast iron, the best consistency associated with a satisfactory range of results is obtained with a plain, machined, and un-notched test bar 0.798 in. in diameter."

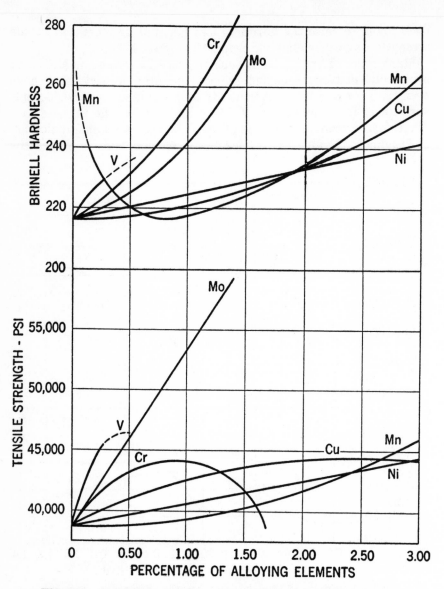

FIG 162 – Comparative Effects of Various Alloying Elements on the Brinell Hardness and Tensile Strength of Gray Cast Iron. Composition of base iron: 3.24% TC, 0.67% CC, 1.88% Si, 0.71% Mn, 0.17% P, 0.09% S (1.2 in. diameter section) (6)

toughness of cast iron appreciably since it increases both the transverse strength and the deflection (Figure 161). Recent work, however, has indicated that the impact values found in single blow impact tests on notched bars of pearlitic copper-molybdenum, molybdenum and molybdenum-nickel irons with 3.2% total carbon are much higher than would be predicted by transverse tests (1).

Accurate modulus of elasticity figures cannot be given for cast irons as they do not follow Hooke's law which is predicated on a linear relationship between stress and strain. Nevertheless, empirical values useful for engineering purposes can be calculated from tensile or, more commonly, transverse tests. The modulus of elasticity so determined rises roughly in proportion to the tensile strength (Figure 163). There is also a general, although not very precise, relationship between the graphitic carbon content and the modulus of elasticity (Figure 163). The shaded band presents 70% of the data. It is believed that the other 30% could be accounted for if it were possible to take into consideration the size and shape, as well as the amount and distribution of the graphite flakes.

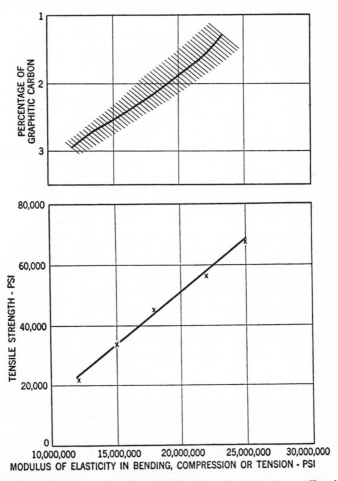

FIG 163 – Modulus of Elasticity in Bending, Compression or Tension of Gray Cast Iron as Affected by Tensile Strength and Graphitic Carbon Content (tensile strength relationship at ¼ breaking load from (3); graphitic carbon relationship from (10))

The well known high damping capacity of cast iron is believed to be due to its graphite content. Inasmuch as the modulus of elasticity is an inverse function of the graphite content (Figure 163), it is also an inverse function of the damping capacity (Figure 164). This means that the higher strength irons will have a lower damping capacity than the weaker irons.

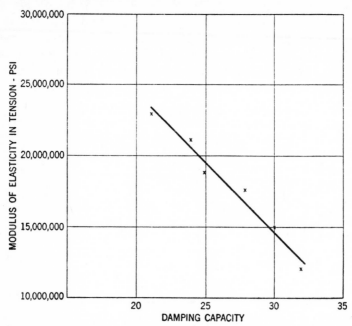

FIG 164 – Correlation of Damping Capacity and Modulus of Elasticity of Gray Cast Irons. Damping capacity expressed as the percent energy dissipated in the first cycle under 20,000 psi torsional stress (11)

The relationships between tensile strength and (a) compressive strength (Figure 165), (b) torsional strength (Figure 166), and (c) the shear strength – tensile strength ratio (Figure 167) appear to be roughly linear. Consequently, any increase in the tensile strength of gray cast iron will normally be accompanied by corresponding increases in the compressive, torsional and shear strengths.

The endurance limit of gray iron varies approximately linearly with the static tensile strength. In reversed or rotary bending the ratio of endurance limit to tensile strength is about 0.4 to 0.6 in the as-cast condition. The meager data available on heat treated cast iron indicate that the endurance limit is not increased by heat treatment to the same extent as is the tensile strength, the endurance ratio actually being decreased to about 0.20 to 0.35 (17, 18). The endurance limit in torsion is generally about the same as that in reversed bending (19). Gray irons are much more resistant to repeated loading in compression than would be calculated from the rotary beam endurance limit (20).

The mechanical properties of unalloyed gray iron deteriorate rapidly as the section size increases. This weakening is due in part to the coarsening of the graphite flakes and often in part to the presence of free ferrite as the result of the slower cooling of large castings. The deterioration is less in high than in low strength irons. With the addition of molybdenum, quite uniform properties may be obtained in large sizes (see Figure 12, p 17). The action of molybdenum in reducing the size sensitivity of gray iron is particularly valuable where a part has a non-uniform section or where castings of a wide range of sizes are to be made from the same iron.

Although machinability normally is poorer as the hardness increases, it is not directly proportional, as microstructure is an important factor. Molybdenum promotes machinability by improving the structural uniformity. Experience in numerous shops substantiates the fact that molybdenum cast iron has better machinability at a given hardness than unalloyed cast iron. Molybdenum irons are regularly produced with machining characteristics comparable to unalloyed irons with a Brinell hardness 50 points lower (21).

It is impossible to express wear resistance in terms of a single number or test since there are many types of wear resistant ap-

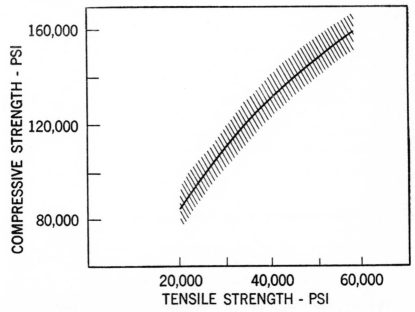

FIG 165 – Relationship between Compressive and Tensile Strengths of Gray Cast Iron (1.2 in. diameter section) (12)

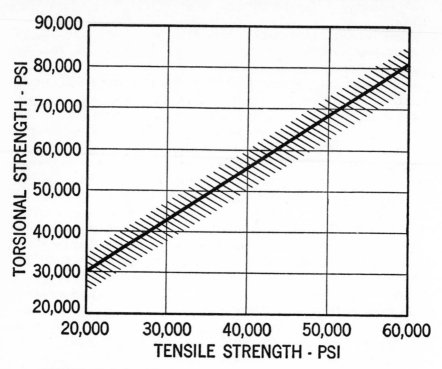

FIG 166 – Relationship between Torsional and Tensile Strengths of Gray Cast Iron (13)

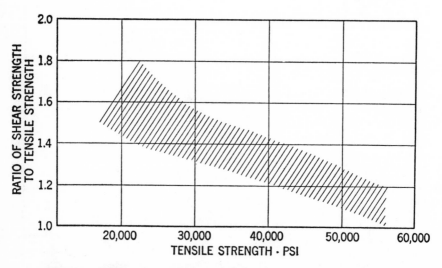

FIG 167 – Relationship between the Ratio of Shear Strength to Tensile Strength and the Tensile Strength of Gray Cast Iron (based on the results of 14, 15, 16)

plications which differ appreciably in their requirements. The wear resistance of gray cast iron has no direct relationship to the mechanical properties usually determined by laboratory tests but depends mainly on structure. Although it is hard to obtain good wear resistance with low hardness, high hardness does not necessarily denote good wearing properties. A recent rating (22) of microstructure in order of decreasing resistance to metal-to-metal wear, as in cylinder liners, piston rings and machine tool ways, is of interest, although it omits heat treated and acicular irons (see pp 279-283; 272-276) which generally have better wear resistance:

Matrix	Graphite
1. fine pearlite	fine, uniformly distributed (AFA Type A)
2. coarse pearlite	fine, uniformly distributed (AFA Type A)
3. pearlite with a small amount of free ferrite	fine, uniformly distributed (AFA Type A)
4. pearlite with a small amount of free cementite	fine, uniformly distributed (AFA Type A)
5. abundant ferrite	fine, uniformly distributed (AFA Type A)
6. abundant cementite	any type
7. secondary ferrite	dendritic (AFA Type D or E)*

The optimum microstructure 1. usually has a minimum Brinell hardness of 190 to 200, but this hardness alone naturally does not guarantee the proper structure. Inoculation (pp 274, 277) is especially advantageous for wear resistant irons as it reduces the possibility of dendritic graphite and free ferrite at the wearing surfaces. Even with proper inoculation, a very thin skin containing dendritic graphite is likely to occur; for best wear resistance, this skin should be removed by machining. This rating shows how molybdenum additions can contribute to wear resistance by aiding the formation of the preferred uniform, fine pearlitic matrix. A secondary advantage is the increased toughness which prevents chipping of sharp edges. If conditions are such that the temperature of the iron is raised in service by friction, the effect of molybdenum in preventing softening at these temperatures is advantageous. Severe abrasive conditions may require the use of white, heat treated or nitrided iron (see pp 304-307; 279-283; 283, 304).

Cast irons are relatively insensitive to stress raisers or notches. The presence of a V notch has little effect on the static tensile, com-

---

* A very fine lacy graphite, frequently in interdendritic pattern and often surrounded by ferrite. It has been referred to by various terms including interdendritic, eutectic, pseudo-eutectic, eutectiform and modified.

pressive and torsional strengths (19). The notch sensitivity is also low under conditions of repeated loading (Figure 168). Numerous tests have been reported where identical endurance limits were found for notched and unnotched bars. This resistance to the effect of notches corresponds to fairly good corrosion fatigue values (19).

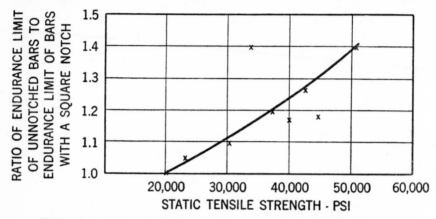

FIG 168 – Relationship between Static Tensile Strength and the Notch Sensitivity of Cast Iron under Repeated Loading (based on data in 23)

Molybdenum has a marked effect in improving the elevated temperature strength (Figure 169) and creep strength of gray iron. Since growth at elevated temperatures is caused partly by graphitization, it can be decreased by the addition of suitable carbide

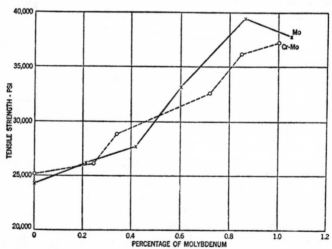

FIG 169 – Effect of Molybdenum on the Short Time Tensile Strength at 930 F of Gray Cast Iron with and without Chromium Additions. Approximate composition of base iron: 3.3% TC, 2.0% Si, 0.5% Mn, 0.15% P, 0.05% S. Chromium series contained 0.29% Cr (24)

[270]

stabilizers. The effect of molybdenum in stabilizing carbides is much milder than that of chromium, so the two are preferably used together to gain the added strength imparted by the molybdenum. As indicated in Figure 170, chromium is the most effective element

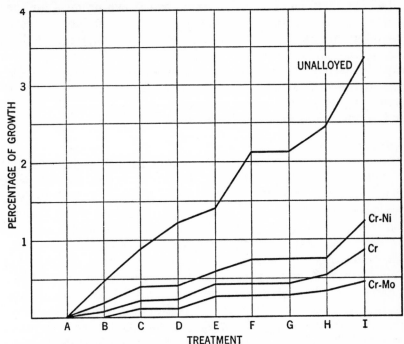

FIG 170 – Results of Growth Tests on One Unalloyed and Three Alloyed Gray Irons

	Analyses				
	%TC	%Si	%Cr	%Mo	%Ni
Unalloyed......................	3.27	1.70	....	....	....
Cr............................	3.18	1.96	0.55	....	....
Cr–Mo.......................	3.15	1.82	0.60	0.50	....
Cr–Ni........................	3.10	1.94	0.52	....	1.78

Treatments
A: 1075 F, 4 hr; furnace cooled to 400 F in 20½ hr
B: 1450 F, 1½ hr; furnace cooled to 400 F in 20 hr
C: 1700 F, 3 hr; cooled to room temperature in 1½ hr; reheated to 1450 F, held 3 hr; furnace cooled to 500 F in 19 hr
D: 1700 F, 10¼ hr; air cooled
E: 1650 F, 1 hr; furnace cooled to 1500 F, held 1 hr; furnace cooled to 1025 F, held 3 hr; reheated to 1500 F, held 2 hr; furnace cooled to 500 F in 20 hr
F: 1520 F, 2 hr; furnace cooled to 500 F in 20 hr
G: 1200 F, 6 hr; furnace cooled to 500 F in 16 hr
H: 1500 F, 6 hr; furnace cooled to 580 F in 18 hr
I: 1700 F, 2 hr; furnace cooled to 1400 F; reheated to 1700 F, held 2½ hr; furnace cooled to 250 F in 38 hr

in reducing growth, but the molybdenum gives an additional improvement. While molybdenum is generally used with chromium alone for alloying iron for elevated temperature service, a high silicon composition with about 2.6% total carbon, 5.5% silicon, 1 to 3% chromium and 1% molybdenum has shown promise for such applications as hearth plates, grate bars and still tube supports, where the impact requirements are not too severe. Heat checking as may occur in brake drums or dies is minimized by high total and graphitic carbon contents. It is often necessary to strengthen such irons by the addition of alloying elements. Molybdenum has proved particularly effective for this purpose (see, for example, the brake drum compositions given in Table 74, pp 284, 285).

High Strength Irons

The lower strength irons in this group with 1.2 in. diameter test bar tensile strengths from about 45,000 to 55,000 psi are being widely produced today. Most of these irons are made with a relatively low carbon content (between 2.7 and 3.2%), which is low enough for good strength but not so low as to cause difficulties in the foundry. The silicon content is usually between 1.25 and 2.75% (with the higher amounts corresponding to the lower carbon contents and smaller sections), which is sufficient to prevent chilled spots without an excessive reduction in the combined carbon. Phosphorus is kept low to avoid the formation of the brittle steadite and to reduce porosity. Inoculation (pp 274, 277) is generally advisable to insure a random distribution of the graphite flakes, while suitable alloys are added to give a fine lamellar pearlite in the matrix, with little if any free ferrite or cementite, and to increase the strength to the required amount. Various single alloying elements or combinations thereof can be used.* Molybdenum, with or without other elements, is a popular and economical choice because of its positive and pronounced action in attaining these objectives. Moreover, since it is not a graphitizing element, its addition rarely requires any adjustment in the silicon content for good results.

Irons with an acicular structure in the matrix, and, of course, fine randomly distributed graphite, have the highest strengths of any of the gray cast irons commercially available at the present. Molybdenum-nickel acicular irons are the most common types although an acicular structure may also be obtained in copper-molybdenum (25) and molybdenum irons. The molybdenum and nickel contents are so adjusted in relation to the cooling rate or size of the casting (Figures 171 and 172) that the austenite transforms to an acicular product at about 900 to 500 F rather than forming pearlite

---

* See, for example, the normally expected tensile strength values in Figure 160, pp 260, 261, and the properties of many of the irons listed in Table 74, pp 284-303.

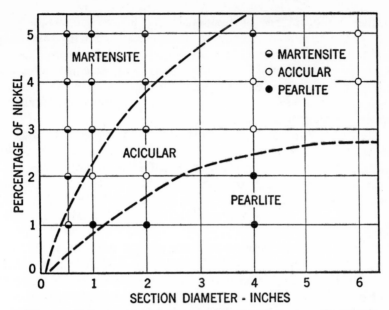

FIG 171 – Effect of Section Size and Nickel Content on the Matrix Structure of Gray Cast Iron. Composition of base iron: 2.5% TC, 2.5% Si, 0.85% Mn, 0.5% Mo (26)

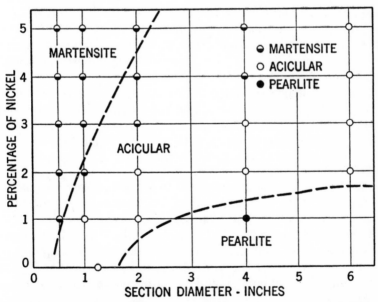

FIG 172 – Effect of Section Size and Nickel Content on the Matrix Structure of Gray Cast Iron. Composition of base iron: 2.5% TC, 2.5% Si, 0.5% Mn, 1.0% Mo. Note: diagram corrected on basis of discussion of paper (26)

at higher temperatures or martensite at lower temperatures. It will be noted that it is difficult to obtain castings with this structure if the section is very thin.* On the other hand, castings having very heavy sections may be produced with an acicular structure. The tensile strength as-cast may not be much higher than that of a high strength molybdenum-nickel pearlitic iron although the transverse strength and deflection are appreciably better (Table 71). However, the tensile strength of the acicular iron may be increased by tempering at 500 to 700 F for five hours or more. Lower tempering temperatures also seem to be effective in some cases (27). Acicular irons are much tougher than any of the pearlitic cast irons of lower or equal strength (see, for example, Table 72). Also, an acicular iron with 2.5% total carbon, 1.81% silicon, 0.93% manganese, 0.11% phosphorus, 0.8% molybdenum and 2% nickel with an as-cast tensile strength of 68,100 psi gave 26 to 27 ft lb (unnotched 0.798 in. diameter test piece broken in an Izod machine) whereas ordinary high phosphorus gray cast iron would have an impact of only 5 to 8 ft lb and pearlitic high strength cast iron 16 to 20 ft lb (29). In spite of the high hardness, which is often well over Brinell 300, the acicular iron is reasonably machinable. A mixture of the acicular structure with some retained austenite in the matrix of cast iron has been found to give remarkable wearing properties, especially in cams, gears and bushings (30). In large sections where cooling rates are slow and near equilibrium conditions prevail, the phosphorus content should be kept to 0.12% maximum as greater amounts will form a complex quaternary eutectic with carbon, iron and molybdenum which removes 1.3 units of molybdenum from the matrix for each unit of phosphorus over 0.12% (31). Acicular irons are finding an increasing use for crankshafts (27, 32) as well as for a number of specialized applications including hot and cold forming dies, machine cut gear wheels, and hammer and press columns (33) (see also Table 74).

Inoculation and Pouring Temperature

Inoculation is now an accepted aid in the production of most high strength cast iron. The addition of an inoculant, usually ferro-silicon**, to the molten cast iron just before tapping, or in the ladle, alters the structure of the cast iron more than would be expected from the change in final chemical composition. A high tapping temperature is essential for the best results in inoculation.*** The type and amount of inoculant should be adjusted to the type of iron

---

* In this case, hot quenching to produce an acicular structure with its attendant advantages might be considered (see pp 282, 283).
** Some inoculants contain alloying elements as well as silicon. Molybdenum silicide, for example, combines the inoculating effect of silicon with the alloying effect of molybdenum. Inoculants containing carbide stabilizing elements are particularly suited for large castings.
*** A minimum temperature of 2750 F has been suggested (22).

TABLE 71

Effect of a Low Temperature Tempering Treatment on the Mechanical Properties of Acicular and Pearlitic Molybdenum-Nickel Cast Irons (26)

| Analyses | | | | | | As-Cast | | | | After Tempering Five Hours at 600 F | |
| | | | | | | Transverse* | | BHN | Tensile Strength psi | BHN | Tensile Strength psi |
%TC	%CC	%Si	%Mo	%Ni	Matrix Structure	Load lb	Deflection in.				
2.26	0.72	2.27	0.33	1.09	pearlitic	4050	0.26	286	71,000	286	72,200
2.31	0.76	2.30	0.81	1.04	acicular**	4600	0.32	321	80,600	321	95,000
2.30	0.75	2.31	1.36	1.03	acicular	4700	0.33	321	71,800	340	98,000
2.25	0.69	2.23	0.32	2.03	pearlitic	4100	0.29	311	67,800†	302	77,000
2.28	0.74	2.31	0.82	2.06	acicular	4600	0.36	340	74,400	364	97,600
2.30	0.77	2.32	1.31	2.08	acicular	4800	0.35	387	82,000	382	98,000a
2.33	0.73	2.36	0.81	3.00	acicular	3850	0.30	375	.....	375	88,000a
2.25	0.60	2.35	0.81	3.05	acicular	3800	0.30	418	.....	387	98,200b
2.29	0.70	2.30	0.30	4.05	acicular	3000	0.25	444	.....	412	92,200a

* 1.2 in. bars; 18 in. span
** 10% pearlite
† flaw

(a) 15 hr temper
(b) Brinell 395 and tensile strength of 105,200 psi after five hours at 700 F

TABLE 72

Comparative Mechanical Properties of Molybdenum-Containing Acicular and Unalloyed Pearlitic Irons (28)

Analyses							Structure	1.2 Inch Section				2.0 Inch Section			
								Tensile Strength psi	Transverse*		Impact** ft lb	Tensile Strength psi	Transverse*		Impact** ft lb
%TC	%CC	%Si	%Mn	%Cu	%Mo	%Ni			Load lb	Defl in.			Load lb	Defl in.	
2.50	0.60	2.82	0.98	.....	.....	.....	pearlitic	69,800	3,806	0.280	.....	54,680	13,790	0.333	44.4
2.50	0.65	2.80	0.99	.....	1.04	.....	acicular	74,100	4,510	0.415	118.1	74,800	17,100	0.455	113.1
2.46	0.64	2.59	1.06	1.06	1.01	.....	acicular	81,500	4,025	0.320	.....	67,400	16,200	0.392	120+
2.49	0.66	2.71	0.97	.....	1.03	1.01	acicular	80,500	5,440	0.570	106.9	65,550	16,800	0.470	120+

* 1.2 in. bars broken on 18 in. centers; 2.0 in. bars broken on 24 in. centers

** unnotched bars, 1⅛ in. in diameter 8 in. long, broken on 6 in. centers in a Charpy machine

[276]

being made and the section being poured.* If less than the amount needed is used, the inoculation may have no effect while over-inoculation in most cases is not detrimental. The Cast Iron Sub-committee of the Institute of British Foundrymen has recommended 0.5 to 1.0% silicon for the late addition, regardless of the amount of silicon charged (34). The effect of inoculation decreases with the time the iron is permitted to remain in the ladle after inoculation. Generally, the time of effectiveness varies from about 10 to 30 minutes. Inoculation promotes the formation of randomly distributed graphite while dendritic graphite** is reduced or eliminated. Likewise, inoculation inhibits chilling. Properly used, inoculation ensures the consistent attainment of optimum mechanical properties and machinability for any given composition.

Many troubles in the production of high strength cast irons are caused by low pouring temperatures.*** As the pouring temperature is lowered, the graphite pattern becomes finer and tends towards the dendritic type while the quantity of ferrite precipitated during the gamma to alpha transformation increases (35). Temperatures as low as 2350 F seem to have little effect upon the tensile and impact properties of relatively low strength irons because the refinement in the graphite flakes apparently offsets the effect of an increase in the amount of ferrite. With higher strength irons, however, reductions in the pouring temperature below 2650 F reduce the tensile strength considerably. Therefore, for high strength irons, a pouring temperature of 2650 to 2800 F (corrected optical temperature) is generally recommended even though the high temperatures will tend to increase shrinkage voids. A more refractory sand, and feeding techniques approaching those used in casting steel, may also be required.

Thermal Treatment

Cast iron is frequently given a stress relieving heat treatment to minimize distortion during machining and in service. A typical treatment involves heating slowly to 850 to 1000 F, holding at this temperature about one hour per inch of section thickness, and cooling slowly in the furnace (4). Apparently, effective relief of stress begins only at temperatures above 850 F, while 975 F is required for substantial relief (36). This treatment has practically no effect upon the microstructure or mechanical properties.†

Annealing of unalloyed gray iron for easier machining is fre-

---

* The thinner the section, the more important is inoculation. Generally, low carbon irons are most improved by inoculation. Inoculation is considered by some to be indispensable for the production of low carbon high strength irons. With high carbon irons (for example, with 3.5% total carbon), inoculation is normally used only where there is danger of chilling in thin sections. See the caption of Figure 160 (pp 260, 261).
** See footnote on p 269.
*** Temperature of the iron as it enters the mold.
† However, a low temperature reheating will increase the strength of acicular cast irons as discussed on p 274.

quently practiced; alloyed gray irons are occasionally annealed before heat treating. The annealing treatment may consist of heating either below the critical range, at say 1200 to 1350 F, in which case slow cooling is not essential, or above the critical at temperatures up to 1600 F in which case slow cooling is required.* The mechanical properties of unalloyed irons are progressively impaired during annealing because of graphitization. Alloy irons, unless they contain large amounts of graphitizers, are less susceptible to damage during annealing since they are more resistant to graphitization during the relatively short heating cycles involved (see Figure 175). Annealing, however, is invariably accompanied by some degree of graphitization which is partly responsible for the lower resultant hardness. This graphitization may become appreciable at about 1250 F and proceeds more rapidly at 1300 to 1450 F at a rate dependent upon composition. Figure 173 shows the effect of annealing temperatures

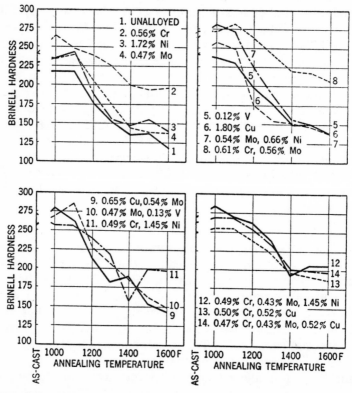

FIG 173 – Effect of Composition and Annealing Temperature on the Annealed Hardness of Gray Cast Iron. Approximate composition of base iron: 3.25% TC, 2.0% Si, 1.0% Mn, 0.11% P, 0.03% S. Specimens furnace cooled after one hour at temperature (37)

* A high temperature anneal at about 1750 F for one to three hours plus one hour per inch of section thickness is sometimes used to graphitize chilled sections to facilitate machining.

in the range of 1000 to 1600 F on the hardness of various irons. The hardness as-annealed is no criterion of the tensile strength which, because of differences in microstructure, will vary among irons annealed to the same hardness. For example, of the irons in Figure 173, the unalloyed iron showed a tensile strength of only 37,800 psi at Brinell 207 to 217 while three of the alloy irons (molybdenum-vanadium iron 10, chromium-molybdenum iron 8, and chromium-molybdenum-nickel iron 12) had tensile strengths of 45,400 to 47,000 psi at the same hardness.

Cast irons may be heat treated to improve their hardness, tensile strength and wear resistance but at some sacrifice in toughness, transverse strength and deflection. The response to heat treatment is more marked for high strength than for the weaker, higher carbon cast irons (Figure 174). Therefore, the total carbon content of irons to be heat treated is generally about 2.5 to 3.2%. The irons are usually oil quenched from about 1550 to 1600 F. Too low a temperature will result in inadequate combined carbon in the matrix for full hardening (Figure 175). The carbon concentration in the austenite at the moment of quenching is controlled by the tempera-

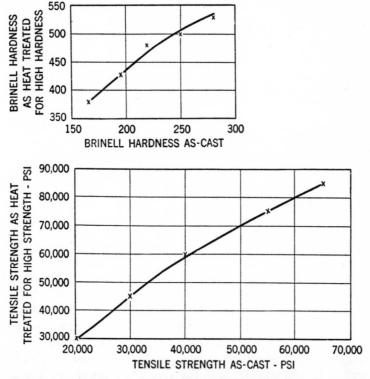

FIG 174 – Approximate Relationship between As-Cast Properties and the Properties that can be Obtained by Heat Treatment (38)

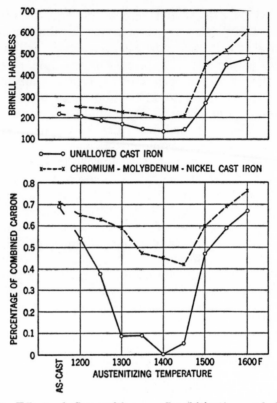

FIG 175 – Effect of Composition on Graphitization and Graphite Re-Solution of Gray Cast Iron. Samples held at temperature one hour prior to oil quenching (39)

	Analyses						
	%TC	%CC	%Si	%Mn	%Cr	%Mo	%Ni
Unalloyed..........	3.19	0.69	1.70	0.76	0.03	0.01	....
Cr–Mo–Ni..........	3.10	0.70	2.05	0.80	0.27	0.45	0.87

ture, time at temperature and chemical composition but is not affected by the combined carbon as-cast. The presence of alloying elements that retard graphitization will ensure a more reproducible response to heat treatment by preventing excessive graphitization on heating. Water quenching is seldom applied while air cooling may be used on very thin sections or on high hardenability alloy irons. Cast iron as-quenched is relatively weak (Figure 176). As the tempering temperature increases, the hardness gradually decreases but the tensile strength increases to a maximum for a tempering temperature of about 800 to 1000 F.

[280]

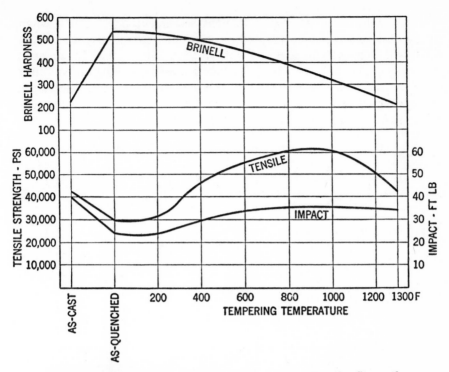

FIG 176 – Effect of Heat Treatment on the Tensile Strength, Hardness and Impact Strength of High Strength Cast Iron. Composite chart based on the results obtained on the following irons, oil quenched from 1575 F:

Analyses

%TC	%CC	%Si	%Mn	%P	%S	%Cr	%Mo	%Ni
3.19	0.69	1.70	0.76	0.22	0.10	0.03	0.01	....
3.22	0.65	1.73	0.75	0.21	0.09	0.03	0.47	....
3.20	0.58	1.76	0.64	0.19	0.05	0.005	0.48	trace
3.22	0.53	2.02	0.66	0.11	0.07	0.02	0.52	1.21
3.21	0.60	2.24	0.67	0.11	0.07	0.50	0.52	0.06
3.36	0.61	1.96	0.74	0.16	0.07	0.35	0.47	0.52

Impact tests made on unnotched bars 1⅛ in. in diameter, 8 in. long, broken on 6 in. centers in a Charpy machine (39)

With higher tempering temperatures there is a recovery of the transverse strength and deflection so these values may sometimes reach, but never materially exceed, the values as-cast. There is also a partial recovery of toughness. For a high degree of abrasion resistance, quenched cast iron is usually tempered at 300 to 800 F to give at least Brinell 400. For high strength, a tempering temperature of 600 to 1000 F is generally used. Engine cylinder liners are commonly heat treated as are many cams, gears, rollers, dies and numerous small machinery parts.

Hardenability is important in heat treatment particularly when large castings are to be treated or when the complexity of section makes it desirable to air cool rather than oil quench. In general, alloying elements have about the same effect on the hardenability of gray cast iron (Figure 177) as on steel (pp 1; 71-93). Therefore, molybdenum is one of the most potent means of increasing the hardenability of cast iron.

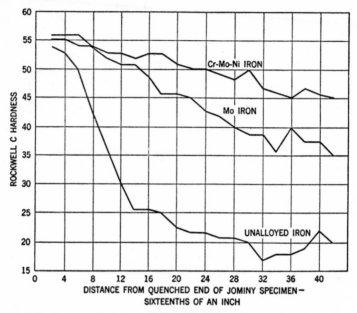

FIG 177 – Jominy End-Quench Hardenability Curves for Three Cast Irons. End-quenched from 1575 F (39)

	Analyses								
	%TC	%CC	%Si	%Mn	%P	%S	%Cr	%Mo	%Ni
Unalloyed.......	3.19	0.69	1.70	0.76	0.22	0.10	0.03	0.01	....
Cr–Mo–Ni.......	3.36	0.61	1.96	0.74	0.16	0.07	0.35	0.47	0.52
Mo.............	3.22	0.65	1.73	0.75	0.21	0.09	0.03	0.47	....

Cast irons may be austempered or, as it is often termed, hot quenched. In this treatment, the castings are quenched from above the critical into a bath at a temperature of about 450 to 800 F, held for a sufficient time (usually two to five hours) for transformation of the matrix to bainite with a hardness of Brinell 250 to 480, and then cooled in air to room temperature. As in the case of steel, the hardenability must be adequate to avoid transformation to pearlite. Therefore, the cast irons used for hot quenching generally contain molybdenum with or without nickel and chromium. Typical mechanical properties of hot quenched molybdenum cast iron are listed in Table 73. In addition to the superior toughness, it is reported (40) that the hot quenched cast iron has better wear resistance than quenched and tempered castings of the same Brinell hardness. Another advantage in the case of thin walled castings such as cylinder liners is the decreased distortion as compared to that produced by quenching (41). This treatment has been used mainly for cams, gears and similar parts which must have good wear resistance.

TABLE 73

Mechanical Properties of Hot Quenched Molybdenum Cast Iron (40)

	As–Cast*	As–Hot–Quenched*
Brinell Hardness Number.............................	223	341
Tensile Strength, psi.................................	47,500	75,500
Impact Strength, ft lb**.............................	44	61

*1.2 in. diameter bars
**unnotched bars, 1⅛ in. in diameter, 8 in. long, broken on 6 in. centers in a Charpy machine
Composition:
    3.25% TC, 1.75% Si, 0.80% Mn, 0.30% P max, 0.10% S max, 0.50% Mo

The surface hardening of cast irons by flame hardening is fairly common while induction hardening has found some application. The thin (1/32 to 5/32 in.), hard (Brinell 450 to 600) layer is especially suitable for wearing surfaces of lathe beds as well as for gears, cams, rollers, plungers and cylinder liners where the surface pressures are light enough so that a hard base is not needed. A tempering treatment at about 400 F may be used to reduce stresses with only a slight loss in hardness. An as-cast combined carbon content of 0.6 to 0.8% is generally considered most suitable for irons to be flame hardened (21). Although hardenability is not a factor when water quenching is used, it is important when hardening is desired with a slower rate of cooling. For example, the wearing surfaces of large dies are sometimes flame hardened without a water spray in order to reduce distortion. In such cases, the alloy content of the iron must be high enough to give adequate hardening without water quenching. Unalloyed cast irons have an extremely rapid rate of graphitization so that even with a fast heating rate some graphitization may occur in flame hardening. As a result, a weak layer with a high ferrite content may be formed below the hardened layer where the higher temperature has caused re-solution of the graphite (39). The moderate retarding action of molybdenum on graphitization is sufficient to prevent the formation of such high ferrite layers.

Cast iron may also be surface hardened by nitriding in the same

TABLE 74

Typical Applications of Gray Cast Irons Containing Molybdenum

Applications	TC %	CC %	Si %	Mn %	P %	S %	Cr %	Cu %	Mo %	Ni %	Other %	Tensile Strength psi	Load lb	Defl in.	Test Bar Diam in.	Section in.	Weight lb	BHN	Remarks	Ref
Annealing Pot Lids	3.30	...	2.65	0.60	0.15 max	...	0.70	...	0.60	...	...	...	...	...	...	...	...	...		
Anvils, forging hammer bases	3.15	0.85	1.80	0.85	0.10 max	...	0.20	...	0.15	...	...	45,000	2650	0.25	1.2	4 to 60	10,000 to 250,000	160		(21)
Brake Drums	3.65 / 3.40	...	2.00 / 1.70	...	...	...	...	1.00 / 0.85	0.40 / 0.50	0.50	...	...	...	...	...	...	...	...		
aircraft	3.75 / 3.25	... / 0.75	1.80 / 2.80	0.70 / 0.70	0.15 / 0.17	0.09 / 0.11	0.40	0.40	0.40 / 0.75	1.25 / 0.75	...	48,000	4900	0.16	1¼	3/8 to 3/4	38	250	poured into mold which becomes part of brake drum (centrifuse process)	(21)
automobile (passenger)	3.50	...	2.25	...	...	...	...	...	0.20	...	...	...	...	...	...	...	...	...	centrifugally cast around an interlocking steel web section	
bus	3.00	...	2.08	0.58	...	...	0.08	...	0.65	1.00	0.10 V	59,400	...	...	...	...	...	248		(43)
railroad (high speed passenger cars)	3.70 / 3.40	...	1.10 / 2.10	0.80 / 0.60	0.03 / 0.15	0.08 / 0.13	... / 0.50	...	0.50 / 0.50	...	...	...	...	...	...	...	...	...	twin plate disk type brake mechanism / twin plate disk type brake mechanism; more susceptible to heat checking than above composition	
truck	3.30	...	1.80	0.70	...	...	0.20	0.20	0.10	...	...	40,000	...	...	...	...	...	215		
truck and automobile	3.00	0.70	2.00	0.70	0.08	0.08	0.40	...	0.35	...	...	48,000	4800	0.16	1¼	3/8 to 1	70	238	hub and drum integral	(21)
truck and bus	3.30	...	1.80	0.70	...	...	0.20	0.45	0.30	...	...	44,500	...	...	...	...	...	220		
truck, bus, trailer	3.40 / 3.40	...	1.90 / 2.10	0.70 / 0.60	0.15 max / 0.20 max	0.13 max / 0.13 max	0.30	0.30 / 0.50	0.30 / 0.50	... / 0.50	...	...	...	...	•	...	...	...		

TABLE 74—(Continued)

Applications	TC %	CC %	Si %	Mn %	P %	S %	Cr %	Cu %	Mo %	Ni %	Other %	Tensile Strength psi	Load lb	Defl in.	Test Bar Diam in.	Section in.	Weight lb	BHN	Remarks	Ref
Brake Drums truck, bus, trailer (high duty)	3.40	...	1.90	0.70	0.15 max	0.18 max	...	...	0.55	...	0.12 V	......	...	...	...	...	...	...	especially recommended for high resistance to wear and heat checking	
	3.70	0.80	1.80	0.80	0.15 max	0.13 max	0.50	...	0.70	...	...	35,000	...	...	...	...	...	229		(21)
truck, bus, trailer, trolley coach	3.25	0.65	2.05	0.70	0.20 max	0.05 max	...	0.75	0.50	...	...	53,500	...	...	...	3/16 to 2 1/4	22 to 270	220		(21)
truck trailer	3.20	...	2.20	...	...	...	0.25	...	0.70	...	...	......	...	...	...	...	...	...		(21)
Cams, control of steam turbine governing mechanism	3.20	0.60	2.05	0.80	0.21 max	0.07 max	none	...	0.50	0.50	...	49,000	3000	0.32	1.2	3/4	8	240		
Camshafts automobile	3.20	...	2.20	0.60	...	0.20 max	1.00	...	0.50	0.30	...	47,000	1860	...	7/8	...	......	260	properties apply to shaft body; cam noses are chilled and file hard	(44)
	3.25	...	2.20	0.65	...	0.10 max	0.90	...	0.20	0.20	...									
	3.10	0.75	2.10	0.80	0.09	0.09	0.90	...	0.50	0.50	...	55,000	5750	...	1.2†	1 to 2	19 to 35	300	cams are heated above critical for a depth of 1/8 in. and air cooled to give Scleroscope 70	(21)
	3.30	0.80	2.30	0.75	0.18	0.15	0.85	...	0.45	0.2	...	50,000	4900	0.18	1.2†	...	18 to 30	280		(21)
automobile, also Diesel camshaft gears	3.25	...	2.25	0.65	0.25 max	0.10 max	0.80	...	0.50	0.35	...	40,000 min	4000	...	1.2†	1 to 1 3/4	1 to 10	210	Scleroscope 65 min on chill cam and eccentric. Brinell 285 on body, also bearings, gear blank. Brinell given is on camshaft gear	(21)
stationary engine	3.00	...	2.10	1.00	0.15 max	0.15 max	0.40	...	1.00	1.20 to 4.00	...	69,500	...	...	...	1/2 to 10	......	300	%Ni increases with section. 0.5 to 0.7% Si as inoculant. TAP unnotched Izod impact 25 to 40 ft lb	(45)
Clutch Plates	3.10	...	2.20	0.75	...	...	0.35	0.35	...	...	...	47,800	2900	...	1.2	...	...	235		
	3.35	...	2.00	...	...	...	0.90	0.55	...	...	...	24,500	...	...	...	...	...	180		
	3.73	...	1.82	...	...	...	0.80	0.50	...	...	...									

TABLE 74—(Continued)

Applications	TC %	CC %	Si %	Mn %	P %	S %	Cr %	Cu %	Mo %	Ni %	Other %	Tensile Strength psi	Load lb	Defl in.	Test Bar Diam in.	Section in.	Weight lb	BHN	Remarks	Ref
Clutch Plates automobile	3.05	0.70	2.15	0.65	0.18	0.09	0.20	...	0.40	...	0.08 Ti	44,000	2900	0.36	1.2	½ to ¾	12	235		(21)
Compressors	3.20	...	2.30	...	...	...	0.35	...	0.35	...	...									
Connecting Rods, gasoline and Diesel	2.35	0.60	1.40	0.40	0.15 max	0.08 max	...	...	0.40	...	...	60,000 to 85,000	4200 to 4500	0.55 to 0.95	1.2	¼ to ¾	40 max	160 to 235	held 6 hr at 1850 F, cooled 60 F per hr for low hardness and 100 F per hr for high hardness	(21)
Crankshafts	3.00	...	2.00	0.90	0.12	...	0.25	...	0.35	...	...	50,000	...	...	1.2	1¼ max	...	250	0.5 to 1.0% Si added late	(46)
	2.60	...	2.35	1.00	0.06 max	...	...	...	1.10	1.10	...	65,000	...	...	1.2	1½ to 4	...	300	0.5 to 1.0% Si added late	(46)
	2.30	...	2.35	1.10	0.03 max	...	0.30	...	1.10	1.10	...	65,000	...	...	2.0	5 to 13	...	310	0.5 to 1.0% Si added late	(47)
	2.75	...	1.59	0.88	0.08	0.07	...	...	0.29	...	...	52,200						245		
	3.28	...	2.19	0.95	0.17	0.09	0.42	...	0.95	...	...	46,600	3400	...	1.2	...	...	280	inoculated	
	3.25	...	1.80	0.70	0.10 max	0.10 max	0.40 max	...	1.20	...	...	49,300						260		
Diesel (8 cylinder marine)	3.00 max	...	2.00	0.90	...	...	0.50	...	0.80	1.50	...	...	...	...	1¼‡	...	...	...	tests from center of 2½ in. bar	(48)
	2.65	...	2.48	1.18	...	...	0.17	...	1.15	1.21	...	72,700	5900	0.49	1¼‡	...	14,000	288		(48)
engine and compressor	2.85	0.80	2.10	0.65	0.20 max	0.10 max	0.20 max	...	0.50	0.85	...	60,000	3350	0.28	1.2	1½ to 3	15 to 40	240		(21)
gasoline and Diesel	2.95	0.75	2.10	0.70	0.20 max	0.10 max	0.20 max	0.15	0.80	1.75	...	65,000	4550	0.36	1.2	1 to 3	40 to 100	300		(21)
gasoline (1 and 2 cylinder)	3.25	...	2.00	0.60	0.20 max	0.11 max	...	0.25	0.25	...	...	49,000	3600	0.42	1.2	⅝ to 1	4 to 5	225		(21)
(starting engine for Diesel)	3.10	0.85	2.15	0.90	0.12	0.11	...	...	0.85	1.65	...	62,500	...	...	...	1 to 2	80	260		(21)

[286]

TABLE 74 — (Continued)

Applications	TC %	CC %	Si %	Mn %	P %	S %	Cr %	Cu %	Mo %	Ni %	Other %	Tensile Strength psi	Transverse* Load lb	Defl in.	Test Bar Diam in.	Casting Section in.	Weight lb	BHN	Remarks	Ref
Crankshafts refrigerator compressor	3.25	…	1.45	1.50	0.20 max	0.11 max	…	0.50	0.55	…	…		…	…	…	6	1,200 to 1,300	200		(21)
stationary engine	2.65	…	1.45	0.75	0.08	…	0.35	…	0.18	0.10	…		…	…	…	¼ to 10	…	…		(45)
	3.00	…	2.10	1.00	0.15 max	0.15 max	0.40	…	1.00	1.20 to 4.00	…	69,500	…	…	…		…	300	%Ni increases with section. 0.5 to 0.7% Si as inoculant. TAP unnotched Izod impact 25 to 40 ft lb	
timing gear (Diesel truck)	3.25	…	2.25	0.65	0.25 max	0.10 max	0.80	…	0.50	0.30	…		…	…	…	1¾	1.6	210		(21)
truck and submarine	2.70	0.65	2.35	0.95	0.08 max	0.08 max	0.15	…	1.00	0.85	…	70,000	6500	0.20	1.2†	1¼ to 3	200 to 1,000	230		(21)
Cylinders	3.00	…	1.10	0.90			0.50		0.50	1.25	…	65,000	…	…	…		…	…		
	3.00	…	1.50						0.60		…		…	…	…		…	…		
forging hammer	3.15	…	1.90	0.85	0.15 max	0.10 max	0.20	…	0.15	0.10	…	47,500	2600	0.25	1.2	¼ to 16	2,500 to 30,000	175		(21)
hydraulic	3.10	…	1.20	0.70	0.20		0.20		0.80		…		…	…	…	3½	…	…		
railroad	3.13	…	1.64	0.99				0.76	0.30		…	50,600	4430	0.13	1.2†		…	241		
	3.20	…	2.13	0.72					0.54		…	65,000	6650	0.18	1.2†		…	255		
	3.13	…	1.29	0.70					0.88		…	61,000	6750	0.22	1.2†		…	262		
	3.11	…	1.50	0.90	0.15	0.12			0.45		…	50,000			1.2		…	255	0.5% Si added late	
	3.20	…	1.90	0.75	0.15	0.10	0.60	1.00	0.60		…	50,000			1.2		…	262	0.5% Si added late	
sluice valve operation	3.00	…	1.95						0.50	1.45	…	up to 78,400	…	…	…	26 ID x 78	…	275		(49)
unaflow steam engine	3.00	…	1.50	0.90			0.50		0.40	1.35	…	50,000 min	…	…	…	2 to 4	2,500 to 3,000	240 min	tensile strength in 2 to 4 in. sections, thermal stability up to 800 F	(21)

TABLE 74—(Continued)

Applications	Compositions											Tensile Strength psi	Transverse*			Casting		BHN	Remarks	Ref
	TC %	CC %	Si %	Mn %	P %	S %	Cr %	Cu %	Mo %	Ni %	Other %		Load lb	Defl in.	Test Bar Diam in.	Section in.	Weight lb			
Cylinder Barrels, aircraft (small)	3.10	....	2.15	0.75	0.15	0.13	0.05	1.00	0.65	0.05	....	57,000	....	....	1.2	....	.....	255	generally stress relieved at 1000 to 1250 F	
	3.20	....	2.15	0.75	0.15	0.13	0.25	0.05	0.35	1.25	....	47,500	....	....	1.2	....	.....	255	generally stress relieved at 1000 to 1250 F	
Cylinder Blocks	3.10	....	2.20	0.70	....	....	0.50	....	0.65	....	....	52,600	3200	....	1.2	....	.....	269		
	3.10	....	2.00	0.90	0.35	0.1 max	0.6	0.6	0.3	....	....	.....	....	....	...	....	.....	...		(25)
automobile	3.30	0.70	1.90	0.80	0.18	0.14	0.18	....	0.18	none	....	39,500	4800	0.15	1¼	3/16 to 2	278	220		(21)
Diesel	3.20	....	1.80	0.80	0.12 max	0.12 max	0.20	0.70	0.30	....	....	.....	....	....	...	....	.....	...	0.20 to 0.25% Si added late	
Diesel truck	3.25	0.75	2.10	0.70	0.18	0.10	0.80	1.10	1.05	0.15	....	51,500	3200	0.39	1.2	3/16 to 2½	220 to 470	259		(21)
gasoline truck and coach (large)	3.25	0.60	2.35	0.70	0.20 max	0.10 max	0.30	....	0.30	0.20	....	45,000	3100	0.32	1.2	¼ to ¾	200 to 215	187		(21)
(small and medium)	3.20	0.65	2.30	0.75	0.19 max	0.08 max	0.40	....	0.40	0.20	....	43,500	2800	....	1.2	¼ to ¾	160 to 210	225		(21)
truck	3.25	....	2.15	0.80	0.12 max	0.15 max	0.50	0.60	0.50	....	....	.....	....	....	...	....	.....	...		
	3.35	....	2.35	0.65	0.16	0.14	0.25	....	0.75	0.75	....	50,000	5800	0.18	1.2†	5/32 to 1	250	200		(21)
	3.35	0.60	2.35	0.65	0.16	0.14	0.25	....	1.25	1.25	....	60,000	6000	0.21	1.2†	5/32 to 1	250 to 400	...	Brinell 200 after annealing at 1400 F	(21)
	3.25	....	2.15	0.85	....	....	0.65	....	0.60	....	....	51,750	3180	....	1.2	....	.....	262		
	3.20	....	2.10	0.80	....	....	0.70	....	1.00	....	....	57,750	3270	....	1.2	....	.....	302		
	3.15	....	2.35	0.60	0.20 max	0.10 max	0.35	....	0.75	0.40	....	.....	2700	....	1.2	5/32 to 3/8	400	230		(21)

TABLE 74—(Continued)

Applications	Compositions: TC %	CC %	Si %	Mn %	P %	S %	Cr %	Cu %	Mo %	Ni %	Other %	Tensile Strength psi	Transverse*: Load lb	Defl in.	Test Bar Diam in.	Casting: Section in.	Weight lb	BHN	Remarks	Ref
Cylinder Blocks truck—(heavy duty)	3.30	....	2.10	0.85	0.20 max	0.12 max	0.40	....	0.35	....	....	40,000	....	....	...	3/16 to 2	75 to 400	215		(21)
(small and medium)	3.25	0.65	2.25	0.70	0.16 max	0.08 max	0.40	....	0.45	none	....	42,000	2950	0.29	1.2	3/16 to 5/8	125 to 165	225		(21)
truck and stationary engine	3.30	....	2.10	0.85	0.20 max	0.12 max	....	....	0.25	....	....	38,000	....	....	...	3/16 to 2	200 to 300	196		(21)
valve-in-head (large) truck and bus	3.25	0.60	2.35	0.70	0.16 max	0.08 max	0.30	....	0.30	0.20	....	42,500	3000	0.32	1.2	3/16 to 3/4	200 to 220	187	cylinder liners used in these blocks	(21)
Cylinder Bushings locomotive	3.20	....	1.60	0.90	0.45	0.10	0.35	....	0.35	....	....	47,000	....	....	...	....	.....	241	0.3% Si added late. stress relieved at 1100 F	
	3.22	....	1.49	0.47	0.49	....	....	....	0.59	....	....	.....	2250	0.18	1.2	....	.....	...		
Cylinder Heads	3.55	....	2.04	0.49	....	....	0.20	....	0.77	....	....	36,000	....	....	1.2	....	.....	217		
	3.10	....	2.00	0.90	0.35	0.1 max	0.6	0.6	0.3	....	....	.....	....	....	...	....	.....	...		(25)
aircraft (small)	3.10	....	2.15	0.75	0.15	0.13	0.05	1.00	0.65	0.05	....	57,000	....	....	1.2	....	.....	255	generally stress relieved at 1000 to 1250 F	
	3.20	....	2.15	0.75	0.15	0.13	0.25	0.05	0.35	1.25	....	47,500	....	....	1.2	....	.....	255	generally stress relieved at 1000 to 1250 F	
Diesel	3.20	....	1.75	....	....	....	0.30	....	0.60	0.75	....	.....	....	....	...	....	.....	...		
	3.00	....	1.50	....	....	....	0.55	....	0.60	1.50	....	.....	....	....	...	....	.....	...		
	3.20	....	2.00	0.80	....	....	0.60	....	1.00	....	....	.....	....	....	...	....	.....	341	annealed to Brinell 241	
	3.60	....	1.60	0.85	....	....	0.40	....	0.90	....	....	.....	....	....	...	....	.....	277	annealed to Brinell 241	
	3.00	....	2.10	....	....	....	....	....	0.50	....	0.10 V	.....	....	....	...	....	.....	...		(50)
	3.05	....	1.85	....	....	....	....	....	0.75	1.25	0.10 V	.....	....	....	...	....	.....	...		(50)
	3.20	....	1.80	0.80	0.12 max	0.12 max	0.20	0.70	0.30	....	....	.....	....	....	...	....	.....	...	0.2 to 0.25% Si added late	
	3.15	....	1.70	....	....	....	0.20	1.00	0.60	....	....	.....	....	....	...	....	.....	...		
	2.63	0.65	1.58	0.70	0.18	0.08	0.20	....	0.40	0.60	....	.....	....	....	...	....	.....	...		
	3.25	....	2.00	....	....	....	0.25	....	0.35	0.35	....	.....	....	....	...	....	.....	...		(51)
	3.35	0.65	2.10	0.75	0.18	0.11	0.40	....	0.55	....	....	36,000	2600	0.28	1.2	5/8 to 1½	450 to 500	220		(21)

TABLE 74—(Continued)

Applications	Compositions: TC %	CC %	Si %	Mn %	P %	S %	Cr %	Cu %	Mo %	Ni %	Other %	Tensile Strength psi	Transverse*: Load lb	Defl in.	Test Bar Diam in.	Casting: Section in.	Weight lb	BHN	Remarks	Ref
Cylinder Heads Diesel—(marine)	3.20	....	1.55	....	....	....	0.20	....	0.15	1.00	....	45,000	....	....	1.2	....	.....	...	inoculated	(52)
	3.10	....	1.50	0.80	....	....	0.40	....	0.70	1.25	....	.....	....	....	...	2	.....	240		
	3.16	....	2.00	....	....	....	0.50	....	0.40	0.75	....	.....	....	....	....	....	.....	...		
Diesel and gas engines used on air, natural gas and ammonia compressors	3.25	....	1.65	0.80	0.12	0.08	....	....	0.45	0.05	0.07 Ti	48,000	3100	0.32	1.2	½ to 2½	500 to 5,000	225		(21)
Diesel truck	3.20	....	2.10	0.85	0.20 max	0.12 max	0.40 min	....	0.75 min	0.40 min	....	50,000	....	....	....	3/16 to 1½	50 to 100	250		(21)
	3.00	....	2.00	....	....	....	0.35	....	0.35	....	....	.....	....	....	...	...	...	...		
gasoline truck and coach (large and medium)	3.05	0.70	2.10	0.70	0.15 max	0.09 max	0.40	0.20	0.55	0.60	....	51,000	3050	....	1.2	¼ to ¾	90 to 105	235		(21)
	3.05	0.75	2.30	0.80	0.15 max	0.07 max	0.25	....	0.70	0.25	....	54,000	3200	....	1.2	¼ to ½	100 to 110	235		(21)
(small and medium)	3.25	0.65	2.15	0.65	0.20 max	0.10 max	0.30	....	0.40	0.45	....	40,500	2550	....	1.2	¼ to ¾	60 to 100	225		(21)
truck (heavy duty)	3.30	....	2.10	0.85	0.20 max	0.12 max	0.40	....	0.35	....	....	40,000	....	....	...	3/16 to 2	75 to 400	215		(21)
(small and medium)	3.25	0.65	2.25	0.70	0.16 max	0.08 max	0.40	....	0.45	none	....	42,000	2950	0.28	1.2	3/16 to ⅝	125 to 165	230		(21)
unaflow steam engine	3.00	....	1.50	0.90	....	....	0.50	....	0.40	1.35	....	50,000 min	....	....	...	2 to 4	2,500 to 3,000	240 min	tensile strength in 2 to 4 in. sections. thermal stability up to 800 F	(21)
valve - in - head (large) commercial	3.00	0.65	2.05	0.75	0.15 max	0.07 max	0.50	....	0.70	0.35	....	48,500	3450	0.33	1.2	3/16 to ¾	100 to 120	235		(21)

TABLE 74—(Continued)

Applications	Compositions											Tensile Strength psi	Transverse*			Casting		BHN	Remarks	Ref
	TC %	CC %	Si %	Mn %	P %	S %	Cr %	Cu %	Mo %	Ni %	Other %		Load lb	Defl in.	Test Bar Diam in.	Section in.	Weight lb			
Cylinder Liners	3.10	....	2.00	....	....	....	0.50	....	0.25	....	....	.....	....	....	...	....	.....	...	cast in permanent mold	
	3.30	....	2.10	0.60	0.10	0.10	0.50	....	0.25	0.50	....	.....	....	....	....	....	.....	...	cast in permanent mold. heat treated to Brinell 241 or 187 by holding 5 hr at 1750 F, cooling in 1 hr to 1500 F, air cooling and tempering at 1200 or 1250 F	
automobile and truck	3.10	0.60	2.30	0.80	0.14	0.10	0.40	....	0.40	0.40	....	50,000	4950	....	1.2†	½ to ⅞	19 to 24	265	liners are heat treated	(21)
automobile, gasoline and Diesel	3.30	0.60 max	2.15	0.70	0.25 max	0.10 max	0.40	....	0.40	0.40	....	.....	....	....	..	....	.....	...	austempered to Brinell 450 to 480	(41)
Diesel	3.30	....	1.90	0.90	0.12 max	0.12 max	0.35	....	0.30	....	....	.....	....	....	..	....	.....	...	0.2 to 0.25% Si added late	
	3.00	....	2.00	....	....	....	0.35	....	0.35	0.35	....	.....	....	....	..	....	.....	...	heat treated	
	3.25	....	1.60	....	....	....	....	....	0.50	....	....	.....	....	....	..	....	.....	...	centrifugally cast	
	3.00	....	1.75	....	....	....	0.35	....	0.40	....	....	50,000	5150	0.10	1.2†	....	.....	262	stress relieved 2 hr at 1100 F after machining	
	2.63	0.65	1.58	0.70	0.18	0.08	0.20	....	0.40	0.60	....	.....	....	....	..	....	.....	...		(51)
	3.10	....	1.25	0.80	0.20 max	0.10 max	0.20	....	0.45	....	0.15 V	45,500	....	....	2.0	1⅝	1,010 to 1,210	220	0.2% ferrosilicon (75% Si) and 0.2% zirconium silicide (40% Zr and 50% Si) added in ladle	(53)
	3.25	0.80	1.70	0.75	0.18	0.10 max	0.45	....	0.65	....	....	36,000	2700	0.25	1.2	1¾	800	230		(21)
	3.25	0.65	2.10	0.75	0.18	0.09	0.35	....	0.45	....	....	35,000	2500	0.28	1.2	1¼	400 to 500	210		(21)
	3.10	0.70	2.30	0.80	0.18	0.11	0.25	....	1.00	none	....	60,000	6250	....	1.2†	½ to ⅞	17 to 24	275	liners are heat treated	(21)
	3.10	0.75	2.10	0.80	0.09	0.09	0.90	....	0.50	0.50	....	55,000	5450	....	1.2†	½ to 1¼	80 to 150	300		(21)
(marine)	3.20	....	1.55	....	....	....	0.35	....	0.35	1.00	....	45,000	....	....	1.2	....	.....	...	inoculated	(52)
(marine main liner)	2.95	0.90	1.30	0.70	0.15	0.07	0.25	....	0.30	1.10	....	47,500	5250	0.12	1¼	2½ to 4	4,000	205	tensile strength and hardness values for casting	(21)

TABLE 74—(Continued)

Applications	Compositions											Tensile Strength psi	Transverse*			Casting		BHN	Remarks	Ref
	TC %	CC %	Si %	Mn %	P %	S %	Cr %	Cu %	Mo %	Ni %	Other %		Load lb	Defl in.	Test Bar Diam in.	Section in.	Weight lb			
Cylinder Liners																				
Diesel (marine, railroad)	3.20	....	1.90	0.85	0.15 max	0.09 max	0.20	....	0.40	0.35	....	40,000 min	2200 min	0.20 min	1.2	....	......	225		(54)
Diesel and gas engines used on air, natural gas and ammonia compressors	3.20	....	1.60	0.80	0.12	0.08	....	....	0.45	0.05	0.07 Ti	48,000	3100	0.31	1.2	½ to 2½	500 to 5,000	225		(21)
Diesel and truck	3.20	0.60	2.20	0.80	0.18	0.12	none	....	0.70	0.70	....	50,000	5300	....	1.2†	½ to ¾	13 to 17	250		(21)
forging hammer	3.05	0.90	1.90	0.85	0.15 max	0.10 max	0.25	....	0.15	0.10	....	45,000	2600	0.25	1.2	1 to 2½	200 to 6,000	195		(21)
locomotive	3.20	....	1.60	0.90	0.45	0.10	0.35	....	0.35	....	....	47,000	....	....	...	....	.....	241	0.3% Si added late. stress relieved at 1100 F	
oil well pump	2.60	....	2.60	0.60	....	....	0.50	....	0.25	....	1.0 Al	.....	....	....	...	....	.....	...	heated to 1750 F, air cooled to 700 F, reheated to 1450 F and cooled slowly. nitrided 10 hr at 960 F	
Cylinder Sleeves	3.30 2.93	....	1.80 2.69	0.70 0.76	....	....	0.35 1.28	....	0.35 0.24	....	.... 1.0 Al 0.16 V	....	....	....	... ...	....	....	... ...	heat treated nitrided	
Diesel	3.10	0.80	2.10	0.60	0.20 max	0.10 max	0.30	....	0.50	0.30	....	46,000	4600	0.18	1.2†	⅜ to ⅞	22	...	heat treated by air cooling from 1550 F, oil quenching from 1575 F and tempering at 450 F. Brinell 260 as-cast, 500 as-hardened	(21)
	3.10	0.80	2.00	1.00	0.20 max	0.14 max	0.75	1.25	0.50	....	....	47,500	2750	0.27	1.2	⅜ to ⅝	20 to 60	248	transverse tests and Brinell as-cast	(21)
Diesel truck	3.25	....	2.25	0.70	0.20	0.10 max	0.60	....	0.45	0.30	....	.....	....	....	...	¼ to ⅜	15 to 30	500	hardened	(21)

TABLE 74—(Continued)

Applications	TC %	CC %	Si %	Mn %	P %	S %	Cr %	Cu %	Mo %	Ni %	Other %	Tensile Strength psi	Load lb	Defl in.	Test Bar Diam in.	Section in.	Weight lb	BHN	Remarks	Ref
Cylinder Sleeves gasoline and truck	3.29	...	2.18	0.73	0.14	0.07	0.34	...	0.69	1.04	...	...	...	...	...	¼ to ⅝	8 to 20	450	hardened	(21)
Dies body	3.10	...	1.60	0.70	...	...	0.35	...	0.35	...	...	...	...	...	...	...	...	230		
	3.40	...	1.40	0.80	...	...	0.25	...	0.50	...	0.10 V	...	...	...	...	...	...	...	flame hardened	
	3.8	...	1.5	0.8	0.12 max	0.12 max	0.5	...	0.5	1.5	...	...	...	...	...	...	800 max	...		
	3.50	...	1.50	0.80	0.12 max	0.12 max	...	...	0.55	...	0.15 V	...	...	...	...	...	...	235		
die block	3.05	...	1.25	1.25	...	...	...	2.00	1.00	...	...	82,000	...	...	1.2	12	...	...	Brinell on test bar	(21)
drop hammer forging	3.00	0.70	1.25	0.80	0.12	0.11	...	...	0.80	...	...	48,000	5200	0.16	1¼	4 to 12	50 to 500	260	properties after 5 hr stress relief at 600 F. Ni may be increased to 5.5% in very heavy dies. 0.15% V may be added	(55)
	2.90	...	1.90	0.85	0.06	0.15 max	0.30	...	0.75	3.25	...	97,500	5000	...	1.2	...	4,000 max	...		
fender	3.20	...	1.50	0.80	0.20 max	0.10 max	0.40	...	0.50	...	0.10 V	...	...	...	...	...	...	...		
forming	3.00	...	1.50	0.75	...	...	0.30	...	0.60	0.90	...	...	...	...	...	6 to 10	400 to 3,600	210		(21)
	3.25	...	1.45	0.65	0.20 max	0.11 max	0.65	...	0.85	0.95	...	...	...	...	...					
forming and hot bending	2.75	0.70	2.20	0.60	0.20 max	0.10 max	0.40	...	0.50	1.55	...	60,000	3400	0.26	1.2	2 to 15	5,000 max	...	Brinell 240 to 270 as-cast and 450 to 550 as-hardened. small dies heat treated by oil quenching from 1550 F and tempering at 350 to 400 F	(21)
forming roll for tube	3.40	...	1.35	0.95	0.09	0.11	0.47	0.81	0.56	...	...	...	...	...	...	...	...	...	0.25% Si added late, heat treated by oil quenching from 1600 F and tempering at 275 F. 1½ in. section will give Rockwell C 55 as-quenched	

[293]

TABLE 74.—(Continued)

Applications	TC %	CC %	Si %	Mn %	P %	S %	Cr %	Cu %	Mo %	Ni %	Other %	Tensile Strength psi	Load lb	Defl in.	Test Bar Diam in.	Section in.	Weight lb	BHN	Remarks	Ref
Dies hot drawing for deep drawn tube	3.80	...	1.05	0.85	0.20 max	0.11 max	0.45	...	1.00	...	0.21 V	36,500	2800	0.21	1.2	2½ to 3½	1,800 to 2,600	230		(21)
hot forming	2.45	0.65	2.05	0.80	0.05	0.06	0.15	...	1.10	0.90	...	61,500	7350	...	1¼	2 to 6	800	...	tensile tests on 2.0 in. diameter test bar. Brinell 311 to 341 on 1 in. section; 240 to 262 on casting	(21)
hot beading	3.05	...	1.86	0.86	0.11	0.11	0.55	...	0.65	2.17	...	63,850	...	...	1.6	...	...	...		(56)
hot work	3.30	...	1.300	0.50	...	...	...	...	0.90	...	...	...	...	...	...	...	...	...		
pipe expanding (large)	2.65	...	1.10	1.00	...	...	0.40	...	0.50	...	...	...	...	...	...	...	...	...		
swaging, reducing diameter of steel tubing	3.90	...	1.05	0.80	0.20 max	0.11 max	0.35	...	1.00	...	0.21 V	30,000 min	2600	0.19	1.2	1½ to 4½	2,000 to 6,000	245		(21)
End Plates and Transmissions truck	3.20	0.70	2.15	0.85	0.14 max	0.14 max	0.35	...	0.55	1.25	...	55,000	3700	0.27	1.2	⅝ to 2	100 to 300	265		(21)
Exhaust Manifolds	3.40	...	2.40	0.60	...	...	0.15	0.60	0.40	...	...	...	...	...	...	...	...	...		
automobile and truck	3.40	0.60	2.00	0.60	0.20	0.12	0.40	...	0.70	...	...	44,000	4100	0.14	1¼	⅝ to ½	25 to 88	225		(21)
	3.50	...	2.40	0.70	0.25	0.12	...	0.60	0.40	...	...	35,000	...	...	...	...	...	212		
Diesel	3.60	1.45	1.45	0.50	0.20	0.12	0.25	1.00	1.00	...	...	46,000	2800	...	1.2	...	...	...	0.2 to 0.25% Si added late	
	3.35	1.90	1.90	0.60	0.20 max	0.12 max	0.40	...	0.30	...	...	...	...	...	...	...	...	...		
Diesel truck (large)	3.00	...	2.00	...	...	...	0.50	...	0.40	...	...	...	...	...	...	...	...	...	annealed	
(small and medium)	3.40	...	2.50	...	...	...	0.20	...	0.50	...	...	...	...	...	...	...	...	...	annealed	
truck	3.40	...	2.20	0.70	0.30	0.12	0.40	...	0.40	...	...	40,000	...	...	...	...	...	228		

TABLE 74—(Continued)

Applications	Compositions											Transverse*				Casting			Remarks	Ref
	TC %	CC %	Si %	Mn %	P %	S %	Cr %	Cu %	Mo %	Ni %	Other %	Tensile Strength psi	Load lb	Defl in.	Test Bar Diam in.	Section in.	Weight lb	BHN		
Flywheels	3.40		1.60	0.85			0.35		0.25			40,000			1.2			...			
automobile and tractor	3.45		1.60	1.10	0.20 max	0.10 max			0.60				3600	0.11	1 sq†	½ to 1½	25 to 60	200		(21)
truck and coach	3.40		2.35	0.60	0.20 max	0.10 max	0.55		0.55			41,000	2700	0.29	1.2	½ to 1¼	35 to 150	225		(21)
Forge Hammers	3.00		1.10	0.80					0.60	1.00		48,000			2.0		...	255		
Frames forging hammer	3.15		1.90	0.85	0.15 max	0.10 max	0.20		0.15	0.10		47,500	2600	0.25	1.2	½ to 16	2,500 to 30,000	175		(21)
Furnace Doors	3.33		1.60	0.77			0.33		0.45								...			
Gears	3.30 3.40 3.30 3.20		1.85 2.30 2.00 1.50	0.60 0.75 0.75	0.35	0.25	0.25		0.40 0.40 0.55 0.75			40,050 44,000 50,000				20 100 500	...		
bevel (heavy duty)	2.95	0.80	2.35	0.60	0.20 max	0.10 max	0.20		0.90	1.95		65,000	3550	0.38	1.2	½ to 1½	150 max	...	stress relieved by furnace cooling from 1050 F. Brinell 280 to 300 as-cast and 265 to 285 as stress relieved	(21)
brake and power transmission	3.00		2.00	0.70	0.18 max	0.10 max			0.70			55,000	3900	0.31	1.2	⅜ to 2	12 to 14	240		(21)
cam (truck)	3.50		2.10	0.65	0.20 max	0.12 max	0.20		0.50		0.14 V					¼ to 1	3 to 15	...	can be heat treated to required hardness. Brinell 187 to 212 green and 269 to 301 heat treated	(21)
Diesel	3.05	0.75	1.60	0.75	0.22	0.11	0.55		0.55			47,500	2900	0.22	1.2	1½	150 to 200	240		(21)

[295]

TABLE 74—(Continued)

Applications	TC %	CC %	Si %	Mn %	P %	S %	Cr %	Cu %	Mo %	Ni %	Other %	Tensile Strength psi	Load lb	Defl in.	Test Bar Diam in.	Section in.	Weight lb	BHN	Remarks	Ref
Gears																				
Diesel (engine gear train) (fuel injection pump drive)	2.95 / 3.25	...	2.25 / 2.25	... / 0.65	0.25 max	0.10 max	0.20 / 0.80	0.75 ...	0.40 / 0.50	0.30 / 0.30	...	40,000 min	4000	...	1.2†	1/2 to 1 1/4	... / 4	210		(21)
general machinery (cut gears)	2.80 / 0.80	...	2.55	0.60	0.25 max	0.10 max	0.40	...	0.50	1.50	...	55,000	3250	0.28	1.2	1/4 to 8	10 to 50	...	heat treated by oil quenching from 1550 F and tempering at 850 to 400 F. Brinell 240 to 270 as-cast and 450 to 550 as-hardened	(21)
idler (camshaft and crankshaft, light 2 cycle Diesel) (tractor)	3.25 / 3.35	0.45	2.30 / 2.15	0.70	0.15 max	0.10 max	0.25 / 0.25	...	0.40 / 0.60	1.20 / 0.30	...	40,000 min	2700	0.24 min	1.2	1/8 to 1 1/2	...	215 / 240		(21)
large	3.00	...	1.80	0.85	...	...	0.25	...	0.75	0.80	...	58,000	...	...	...	...	...	...		
lawn mower	3.30	...	1.90	...	...	...	0.30	...	0.30	...	...	...	...	...	...	...	...	...		
stoker	3.20	...	2.10	0.80	...	...	0.50	...	0.50	...	...	...	...	...	...	...	...	...		
truck	3.00	...	2.00	...	0.18 max	0.10 max	...	...	0.70	...	0.14 V	52,500	3750	0.33	1.2	3/4 to 1 1/2	8 to 20	225		(21)
washing machine	3.30	...	2.20	0.60	0.20	0.12	...	...	0.50	0.90	...	...	...	...	...	...	...	...		
Gear Box Housings	3.40	...	2.25	...	...	...	0.25	...	0.50	...	...	40,000	...	...	...	...	...	...		
Goosenecks aluminum die casting	3.30	...	1.60	0.85	...	...	0.50	...	1.00	0.75	...	...	...	...	...	...	...	...		
Grate Bars	3.50 / 3.25	...	1.50 / 1.75	0.70 / 0.70	...	...	0.85 / 0.50	...	0.30 / 0.40	...	...	...	...	...	...	...	...	...		
Grinding Machine Bases	3.25	...	1.75	0.75	...	...	...	...	0.60	0.75	...	50,000	...	...	...	...	...	248		
Guides rolling mill (finishing)	3.20	...	1.70	0.75	0.15 max	0.12 max	...	...	0.50	...	...	...	...	...	...	...	...	...		

TABLE 74—(Continued)

Applications	TC %	CC %	Si %	Mn %	P %	S %	Cr %	Cu %	Mo %	Ni %	Other %	Tensile Strength psi	Load lb	Defl in.	Test Bar Diam in.	Section in.	Weight lb	BHN	Remarks	Ref
Guides sleeve (gear cutting machine)	3.20	...	2.10	0.80	0.22	0.09	none	...	0.50	none	...	48,000	3000	0.32	1.2	1¼	100	...	heat treated by quenching from 1575 F and tempering at 600 F. Brinell 225 to 235 as-cast, about 490 as-hardened	(21)
valve (aircraft and truck)	3.00	...	2.40	0.80	0.15	...	0.50	...	0.50	...	...	......	...	...	...	...	...	...	heat treated by oil quenching from 1600 F and tempering at 850 F. Rockwell C about 50 as-hardened	
valve stem (Diesel)	3.50	...	2.40	0.70	0.20	0.10	0.40	...	0.40	...	...	......	...	...	...	...	...	...		
Headers	2.60	...	2.60	0.85	...	...	...	...	1.20	0.62	...	88,900	...	...	...	...	...	...		
Ignition Distributors	3.20	...	2.25	0.65	0.25 max	0.10 max	0.80	...	0.50	0.30	...	40,000 min	4000 min	...	1.2†	⅜ to ⅝	0.82 to 0.85	285		(21)
Lapping Plates ball bearing lapping	3.25	...	1.60	0.80	0.22	0.11	...	...	0.50	2.05	...	45,000	3100	0.28	1.2	1½ to 3	800 to 600	265		(21)
Lathe Beds	3.10 3.20 3.10	...	1.50 1.80 1.25	0.75 0.70 0.75	...	...	... 0.25 ...	...	0.35 0.40 0.50	1.00 0.50 0.50	...	44,000 47,000	...	...	...	...	...	255 255	flame hardened	
Liners	3.20	...	2.10	...	...	...	...	...	0.50	...	...	......	...	...	2.0	...	...	...	centrifugally cast	
Mandrels	2.85	...	1.60	...	...	...	0.85	...	0.35	1.25	...	......	...	...	...	...	...	259		
Melting Pots aluminum	3.25	...	1.80	0.70	0.15	...	0.50	...	0.60	...	...	......	...	...	...	...	...	...		
zinc alloys	3.25	...	1.50	0.75	...	...	1.15	...	0.50	2.25	...	......	...	...	...	...	...	...	heat treated to produce oxidized surface by holding 4 hr at 1200 to 1400 F and cooling to room temperature in 12 hr min. life further increased by application of an iron oxide solution prior to use	(57)

TABLE 74—(Continued)

Applications	TC %	CC %	Si %	Mn %	P %	S %	Cr %	Cu %	Mo %	Ni %	Other %	Tensile Strength psi	Load lb	Defl in.	Test Bar Diam in.	Section in.	Weight lb	BHN	Remarks	Ref
Mine Hoist Drums	3.10		1.40	0.75					0.35	0.95		50,000	2700	0.29	1.2			269		
Mold Boards plow shares	2.95		2.60					1.25	0.65			50,000								
Molds glass	3.65		2.15	0.70	0.30 max	0.12 max			0.50	0.50										
	3.55		2.15	0.65	0.35 max	0.08 max			0.60											
(optical lens)	3.30	0.62	2.43	0.41			0.28		0.49											(58)
permanent (centrifugal casting of nonferrous metals)	2.9		1.80	1.00	0.20 max	0.12 max	0.60		0.70	2.75										
(copper and aluminum alloys)	3.40		3.20	0.25	0.10 max	0.10 max			0.60											
(copper ingots)	3.75		1.25	1.25					1.00											
Outboard Bearing starting motor	3.35		2.20	0.70	0.20 max	0.11 max			0.40		0.14 V	41,000	2800	0.24	1.2	3/8 to 7/8	9 to 16	215		(21)
Outboard Motors	3.25		2.60	0.60	0.50				0.25	0.50										
Packing Rings	3.10		1.90	0.60	0.50				0.50									215	inoculated	
locomotive	3.20		1.60	0.90	0.45	0.10	0.35		0.35			47,000						241	0.3% Si added late, stress relieved at 1100 F	
Pistons	3.15		2.50	0.75			0.30		0.35			46,000	2700		1.2			228		
accumulator	2.50		2.60	0.70	0.20	0.10			0.40										0.2% Si added late	
automobile	3.35	0.60	2.40	0.60	0.19	0.07	0.15		0.50			43,000				0.08 to 1/4	3/4 to 4	230		(21)
Diesel	2.63	0.65	1.58	0.70	0.18	0.08	0.20		0.40	0.60		53,000								(51)
	3.20		2.00	0.70		0.35	0.35		0.60	1.25										

TABLE 74—(Continued)

Applications	TC %	CC %	Si %	Mn %	P %	S %	Cr %	Cu %	Mo %	Ni %	Other %	Tensile Strength psi	Load lb	Defl in.	Test Bar Diam in.	Section in.	Weight lb	BHN	Remarks	Ref
Pistons Diesel	2.60	0.60	1.70	0.60	0.15 max	0.07 max	....	....	0.60	1.50	0.12 V	65,750	....	....	....	1 to 1¼	60 to 90	235		(21)
Diesel and gas engines used on air, natural gas and ammonia compressors	3.20	....	1.60	0.80	0.12	0.08	....	....	0.40	0.05	0.06 Ti	48,000	3100	0.32	1.2	½ to 2½	500	225		(21)
truck	3.35	0.50	2.85	0.65	0.16	0.14	0.25	....	0.40	0.75	....	48,000	5600	0.17	1.2†	⅝ to 1	....	200		(21)
unaflow steam engine	3.00	....	1.50	0.90	....	....	0.50	....	0.40	1.85	....	50,000 min	....	....	....	2 to 4	2,500 to 3,000	240 min	tensile strength in 2 to 4 in. sections, thermal stability up to 800 F	(21)
Piston Heads Diesel	3.10	....	1.50	0.80	....	....	0.25	....	0.40	....	....	....	....	....	....	....	....	....	0.25 to 0.35% Si added late	
Piston Rings	3.50	....	1.60	....	0.35 max	0.10 max	0.40	....	0.60	2.00	....	....	....	....	....	....	....	....	tempered at 1250 F	(59)
	3.50	0.60	2.45	0.70	....	....	....	....	1.10	1.00	....	....	....	....	....	....	....	....		
	3.75	....	2.75	0.45 max	....	....	0.50	....	....	....	0.20 V	....	....	....	....	....	....	....		
aircraft	3.75	....	2.70	0.60	0.80	0.10	0.40	0.70	0.60	....	....	....	....	....	....	....	....	....	about Rockwell C 35 as-cast; tempered at about 1100 F to about Rockwell C 26 treated to Rockwell C 20 to 24 piston ring pots; if chill cast, whole of chill removed by machining	(60)
	2.90	....	2.27	0.76	0.08	0.06	0.65	....	0.68	....	....	....	53,760a min	....	....	....	....	....		
	3.4 max	0.75	2.0	1.0	0.60	0.12	0.25 max	0.6	0.85	0.60	....	....	....	....	....	....	....	....		
	2.95	0.95	2.20	0.85	0.08	0.95	....	....	0.90	0.3 max	....	....	58,240a min	....	....	....	....	285	heat treated by holding at 1740 to 1920 F and cooling slowly	(61)
	3.25	0.75	2.30	0.85	0.50	0.08	0.45	....	0.75	....	....	....	44,800a min	....	....	8 OD max	....	275	centrifugally cast	(62)
	3.30	....	1.80	....	....	....	....	....	1.00	1.00	....	....	....	....	....	....	....	....		
aircraft, tank and Diesel	3.75	0.70	2.80	0.65	0.45 max	0.10 max	0.10	0.75	0.50	0.50	0.07 V	48,500	....	....	....	⅛ to ⅜	2 to 4 oz	....	Rockwell B 102 to 108	(21)

[299]

TABLE 74—(Continued)

Applications	Compositions TC %	CC %	Si %	Mn %	P %	S %	Cr %	Cu %	Mo %	Ni %	Other %	Tensile Strength psi	Transverse* Load lb	Defl in.	Test Bar Diam in.	Casting Section in.	Weight lb	BHN	Remarks	Ref
Piston Rings																				
Diesel and gasoline	3.70	0.50	2.70	0.70	0.35	0.08	0.20	....	0.20	....	....	24,000	....	....	...	1/8 to 3/16	0.1 to 0.25	...	Rockwell D 40 to 45	(21)
(compressors)	3.65	0.65	1.65	0.65	0.40	0.08	0.40	....	0.40	1.00	....	37,500	1450	0.15	7/8	0.375 to 0.10; 5.0 to 30.0 OD	0.25 to 0.30	205	tensile strength of rings	(21)
tractor	3.25	....	2.75	0.70	....	....	0.06	....	0.95	1.30	....	.....	....	....	...	....	.....	...	Rockwell C 35 to 40 as-cast. annealed at 1300 F to Rockwell B 85 to 90. after machining hardened to Rockwell C 45 to 55 by oil quenching from 1560 F and tempering at 600 to 700 F	
Plungers																				
glass house	3.60	....	1.10	0.65	0.16 max	0.10 max	0.25	....	0.35	....	0.14 V	37,500	2900	0.30	1.2	1½ to 2¼	12 to 30	240		(21)
valve (large)	2.90	....	2.00	0.90	0.15	0.12 max	0.35	....	0.30	1.60	.....	50,000	3000 min	....	1.2	1½ to 2½	1,500 to 3,500	270		(21)
Pressure Castings, Chemical Machinery	2.70	0.85	1.70	0.50	0.15	0.06	0.55	....	0.90	0.45	0.15 Ti	65,000	4500	....	1.2	¾ to 1½	5 to 25	260		(21)
steam	3.05	0.65	1.35	0.85	0.15	0.10	....	....	0.25	....	....	42,500	5400	0.18	1¼	¾ to 1½	2,000 to 7,000	200		(21)
	2.85	0.65	1.95	0.70	0.15	0.06	0.20	....	0.50	0.20	....	51,500	3450	....	1.2	¾ to 1¼	5 to 25	230		(21)
Pressure Plates	3.70	....	2.00	0.60	....	0.10	0.35	....	0.50	....	....	.....	....	....	...	....	.....	...	0.25% Si added late	

TABLE 74—(Continued)

Applications	TC %	CC %	SI %	Mn %	P %	S %	Cr %	Cu %	Mo %	Ni %	Other %	Tensile Strength psi	Load lb	Defl in.	Test Bar Diam in.	Section in.	Weight lb	BHN	Remarks	Ref
Pumps	3.25		2.50	0.70	0.15	0.10			0.35							⅜ to ⅝		...		
	3.25		2.25	0.70	0.15	0.10	0.25		0.50							¼ to 1¼		...		
	3.25		2.00	0.70	0.10	0.08	0.50		0.50							½ to 2		...		
	3.10		1.75	0.70	0.10	0.08			0.75	0.75						1 to 3		...		
	3.00		1.25	0.70	0.08	0.08			1.00	1.00						2 to 6		...		
	3.16	1.02	1.86	0.55	0.06	0.08	0.41		0.73	1.03		60,500	11,700	0.25	2.0			286		
boiler feed	3.23	0.71	1.93	0.95	0.15	0.05	0.28		0.57	1.08		62,500	3820	0.33	1.2	¾ to 3				
high pressure	2.90		0.95	0.75					0.27	1.80		40,000	9050		2.0			248		(21)
	2.85		2.60	0.77					0.57			53,750	3150		1.2			255		
	3.00		1.70	0.83					0.75	1.25		57,500	3280		1.2			269		
(centrifugal)	3.35		1.90	0.90	0.05				0.67	0.97		61,100				2 to 6	4,000 to 16,000	255	5000 psi pressure, hardness on 2 in. section	
(well drilling)	3.00	0.85	1.80	0.90	0.10	0.10	0.50		0.70	0.95		59,350						280		
oil	2.86	1.69	1.05	1.05	0.12	0.10	0.42	0.38	0.38	1.58		52,800						255	generally stress relieved at 1000 to 1250 F	
(aircraft)	3.10	2.15	2.15	0.75	0.15	0.13	0.05	1.00	0.65	0.05		57,000								
	3.20		2.15	0.75	0.15	0.13	0.25	0.05	0.35	1.25		47,500						255	generally stress relieved at 1000 to 1250 F	
oil well drilling	3.00		0.90	0.75	0.17	0.12	none		0.40	2.00		51,000				2 to 6	7,000 to 10,000	305		(21)

[301]

TABLE 74—(Continued)

Applications	TC %	CC %	Si %	Mn %	P %	S %	Cr %	Cu %	Mo %	Ni %	Other %	Tensile Strength psi	Transverse* Load lb	Defl in.	Test Bar Diam in.	Casting Section in.	Weight lb	BHN	Remarks	Ref
Pump Casings boiler feed pump	2.62	....	2.38	....	....	....	....	....	0.50	1.25	....	81,200	....	....	....	....	....	....		(49)
Pump Liners sludge pump	3.00	0.70	1.30	0.75	0.14	0.12	none	....	0.50	none	....	49,500	5050	....	1.2†	1 to 2	200 to 700	245		(21)
Rollers rolling mill	3.50	....	1.50	0.55	0.60	0.06	0.95	....	0.55	....	....	40,000	3500	0.25	1.2	1 to 1½	1,000 to 5,000	275		(21)
Seal Bearings	3.10	....	1.90	0.70	0.20	0.10	0.45	....	0.65	1.30	....	....	....	....	....	....	....	....		
Sprockets agricultural	3.25	....	1.55	0.90	0.40 max	0.15 max	....	....	0.30	....	....	....	....	....	....	....	....	....		
Stove Girders blast furnace	3.00	....	1.90	0.90	0.20 max	0.12 max	0.40	....	0.40	1.00 min	....	50,000	....	....	....	....	....	....	suitable for use at a working temperature of 800 F	(63)
Tables machine tool	2.90	....	1.85	0.90	....	....	....	....	0.35	0.50	....	50,000	....	....	....	....	....	255		
Turrets machine tool	3.25	....	1.25	0.90	....	....	....	....	0.35	....	....	45,000	....	....	....	....	....	262		
Valves	2.50	0.70	2.00	0.50	0.17	0.06	....	0.90	0.35	....	....	60,000	4500	....	1.2	....	....	230		
	3.21	....	2.16	0.81	....	....	0.31	0.35	0.41	0.77	....	46,000	2900	....	1.2	....	....	248		
	3.27	....	1.77	0.70	....	....	0.36	0.77	....	0.78	....	50,000	3000	....	1.2	....	....	269		
control, very light for superheated steam	3.10	....	2.45	0.75	0.20	0.08	none	....	0.75	none	....	39,500	2750	0.30	1.2	¾	3 to 25	240 max		(21)
gate (river lock) (water works sluice)	3.00	....	2.00	0.45	0.20	0.12	0.95	0.50	0.50	1.45	....	69,750	3700	0.31	1.2	....	1,500 to 8,000	275		(21)
	2.50	....	1.90	0.80	0.20	0.12	....	0.95	0.35	1.35	....	....	....	....	....	....		...		
	2.85	....	2.40	0.80 max	0.20 max	0.35 max	0.40 max	0.40	0.40	1.35	....	62,500	3650	0.35	1.2	....		275	Cr+Mo=0.75% max	(21)

TABLE 74—(Continued)

Applications	Compositions TC %	CC %	Si %	Mn %	P %	S %	Cr %	Cu %	Mo %	Ni %	Other %	Tensile Strength psi	Transverse* Load lb	Defl in.	Test Bar Diam in.	Casting Section in.	Weight lb	BHN	Remarks	Ref
Valve Cages Diesel	2.63	0.65	1.58	0.70	0.18	0.08	0.20	....	0.40	0.60	....	......	......	....	....	....	......	....		(51)
Valve Gages Diesel	3.45	....	1.65	0.65	0.18	0.10 max	0.35	....	0.40	....	....	42,500	2950	0.2	7/8	1/2 to 1	25	230		(21)
Valve Liners locomotive	3.20	....	1.60	0.90	0.45	0.10	0.35	....	0.35	....	....	47,000	......	....	....	....	......	241	0.3% Si added late. stress relieved at 1100 F	
Valve Seat Inserts	3.25	....	2.25	0.75	0.15	0.10	0.35	....	1.10	0.35	....	......	......	....	....	....	......	....	Rockwell C 30. machined from solid bar	
Wedge Blocks locomotive	3.00	....	1.60	0.90	....	....	....	....	0.75	1.25	....	......	......	....	....	....	......	....		
Wheels chain hoist	3.25	0.70	2.10	0.75	0.22	0.09	none	....	0.50	0.50	....	50,000	3100	0.36	1.2	3/8 to 3/4	5 to 10	230		(21)
Zinc Die Casting Machine Parts	3.25	....	1.50	0.70	0.50	....	....	....	0.40	....	....	......	......	....	....	....	......	....	if parts must fit closely, anneal by furnace cooling from 1600 to 1600 F to below 1000 F	

*unless otherwise noted, the following test conditions apply for transverse tests:

test bar diameter—in.	distance between supports—in.
7/8	12
1 1/2	18
1 1/4	12
1.6	18
2.0	24

†12 in. distance between supports in transverse test
‡18 in. distance between supports in transverse test
(a) transverse breaking stress calculated by formula

$$S = \frac{PD \times 2240}{b t^2 \times 1200}$$

where
S = transverse breaking stress in psi
P = load in lb
D = external diameter of unsplit ring in in.
b = axial breadth of ring in in.
t = radial thickness of ring in in.

[303]

way as steel. Special compositions are generally used, two of which are given below: (21)

%TC	%Si	%Mn	%Al	%Cr	%Mo	%V
2.70	1.55	0.60	1.10	0.30	0.70	....
2.75	2.58	0.73	1.01	1.22	0.24	0.16

Other compositions have been proposed with up to 3% nickel. The presence of molybdenum has been stated to minimize the decrease in strength that occurs as a result of the long holding at 950 F for nitriding (42).

Applications

In the selection of an iron for a specific application, it is often helpful to know what compositions have been used successfully in similar parts. Table 74 offers some applications of molybdenum-containing gray irons reported to have been satisfactory. Where available, mechanical properties and size of casting are also indicated.

WHITE IRON

Molybdenum is added to both types of white iron castings—those that are white throughout and those that have a gray iron backing. Reports from users indicate that the most important effect of small additions of molybdenum is to improve the toughness of white iron.

Molybdenum is about a third as effective as chromium in increasing the depth of chill (Figure 178). It refines the grain structure

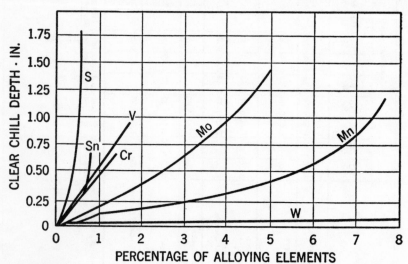

FIG 178 – Relative Effect of Chill Increasing Elements on the Depth of Chill (21)

TABLE 75

Typical Applications of White Cast Irons Containing Molybdenum

Applications	Compositions								Remarks
	%C	%Si	%Mn	%Cr	%Cu	%Mo	%Ni	%W	
Augers for clay machines	3.00	0.9	....	...	...	1.50	...	...	
Balls for grinding	3.70	1.1	0.8	0.6	...	0.30	...	...	3½ in. balls cast in chilled metal molds have surface Brinell of 550 and center Brinell of 350
Blades for shot blasting and peening (Wheelabrator type)	1.50	0.5	0.8	1.8	...	1.75	...	...	short blades, quenched from 1700 F into salt bath at 400 F for three minutes, then water quenched
	3.40	1.7	0.7	2.8	...	4.75	...	...	cast in permanent molds. Rockwell C 61 to 64
	1.00	0.5	0.7	2.0	...	5.00	...	...	short blades, air cooled from 1750 F. Rockwell C 60
	2.35	1.4	0.7	2.2	...	7.00	...	...	long blades, usually not heat treated. if hardness as-cast low, stress relieved by air cooling from 1100 to 1200 F. Rockwell C 60
	2.75	1.3	0.4	4.0	...	7.50	...	...	Rockwell C 65 as-cast
	3.60	1.2	0.5	6.3	...	10.20	...	...	Rockwell C 69.5
Coke sizer	3.00	0.8	0.8	...	...	2.00	...	...	
Conveyor parts for ash handling	3.00	1.2	....	1.0	...	0.35	...	...	
Conveyor shovel plates	4.00	0.6	1.3	2.0	...	1.00	0.8	...	Brinell 650
Guides for rolling mills	3.30	1.6	0.6	0.7	...	0.50	1.3	...	
Knives for pug mills	3.12	0.8	2.9	...	...	1.35	...	...	Brinell 601
Liners for ball mills	2.70	1.1	0.6	0.4	...	0.40	...	...	
	3.40	0.8	0.4	1.4	1.5	0.45	...	...	Rockwell C 48
Liners for deep well pumps	1.75	0.8	....	2.5	...	2.50	3.7	...	
Mine car wheels	3.40	1.1	0.4	...	...	0.15	...	...	½ in. chill
	3.50	0.9	....	0.2	...	0.40	...	...	
Mold boards for plows	3.50	1.9	....	...	...	0.3	...	...	face cast against a chill; gray iron backing
Nozzles for sand blasting	2.50	1.0	....	1.5	...	0.75	4.5	...	
Plates for jaw crushers	3.40	0.7	0.4	0.3	...	0.50	0.3	...	Scleroscope 65 on chill; gray iron backing
Plow tips	2.40	0.3	2.9	1.6	...	0.40	2.7	...	Brinell 353
Plungers for deep well pumps	1.75	0.8	....	2.5	...	2.50	3.7	...	
Rolls for rolling mills	3.00	0.6	0.4	...	...	0.25 to 0.50	...	...	for finishing stands, tinplate, medium and heavy sheet, and, to some extent, universal and plate mills
	3.02	0.7	0.3	0.1	...	0.85	...	...	sheet mill (65)
	2.90	0.6	0.3	0.4	...	0.24	...	...	two and three high mills. ⅝ to ⅞ in. chill (65)

TABLE 75 — (Continued)

Applications	Compositions								Remarks
	%C	%Si	%Mn	%Cr	%Cu	%Mo	%Ni	%W	
Rolls for rolling mills	3.20	0.7	0.3	0.5	...	0.30	...	...	two and three high mills. ⅝ to ⅞ in. chill (65)
	3.40	1.2	0.4	1.2	...	0.30	...	...	
	3.50	0.5	0.4	...	...	2.00	2.0	...	Scleroscope 102 on chill with machinable necks
	3.20	1.0	....	0.9	...	0.40	0.5	...	
	3.65	1.5	0.8	1.4	...	0.30	1.0	...	Scleroscope 75 on collar, 47 on journal. for rod mills and for rolling other small sections
	3.10	0.5	0.2	0.5	...	0.80	2.5	...	for two high mills, roughing stands for hot rolling sheet and strip and finishing stands for sheet bar and plate
	3.10	0.5	0.2	0.8	...	0.80	4.0	...	Scleroscope 75 to 85, for working rolls on continuous three and four high water cooled mills and for hot rolling sheet and strip
	3.20	0.5	0.2	1.0	...	0.85	5.2	...	Scleroscope 85 min for cold rolling ferrous and nonferrous sheet and strip
Tappets	3.50	2.5	....	....	...	0.60	...	...	
	3.40	2.5	0.5	0.2	...	0.60	0.2	...	Rockwell C 57 on chill
	3.30	2.6	0.4	0.2	...	0.60	2.0	...	Rockwell C 58 on chill
Valve seat inserts for automobile and truck engines	2.75	1.8	0.7	3.0	...	4.50	...	...	stress relieved by air cooling from 1100 to 1200 F. Rockwell C 60
	2.60	1.3	....	2.0	...	5.00	...	...	
	2.00	1.4	0.5	3.0	...	5.00	...	...	no subsequent heat treatment. Rockwell C 60 as-cast
	1.80	0.5	0.5	3.5	...	6.50	...	5.5	annealed by furnace cooling from 1500 to 1200 F. Rockwell C 40
	1.30	0.6	....	3.0	1.1	8.50	...	1.5	
	1.00	2.5	0.6	4.0	...	8.50	...	...	annealed to about Rockwell C 35 by heating to 1675 F, furnace cooling to 1200 F, heating to 1400 F and air cooling. used in annealed condition
	1.40	0.6	0.6	4.0	1.5	8.50	...	1.8	
	1.00	2.1	....	4.6	...	8.80	...	...	annealed to Rockwell C 45 so inserts can be machined, by furnace cooling from 1425 F; inserts work harden in motor to Rockwell C 52
	1.35	0.8	0.5	4.4	...	12.00	...	...	
Vanes for flotation impellers	3.35	0.8	....	1.1	0.9	0.45	...	...	Rockwell C 47
	3.35	0.8	....	0.3	...	0.35	...	...	Rockwell C 45
Vanes for pump runners (Wilfley type)	3.08	0.6	....	1.3	0.9	0.60	...	...	Rockwell C 43
Wear plates for centrifugal casting machines	2.49	0.9	0.3	1.4	...	1.30	3.0	...	
Wear plates for coke ovens	3.71	0.8	0.4	0.5	...	0.50	...	...	
Wear shoes (Aitkens type)	3.20	0.3	0.3	...	...	0.30	...	...	

of the chilled and mottled iron. In large amounts, as in valve seat inserts, molybdenum raises the resistance to wear, corrosion and softening at high temperatures.

The action of molybdenum in markedly increasing the resistance of rolls to breakage, chipping, heat checking and spalling in service has been repeatedly observed. Its usefulness has been proved not only in chilled rolls but also in grain rolls.

Molybdenum appears to be the most effective element in promoting resistance to heat checking (Figure 179). The addition of 0.47%

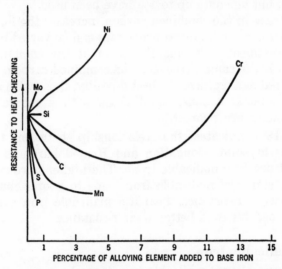

FIG 179 – Comparative Effect of Various Alloying Elements on the Resistance of White Iron to Heat Checking on Repeated Water Quenching from 1110 F. Composition of base iron: 3.7% C, 0.45% Si, 0.94% Mn, 0.05% P, 0.023% S (64)

molybdenum increased the heat check resistance by 1.5 times while the simultaneous addition of 1% chromium, 0.3% molybdenum and 4% nickel to a 3.5% carbon white iron doubled the resistance to heat checking as compared with unalloyed white iron (64).

Specific compositions of molybdenum-containing white irons reported to be successfully used for typical applications are listed in Table 75.

MALLEABLE IRON

Pearlitic Malleable Iron

"Pearlitic" malleable iron differs from regular malleable iron in that it is not completely graphitized but contains significant amounts (such as 0.30 to 0.60%) of combined carbon, usually in the form of pearlite but sometimes as spheroidite or another decomposition product of austenite. There are three methods of producing pearlitic malleable iron: 1) the annealing cycle of regular malleable iron is interrupted before second stage graphitization is complete; 2) completely graphitized castings are reheated to dissolve part of the carbon in the ferritic matrix and cooled so as to give the desired structure; 3) suitable alloying elements are added to retard or prevent second stage graphitization even with the regular annealing cycle. Molybdenum is particularly advantageous with the third method of treatment as it retards second stage graphitization moderately but has little effect on first stage graphitization. The most common addition is about 0.25%, often in conjunction with increased manganese, but amounts up to 1% have been used.

Any increase in the combined carbon increases the hardness and strength. Also, the mechanical properties can be varied by changing the heat treatment and thus the form of the combined carbon. Generally, for the same percentage of combined carbon, irons with a spheroidized matrix have the best ductility, those with a tempered martensitic matrix are next and those with a coarsely lamellar pearlitic matrix are poorest.

Figure 180 indicates the relationship between the tensile strength, yield point, elongation and Brinell hardness of certain commercial pearlitic malleable irons. The higher hardness as compared with standard malleable iron leads to poorer machinability but better wear resistance. Pearlitic malleable iron can be selectively hardened for even better wear resistance.

Ferritic Malleable Iron

Molybdenum alloyed malleable iron is made commercially by the addition of 0.25 to 0.50% molybdenum to the standard malleable iron. A small amount of pearlite will normally be retained with such an addition unless the annealing time is increased. If the malleable iron is free from pearlite, the molybdenum addition will increase the tensile strength by about 7,000 psi, the yield point by about 3,000 psi and the hardness by about 15 points Brinell. If a normal annealing cycle is used so that a small amount of pearlite is retained, the molybdenum malleable iron will show an increase in tensile strength of about 5,000 to 10,000 psi, an increase in yield point of about 4,000 to 7,000 psi and an increase in Brinell hardness of about 20 points, as compared with the standard ferritic malleable iron.

With properly balanced copper and molybdenum additions, the action of the molybdenum in retarding graphitization is neutralized by the copper so that a completely graphitized product can be obtained with a normal annealing cycle. Despite the somewhat higher strength (Table 76), the machinability of the copper-molybdenum malleable iron is about the same as that of the "higher strength"

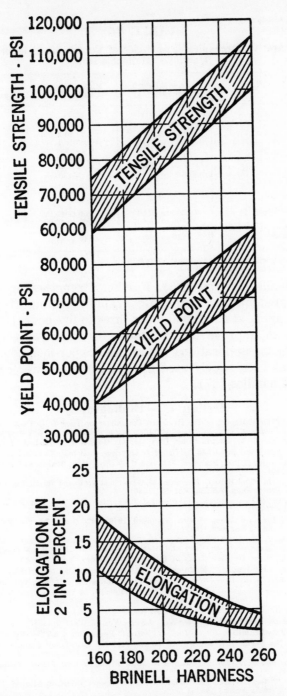

FIG 180 – Relationship between Tensile Strength, Yield Point, Elongation and Brinell Hardness of Certain Commercial Pearlitic Malleable Irons (66)

TABLE 76
Comparative Mechanical Properties of Copper-Molybdenum and Unalloyed Malleable Iron

	Lower Strength Unalloyed (13)	Higher Strength Unalloyed (13)	Copper-Molybdenum
Composition*:			
%C	2.25 to 2.70	1.75 to 2.30	2.00 to 2.45
%Si	0.80 to 1.10	0.85 to 1.20	0.85 to 1.20
%Mn	0.40 max	0.40 max	0.55 max
%P	0.20 max	0.20 max	0.20 max
%S	0.07 to 0.15	0.12 max	0.18 max
%Cu	....	....	0.50 to 1.00
%Mo	....	....	0.25 to 0.50
Mechanical Properties:			
Tensile Strength, psi	50,000 to 52,000	53,000 to 60,000	58,000 to 65,000
Yield Point, psi	32,500 to 35,000	35,000 to 40,000	40,000 to 45,000
Elongation, percent**	10 to 18	18 to 25	15 to 20
Brinell Hardness	110 to 135	110 to 145	135 to 155

*chemical compositions apply to original white iron castings
**in 2 in. on a ⅝ in. diameter specimen

unalloyed malleable iron (66). Further strengthening can be obtained by precipitation hardening (rapidly cooling from 1300 to 1350 F and aging at about 900 F for three to five hours). The copper also serves to improve the corrosion resistance of the malleable iron. Among the applications where this copper-molybdenum malleable iron has been widely used are freight car buffer castings and pipe wrench handles (67).

Section IX – Bibliography

(1) J. G. Pearce "Third Report of the Research Committee on High-Duty Cast Irons for General Engineering Purposes" Proceedings of the Institution of Mechanical Engineers, Vol 149 (1943)

(2) H. Bornstein and J. W. Bolton "Cast Iron" Metals Handbook, published by the ASM (1939)

(3) High Duty Cast Iron, published by Sykes & Harrison Limited, Manchester, England (1945)

(4) Data on Cast Iron, British Standard 991, issued by the British Standards Institution, London, England (1941)

(5) J. T. MacKenzie "The Brinell Hardness of Gray Cast Iron and its Relation to Some Other Properties" Proceedings, ASTM, Vol 46 (1946)

(6) V. A. Crosby "Microstructure and Physical Properties of Alloy Cast Irons" Transactions, AFA, Vol 45 (1937)

(7) Impact Test for Cast Iron, British Standard 1349:1947, issued by the British Standards Institution, London, England (1947)

(8) A. B. Everest, J. W. Grant and H. Morrogh "The Development of a Single Blow Impact Test for Cast Iron" Journal of the Iron and Steel Institute, Vol CLII, No. 2 (1945)

(9) J. S. Vanick "Some Unusual Tests of Cast Iron" Foundry, Vol 75 (1947)

(10) A. J. Herzig "Cast Iron . . . Modulus of Elasticity" American Foundryman, Vol 9 (1946)

(11) J. T. MacKenzie "Gray Iron–Steel Plus Graphite" Transactions, AIME, Vol 158 (1944)

(12) The Engineering Properties of Gray Cast Iron, published by the Gray Iron Founders' Society (1939)

(13) Cast Metals Handbook, published by the AFA (1944)

(14) "Symposium on Cast Iron" Proceedings, ASTM, Vol 33, Part 2 (1933)

(15) "Report of Sub-Committee XV on Impact Testing" Proceedings, ASTM, Vol 33 Part 1 (1933)

(16) W. Jolley "The Shear Test not a Satisfactory Test for Cast Iron" Foundry Trade Journal, Vol 40 (1929)

(17) H. F. Moore and J. J. Picco "Fatigue of High Strength Cast Irons" Transactions, AFA, Vol 42 (1934)

(18) T. E. Eagan "Effect of Heat Treatment on the Endurance Limit of Alloyed Gray Cast Iron" Transactions, AFA, Vol 54 (1946)

(19) W. L. Collins and J. O. Smith "The Notch Sensitivity of Alloyed Cast Irons Subjected to Repeated and Static Loads" Proceedings, ASTM, Vol 42 (1942)

(20) A. Pomp and M. Hempel "The Behavior of Cast Iron under Alternating Tension-Compression Stresses" Stahl und Eisen, Vol 57 (1937)

(21) Alloy Cast Irons, published by the AFA (1944)

(22) F. G. Sefing "Gray Iron Wear Resistance" Transactions, AFA, Vol 54 (1946)

(23) Battelle Memorial Institute, Prevention of the Failure of Metals under Repeated Stress, published by John Wiley and Sons, Inc. (1941)

(24) W. West "Cast Materials for Crankshafts" Appendix I of "First Report of the Research Committee on High-Duty Cast Irons for General Engineering Purposes" Proceedings of the Institution of Mechanical Engineers, Vol 140 (1938)

(25) Copper in Cast Steel and Iron, issued by the Copper Development Association, London, England (1946)

(26) R. A. Flinn and D. J. Reese "The Development and Control of Engineering Gray Cast Irons" Transactions, AFA, Vol 49 (1941)

(27) J. J. Sheehan "High Duty Cast Irons" Foundry Trade Journal, Vol 78 (1946)

(28) G. A. Timmons, V. A. Crosby and A. J. Herzig "Produces High Strength Iron" Foundry, Vol 66 and 67 (1938, 1939)

(29) A. H. Horton "Some Notes on High-Duty Cast Irons" Foundry Trade Journal, Vol 78 (1946)

(30) E. L. Bartholomew, discussion of R. A. Flinn, M. Cohen and J. Chipman "The Acicular Structure in Nickel-Molybdenum Cast Irons" Transactions, ASM, Vol 30 (1942)

(31) F. B. Rote and W. P. Wood "Segregation of Molybdenum in Phosphorus-Bearing Alloyed Gray Cast Iron" Transactions, ASM, Vol 35 (1945)

(32) A. E. McRae Smith "The Year's Progress in the Production and Application of Alloy Cast Irons" Metallurgia, Vol 35 (1946)

(33) A. E. McRae Smith "A Review of the Major Changes in Grey-Iron Foundry Practice During the Period 1914-1944" Foundry Trade Journal, Vol 77 (1945)

(34) J. E. Hurst "Cast Iron and the Foundry Industry" Metallurgia, Vol 29 (1943)

(35) G. A. Timmons and V. A. Crosby "Effect of Pouring Temperature on the Strength and Microstructure of Gray Cast Iron" Transactions, AFA, Vol 49 (1941)

(36) P. A. Russell "Heat-Treatment of Grey Cast Iron for Relief of Internal Stresses" Foundry Trade Journal, Vol 80 (1946)

(37) G. A. Timmons and V. A. Crosby "Alloy Additions to Gray Cast Iron" Foundry, Vol 69 (1941)

(38) J. S. Vanick "Engineering Properties of Heat Treated Cast Irons" Transactions, AFA, Vol 54 (1946)

(39) G. A. Timmons, V. A. Crosby and A. J. Herzig "Some Factors Involved in Hardening and Tempering Gray Cast Iron" Transactions, AFA, Vol 47 (1939)

(40) E. L. Bartholomew "Gray Cast Iron" Iron Age, Vol 146 (1940)

(41) C. W. Ohly "Austempered Cast Iron Serves as Cylinder Liners" Materials and Methods, Vol 25 (1947)

(42) J. E. Hurst "Temper Brittleness in Cast Iron and the Influence of Nickel and Molybdenum" Foundry Trade Journal, Vol 53 (1935)

(43) R. G. McElwee and T. E. Barlow "The Role of Vanadium in Gray Iron Castings" Vancoram Review, Vol 5 (1946)

(44) Anonymous "Automobile Castings" Automobile Engineer, Vol 34 (1944)

(45) Anonymous "Acicular Iron Castings used in the Manufacture of 'Douglas' Stationary Engines" Automobile Engineer, Vol 36 (1946)

(46) E. M. Currie and R. B. Templeton "The Manufacture of Crankshafts in High-Duty Cast Iron" Foundry Trade Journal, Vol 66 (1942)

(47) Anonymous "Cromol Crankshafts—Factors Involved in the Use of High-Duty Alloy Iron Castings" Automobile Engineer, Vol 35 (1945)

(48) G. Vennerholm "Developments in Gray Iron and Malleable" Metal Progress, Vol 49 (1946)

(49) W. F. Chubb "Molybdenum in Cast Iron" Proceedings of the Institute of British Foundrymen, Vol 32 (1938-39)

(50) E. Piwowarsky "Vanadium in Cast Iron" Foundry Trade Journal, Vol 63 (1940)

(51) P. Dwyer "Pours Engine Castings in Dry Sand Molds" Foundry, Vol 75 (1947)

(52) "Alloys Contribute to Diesel Engine Performance" Nickel Cast Iron News, Vol 17 (1946)

(53) W. W. Levi "Cylinder Liners for Diesel Engines" Vancoram Review, Vol 4 (1945)

(54) N. A. Kahn and B. N. Ames "The Casting of a Gray Iron Diesel Engine Liner" Foundry, Vol 75 (1947)

(55) R. R. Taylor, letter to the editor, Metals and Alloys, Vol 19 (1944)

(56) A. E. McRae Smith "Melting and Casting Problems in the Production of High Strength and Special Duty Alloy Iron Castings" Foundry Trade Journal, Vol 64 (1941)

(57) S. Menton "Casting Zinc Alloy Dies" Foundry, Vol 75 (1947)

(58) F. Hudson "Permanent Moulds and Their Application to the Production of Non-Ferrous Castings" Foundry Trade Journal, Vol 64 (1941)

(59) D. M. Smith "Piston Rings in the War" SAE Journal, Vol 53 (1945)

(60) Ministry of Aircraft Production (Great Britain) Material Specification D.T.D. 413 (1940)

(61) Ministry of Aircraft Production (Great Britain) Material Specification D.T.D. 485A (1945)

(62) Ministry of Aircraft Production (Great Britain) Material Specification D.T.D. 233A (1945)

(63) T. H. Stayman "Some Notes on Recent American Blast-Furnaces" Journal of the Iron and Steel Institute, Vol 155, No. 1 (1947)

(64) K. P. Bunin, E. P. Troitskaya and S. N. Khitrik "Effect of Individual Elements on the Thermal Stability of White Iron" Stal, No. 11/12 (1946)

(65) J. H. Mort "Sheet and Tinplate Mills—Roll Dressing Formulae" Iron and Steel, Vol 20 (1947)

(66) American Malleable Iron, published by the Malleable Founders' Society (1944)

(67) J. H. Lansing "Malleable Iron Castings" Product Engineering, Vol 18 (1947)

SECTION X

SPECIAL PURPOSE AND NONFERROUS ALLOYS

There are a large number of special purpose and nonferrous alloys that contain molybdenum as an essential constituent. The versatility of molybdenum as an alloying element is nowhere better shown than in these alloys where it may contribute added corrosion resistance, elevated temperature strength, hardness, resistivity or some other desired property depending upon the type of base alloy. It is impossible to do more.here than to present a few data on some of the most widely used of these alloys.

HIGH PERMEABILITY ALLOYS

The iron-nickel alloys developed for very high magnetic permeability at low field strengths are sensitive to heat treatment. For example, the initial permeability of a 78.5% nickel alloy is decreased from about 10,000 to 1500 by furnace cooling. Therefore, its use is restricted to sizes that can be effectively heat treated by air cooling as more drastic quenching may result in strains which will be highly detrimental to the magnetic properties. The addition of molybdenum decreases the sensitivity to cooling rate, so high permeability is retained even with slow cooling rates (Table 77). Molybdenum also increases the initial permeability as "quenched".* Another advantage of the molybdenum addition is that it increases resistivity and consequently decreases the eddy current losses. The highest permeability values are found at 1.6% molybdenum for quenched alloys and 3.8% molybdenum for annealed alloys, while the resistivity increases continuously with the molybdenum (1). The 3.8% molybdenum – 78.5% nickel alloy is used for applications such as audio transformers, retardation coils, telephone toroid cores, coils for continuous loading of cables and cable sheathing. The 5% molybdenum alloy of Table 77 is used for transformer cores where it permits a threefold increase in the range of frequencies

* See Table 77 for "quenching" treatment.

TABLE 77

Electrical and Magnetic Properties of High Permeability Alloys

Compositions*			Initial Permeability	Maximum Permeability	Hysteresis Loss erg per cc per cycle**	Residual Induction gauss	Coercive Force oersted	Saturation Value of Intrinsic Induction gauss	Resistivity microhm-cm	Reference
%Cu	% Mo	% Ni								
...	...	78.5a	10,000	105,000	200	6,000	0.05	10,700	16	(1)
...	3.8	78.5b	20,000	75,000	200	5,000	0.05	8,500	55	(1)
...	5.0	79.0c	50,000 to 150,000	600,000 to 1,200,000	5	.....	0.002 to 0.005	7,900	65	(2)
14	3	72	50,000	100,000	50	.....	.....	6,000	56	(3, 4)

* balance iron
** for saturation value of flux density for first two alloys and for B = 5,000 for last two alloys
(a) "quenched" by cooling at about 70 F per sec from 1110 F
(b) "annealed" by furnace cooling from 1880 F
(c) vacuum melted, poured at atmospheric pressures under a helium or nitrogen atmosphere, heat treated by holding at 2370 F in pure dry hydrogen, then cooling through the range 1110 to 570 F at a "critical rate" (tests on 0.014 in. sheet)

transmitted and a pulse duration three times that obtainable with the older alloys (2).

The cores of inductance coils for use at the high frequencies of communication circuits are generally made by powder metallurgy* to prevent the excessively high eddy current losses that would occur with the solid cores.** The use of a 17% iron – 2% molybdenum – 81% nickel alloy permits a reduction of about 50% in the size of these cores as compared to those made from the plain iron-nickel alloy, since the molybdenum alloy cores have about 70% higher permeability and markedly lower hysteresis and eddy current losses (8). The decreased losses result in improvements and economies for loading and filter coils for voice and carrier frequency operation. A further modification must be made in quartz crystal filters used in wide band carrier systems since any departure from initial frequency adjustment due to changes in core permeability ordinarily occurring with room temperature changes must be avoided. About 0.25 to 1% of a "stabilizing" powder containing approximately 12% molybdenum, 80% nickel and balance iron, which has a Curie point close to room temperature and a negative temperature coefficient of permeability, is added to the 17% iron – 2% molybdenum – 81% nickel alloy powder to give a core with an extremely small net temperature coefficient of permeability (9).

Likewise, molybdenum is added to the 50% iron – 50% nickel alloy (which has a much higher permeability at low flux densities than the ordinary iron-silicon alloys) to increase the resistivity and thus to reduce eddy current losses to a point below that which could be obtained by gage reduction alone. For example, molybdenum increases the specific resistance from 52 to 80 microhm-cm with only a slight decrease in the saturation value from 16,000 to 15,000 gauss (10). Molybdenum also raises the knee of the magnetization curve and simultaneously brings about a high rate of change of flux density relative to magnetizing force. These effects of molybdenum have been of considerable importance in the design of special transformers for high frequency communication applications. A modification with 4% molybdenum, 43% nickel and balance iron has been used to a limited extent in radar transformers because of its high resistivity and low core loss values (7).

CONSTANT PERMEABILITY ALLOYS

These alloys exhibit a constant permeability over a considerable

---

* A small amount of sulphur is added to give an alloy which can be hot rolled but which is extremely brittle when cold and thus can be easily pulverized. The powder is annealed, coated with a ceramic type insulation, compressed and then annealed to remove strains (5, 6).

** Insulated tape, 2 mils or less in thickness, of a 17% iron – 4% molybdenum – 79% nickel alloy has been applied for some cores to be used at high frequencies where powder cores do not meet severe requirements of faithful transmission of the pulse shape and high effective permeability (7).

range of relatively low flux densities. Their major use is in applications where a constant inductance or reactance is essential and where distortion would be fatal to good quality of transmission. Molybdenum is added to the basic cobalt-iron-nickel alloy primarily to increase its resistivity (Table 78). This advantage more than offsets the fact that the permeability of the molybdenum alloy is not quite so independent of the magnetizing force nor is the hysteresis loss quite as low as in the molybdenum-free alloy. The molybdenum modification with its high resistivity is an especially suitable continuous loading material for certain types of loaded cables, such as long submarine telephone cables.

PERMANENT MAGNET ALLOYS

Molybdenum is used in both the quench hardening and the precipitation hardening types of permanent magnets, as indicated in Table 79.

The presence of molybdenum in the chromium-molybdenum quench hardening magnet Steel 2 improves the working and heat treating characteristics. The chromium-cobalt-molybdenum quench hardening magnet Steels 4 to 8 have appreciably better magnetic properties than the chromium and tungsten magnet Steels 1 and 3. These steels can be hot worked and are machinable in the annealed condition.

The precipitation hardening Alloys 10 and, particularly, 11 have magnetic properties at least comparable to those of the 36% cobalt Steel 9. These alloys can be formed by casting or by hot working. Alloy 11, for example, can be hot rolled to thin sheet from which the desired shapes may be punched. Decarburization is not a problem with these materials as it is with the quench hardening steels where decarburization impairs their magnetic properties. They can be readily machined to close tolerances after quenching from a high temperature and prior to precipitation hardening. Alloys 10 and 11 are structurally more stable than the quench hardening steels since their magnetic properties result from precipitation hardening at 1100 to 1200 F rather than from quenching. While aluminum-iron-nickel and aluminum-cobalt-iron-nickel alloys have higher energy products than Alloys 10 and 11, they have the disadvantage that they cannot be hot worked or machined and must be formed by sintering or casting and grinding. The cobalt-molybdenum Alloy 11 has been described as a "natural choice" where a high flux density is required in a short air gap (16) and has found extensive application in small telephone magnets.

TABLE 78

Electrical and Magnetic Properties of Constant Permeability Alloys (1)

Compositions*				Initial Permeability	Maximum Permeability	Hysteresis Loss erg per cc per cycle**	Residual Induction gauss	Coercive Force oersted	Saturation Value of Intrinsic Induction gauss	Resistivity microhm-cm
%Co	%Fe	%Mo	%Ni							
25	30	..	45	400	2,000	2,500	3,000	1.2	15,500	19
25	23	7	45	550	3,700	2,600	4,300	0.65	10,300	80

* alloys "baked" by holding 24 hr at 800 F, followed by slow cooling
** for saturation value of flux density

TABLE 79

Typical Magnetic Properties of Permanent Magnets

No.	Compositions*						Heat Treatment	Coercive Force Hc oersted	Residual Induction Br gauss	BdHd max** x 10⁻⁵	Reference
	%C	%Co	%Cr	%Mo	%W						
1	0.9	....	3.5	....	....	1640 F oil quench	63	9,500	0.25	(11)
2	1.0	....	4.0	0.4	....	1500 F oil quench	65	9,000	....	(12)
3	0.6	....	....	....	5.5	1640 F water quench	65	10,000	0.27	(11)
4	1.0	3.0	9.0	1.5	....	2100 F air cool+1440 F furnace	115	7,800	0.40***	(13)
5	1.0	6.0	9.0	1.5	....	cool+1830 F air cool+1440 F air cool	135	7,500	0.43***	(13)
6	1.0	9.0	9.0	1.5	....	2100 F air cool+1440 F furnace cool+1830 F air cool	150	8,000	0.54***	(13)
7	1.0	10.0	6.5	1.5	....		120†	8,000†		(14)
8	1.0	15.0	9.0	1.5	....	2100 F air cool+1440 F furnace cool+1830 F air cool	180	8,600	0.65***	(13)
9	0.8	36.0	2.0	....	5.0	1740 F oil quench	230	9,000	0.87	(11)
10	low	12.0	....	23.4	....	2320 F quench +1200 F	219	7,000	....	(15)
11	low	....	....	17.0	....	2190 F oil quench +1110 F	250	10,500	1.10	(11)

* balance iron
** maximum value of the energy product as obtained from the product of the flux and magnetizing force values of the demagnetization curve
*** BfH max where Bf =4πI or the ferric induction; the values corresponding to Bf are slightly above the absolute values of B
† minimum

[316]

COMPOSITE CONTACT MATERIALS

No pure metal meets the requirements of an ideal contact material. Silver, for example, has satisfactory thermal and electrical conductivity but does not meet the other requirements of high hardness, high density and low material transfer. Molybdenum fulfills the latter specifications well but has low conductivity. Powder metallurgy makes it possible to combine the desirable characteristics of these two metals even though they do not alloy in the usual sense of the term. The two most common molybdenum-silver contact materials contain 30 and 60% molybdenum with the balance silver (17). Table 80 indicates typical properties of two sintered molybdenum-silver contact materials which have been widely used on circuit-interrupting equipment such as arcing tips and combination arcing-current carrying tips. These materials have a very high resistance to the erosion of electric arcs and are used where it is essential that the contacts do not weld when the current is interrupted.

TABLE 80
Typical Properties of Molybdenum-Silver Contact Materials (18)

No.*	Electrical Conductivity % IACS	Rockwell B Hardness	Tensile Strength psi	Modulus of Rupture psi
1..................	45 to 50	80 to 90	60,000	135,000
2..................	50 to 55	70 to 80	45,000	110,000

* no. 1 has higher molybdenum content than no. 2

WIRES FOR GRIDS OF ELECTRONIC DEVICES

Only a limited number of materials has been found capable of meeting grid wire requirements, which have been listed as: high hot strength, freedom from back or secondary emission, good ductility, uniform spring back and low thermal expansion (19). Pure molybdenum wire finds application in many cases, while one of the most widely used grid wire alloys contains approximately 20% iron, 2% manganese, 20% molybdenum and 58% nickel (20).

MOLYBDENUM-TUNGSTEN ALLOYS FOR ELECTRIC AND ELECTRONIC EQUIPMENT

An entire series of molybdenum-tungsten alloys (Table 81) has been developed primarily for use as hooks in high wattage lamps, supports and springs in discharge tubes and heaters in radio tubes. They are also used as resistance wire in high temperature electric furnaces.

TABLE 81
Molybdenum-Tungsten Alloys (21)

Compositions		Specific Resistance ohms per sq mm per m at 68 F	Temperature Coefficient of Resistivity between 68 and 212 F
%Mo	%W		
		about	
20	80	0.081	1.8×10^{-3}
51	49	0.090	1.6×10^{-3}
72.5	27.5	0.083	1.81×10^{-3}
80	20	0.076	1.94×10^{-3}
90	10	0.067	2.23×10^{-3}

GLASS SEALING ALLOYS

Molybdenum-containing alloys with expansion coefficients suitable for metal-to-glass seals in soft glasses are listed in Table 82.*

TABLE 82
Glass Sealing Alloys

Compositions*				Coefficient of Thermal Expansion $\times 10^6$ per degree F	Reference
%Co	%Cu	%Mo	%Si		
..	1	10	...	6.13 (68 to 1110 F)**	(23)
..	1	15	...	5.55 (68 to 1110 F)**	(23)
..	1	20	...	5.08 (68 to 1110 F)**	(23)
19	..	10	0.8	5.0 to 5.3 (68 to 212 F)	(24)

* balance iron
**prepared from sintered ingots

THERMOSTATIC BI-METALS

Iron-molybdenum-nickel alloys are used for the high expansion component of thermostatic bi-metals, as indicated in Table 83.

THERMOCOUPLE ALLOYS

A thermocouple of a 25% molybdenum – 75% tungsten alloy and pure tungsten is reported to have been satisfactory in inert gases up to 5430 F (26).** In recent years, use has been made of a thermocouple composed of very pure nickel and a molybdenum-nickel alloy containing 18% molybdenum. The major application is in hydrogen brazing furnaces, operating at about 2000 F. Highly

---

* Molybdenum with a mean coefficient of linear expansion of about 3.2×10^{-6} between 32 and 930 F is satisfactory for hard glass. With proper joint design, it can also be used for "unmatched" seals to glass with a lower coefficient of expansion (22).
** Thermocouples of pure molybdenum vs pure tungsten have found some use for high temperature measurements although the emf is relatively low.

TABLE 83

Molybdenum-Containing Thermostatic Bi-Metals

Compositions*			Highest Operating Temperature F	Reference
High Expansion Component		Low Expansion Component		
%Mo	%Ni	%Ni		
5	27	36	390	(25)
5	27	42	750	(25)
5	42	42	750**	(24, 25)

* balance iron
** useful range 265 to 750 F

accurate temperature control can be obtained with this thermocouple because its emf is much greater than that of other types of high temperature thermocouples. It is suitable only for use in hydrogen or other reducing atmospheres.

HARD SURFACING ALLOYS

Molybdenum is used in various iron base welding rods for hard surfacing (Table 84). In the high manganese type (Alloy 1), it is reputed to give superior work hardening and abrasion resistance to straight manganese steels. Alloy 11 has been stated to have almost as high hot hardness as the nonferrous chromium-cobalt-tungsten alloys and has been advocated for aircraft exhaust valve seats, faces and stem ends (27, 28). The other alloys have found a definite field of application where moderate abrasion or heat resistance is required but where a lower cost material than the cobalt base alloys is welcome.

For very high wear resistance, diamond-hard synthetic granules may be used with a ferrous base bonding material containing 0.05% boron, 0.20% carbon, 30% chromium, 8% cobalt, 8% molybdenum and 5% tungsten (29).

Molybdenum is likewise added to nickel and cobalt base hard surfacing alloys. A typical analysis of a cobalt base alloy for this purpose is 2.38% carbon, 29.52% chromium, 3.20% molybdenum, 9.72% tungsten and the balance cobalt. The hardness of the deposit is about Rockwell C 54.5 (30). A nickel base alloy containing about 17% chromium, 19% molybdenum and 5% tungsten is reported to have given excellent results on applications requiring resistance to heat, friction, pressure and impact, such as hard surfacing hot shear blades, rolling mill entry guides, and hot forming and punching dies. The deposited hardness is only about 210 Brinell, but the alloy

TABLE 84
Iron Base Hard Surfacing Alloys

No.	%C	%Mn	%Si	%B	%Co	%Cr	%Cu	%Mo	%Ni	%Ti	%V	%W
						Compositions*						
1	1.2	14	...	....	...	....	1	0.5	...	...	1.5	..
2	2.7	...	...	....	15	25	....	0.6	...	...	1.5	13
3	...	...	...	....	10	5	....	1	...	...	...	19
4	1.0	0.5	0.8	....	..	5	....	1.5	...	...	...	..
5	4.0	...	...	1	..	12	....	2	8	4	...	..
6	3.5	0.5	1.0	....	..	7.5	....	2	...	...	...	..
7	1.2	...	...	0.5	..	4	....	2	6	...	3	..
8	1.5	...	...	....	..	5.5	....	2.5	...	...	...	..
9	8.0	low	1.0	....	..	5	....	2.5	...	...	1	17
10	0.9	0.2	1.7	0.3	..	13.5	1.3	4.4	...	...	...	..
11	1.6	0.6	2.3	....	19	27	....	4.5	...	...	...	4
12	3.0	low	1.0	....	..	5	....	4.5	...	...	...	..
13	1.3	...	...	....	10	6	....	7	...	...	1.6	4
14	4	...	...	....	..	16	....	8	4	...	...	..
15	0.6	...	...	0.02	6	35	14	10	...	...	...	8
16	3.4	...	...	....	9	19	....	12	1	...	...	1
17	...	...	...	....	6	17	....	15	...	...	2	..
18	0.1	...	...	0.05	8	....	....	16	...	...	...	35
19	0.9	0.5	1.9	1	..	0.5	....	16.3	3.8	...	...	7

* balance iron

readily work hardens to as much as 400 Brinell. The resistance to chipping and checking is stated to be excellent (31).

A nonferrous composition with about 35% chromium, 5% molybdenum and 60% copper crystals (one micron in size) is used for resistance to heat and corrosion as well as wear (29).

HIGH TEMPERATURE NONFERROUS ALLOYS*

The severe service requirements of turbosupercharger blades and, particularly, of gas turbine parts have accelerated the development of essentially nonferrous alloys with unusually high strengths at elevated temperatures. Generally the use of these alloys does not become economical until the temperature of the metal exceeds about 1200 F and the stresses are too high for the conventional austenitic steels. Table 85 gives the compositions, applications and usual treatments of some of these alloys that are either being applied commercially or being seriously considered. Representative data on elevated temperature properties are reproduced in Figures 181 through 185 and Tables 86 and 87. Some 40 million turbosupercharger blades of Alloy 5 have been produced** in addition to a large number of gas turbine blades and other high temperature parts (52). Alloy 9, in spite of its susceptibility to oxidation because of the absence of chromium†, has been widely used for gas turbine blades.

* Information on compositions with higher iron contents will be found in Section VI, pp 179-192. In both cases, the information given is based on publications through 1947. For later developments it is suggested that current literature be consulted.
** For a discussion of the effect of processing variables on the elevated temperature properties of this alloy see (46, 47, 48, 49, 50, 51). Carbon content also has a marked effect on the strength at elevated temperatures of Alloy 5 as well as Alloy 1 (51).
† For this reason, a top temperature of 1400 F has been suggested for a life of 300 to 400 hr and 1300 to 1350 F for a longer life up to 10,000 hr (49).

TABLE 85

Compositions, Conditions and Applications of Nonferrous High Temperature Alloys (32 to 42)*

No.	Designations	Type Compositions											Form	Usual Treatment (a)	Applications
		%C	%Mn	%Si	%Cb	%Co	%Cr	%Fe	%Mo	%Ni	%W	% Other			
1	N 155 Multimet (AMS 5532–sheet) (AMS 5767 and 5768 –bars, billets, forgings)	{0.15} {0.30} †	1.5	0.5	1	20	21	bal	3.2	20	2.8	0.15 N	mainly wrought; some precision cast	hot worked; hot worked +aged; solution treated +aged	gas turbine blades, bolts, diaphragms, disks, shrouding, tail cones
2	Refractaloy 26 NR 93 (AMS 5760–bars, billets, forgings)	0.03	0.7	0.6	..	20	18	bal	3.2	37	..	0.25 Al 3.0 Ti	wrought	quenched from 2100 F, double aged at 1500 F +1350 F	experimental blades, bolts, disks
3	S 590 NR 74 (AMS 5533–sheet, strip) (AMS 5770–bars)	0.45	1.6	0.5	4	20	20	bal	4	20	4	....	wrought; precision cast	quenched from 2150 to 2350 F +aged at least 10 hr at 1400 F	gas turbine blades, bolts, disks, rotors
4	S 816 NR 76 (AMS 5534–sheet, strip) (AMS 5765–forgings)	0.40	0.5	0.5	4	bal	20	5 max	4	20	4	....	wrought; precision cast	quenched from 2150 to 2350 F +aged at least 6 hr at 1400F (b)	gas turbine blades, disks
5	Vitallium Haynes Stellite 21 NR 10 (AMS 5385)	0.25	1.0 max	1.0 max	..	bal	27	2 max	5.5	2.8	..	....	mainly precision cast (c)	as-cast or solution treated +aged	gas turbine blades, heat exchangers, nozzle vanes, tail cones; turbosupercharger blades
6	6059 Haynes Stellite 27 NR 63 (AMS 5378)	0.40	1.0 max	1.0 max	..	bal	24.5	2 max	5.5	32.5	..	....	precision cast	as-cast	gas turbine blades

[321]

TABLE 85—(Continued)

No.	Designations	Type Compositions											Form	Usual Treatment (a)	Applications
		%C	%Mn	%Si	%Cb	%Co	%Cr	%Fe	%Mo	%Ni	%W	% Other			
7	422-19 Haynes Stellite 30 NR 12 (AMS 5380)	0.45	1.0 max	1.0 max	..	bal	26	2 max	6.2	15	...	....	precision cast	as-cast	gas turbine blades, nozzle diaphragm blades
8	Refractaloy 70 Refractaloy M-284 NR 62	0.05	2	0.2	..	bal	20	15	8	20	4	....	wrought	quenched from 2350 F + aged at 1500 F	experimental blades
9	Hastelloy B* (d)	0.05	0.6	0.5	..	...	...	5	30	bal	...	0.35 V	mainly wrought	24 hr at 1900 to 1950 F (e)	gas turbine blades

* some interest has been shown in a nickel base alloy similar to Alloy 7 of Table 90 (Hastelloy C type) (AMS 5530 and 5389) for tail cone stacks and some other parts operating above 1500 F (37); for pertinent data, see (33)

† the low carbon modification is preferred for wrought products and the high carbon for castings

(a) in general, the higher the solution temperature, the higher the elevated temperature strength and the lower the ductility. Therefore, exact solution temperature usually depends on application. Many parts are given an aging treatment at or near service temperature before use. Aging considerably increases the short time tensile strength at 1000 to 1200 F of the cobalt base alloys but the ductility is greatly reduced (32)

(b) heat treatment is generally considered unnecessary for precision cast parts (38, 39)

(c) a small amount has been produced in the form of rolled sheet and has given by far the best experimental results for combustion chamber liners of gas turbines

(d) for corrosion resistant properties of this alloy, see pp 382-384

(e) 72 hr at 1750 F is a more effective stabilizing treatment to minimize aging in service but is too long to be practical in mass production   37)

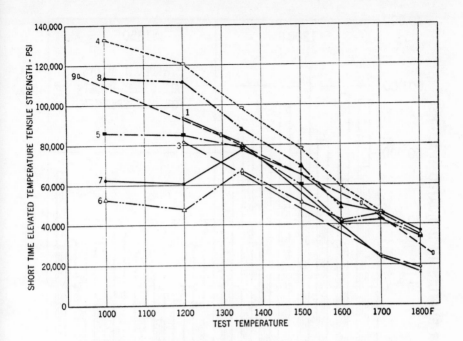

FIG 181 – Short Time Elevated Temperature Tensile Strengths of Some Nonferrous High Temperature Alloys

No.*	Condition	Reference
1 (low C)........	(1200 and 1350 F) hammer forged from 2 in. to 1 in. at 2100 to 1350 F	(40)
	(1700 and 1800 F) 2280 F air cooled...............................	(40)
3..............	(1200 and 1350 F) 20 in. diameter x 3 ¼ in. thick disk; 2300 F water quenched; aged 16 hr at 1400 F	(40)
	(1700 and 1800 F) 2270 F water quenched; aged 16 hr at test temperature	(40)
4..............	2300 F water quenched; aged 16 hr at 1400 F....................	(41)
5..............	(1600 F and lower) precision cast; aged 50 hr at 1350 F.............	(42)
	(1000 and 1200 F) precision cast..............................	(33)
6, 7...........	(1350, 1500 and 1600 F) precision cast; aged 50 hr at 1350 F........	(42)
	(1700 and 1800 F) precision cast..............................	(33)
8..............	2350 F quenched; aged at 1500 F..............................	(35)
9..............	2100 to 2150 F quenched......................................	(43)

* for type composition, see Table 85

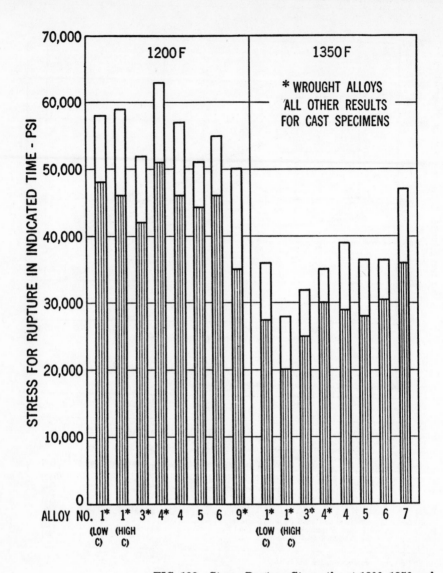

FIG 182 – Stress Rupture Strengths at 1200, 1350 and

No.*	Condition	Reference
1 (low C)........	(1200 and 1350 F) hammer forged from 2 in. to 1 in. at 2100 to 1350 F	(40)
	(1500 F) 2280 F air cooled..	(32)
1 (high C).......	(1200 and 1350 F) 21.73% reduction by rolling at 1700 F; stress relieved at 1200 F	(40)
	(1500 F) 2200 F water quenched; aged 50 hr at 1500 F.............	(42)
2...............	2100 F oil quenched; aged 20 hr at 1500 F +20 hr at 1350 F........	(42)
3...............	(1200 and 1350 F) 20 in. diameter x 3 ¼ in. thick disk; 2300 F water quenched; aged 16 hr at 1400 F	(40)
	(1500 F) 2300 F water quenched; aged 50 hr at 1500 F.............	(42)
4 (wrought)......	(1200 F) 2150 to 2300 F quenched; aged at 1350 to 1500 F.........	(39)
	(1350 F) 2300 F water quenched; aged 16 hr at 1400 F............	(40)
	(1500 F) 2300 F water quenched; aged 50 hr at 1500 F.............	(42)
4 (cast)..........	(1200 and 1350 F) precision cast.................................	(39)
	(1500 F) precision cast; 2300 F water quenched; aged 50 hr at 1500 F	(42)
5...............	(1200 F) precision cast..	(44)

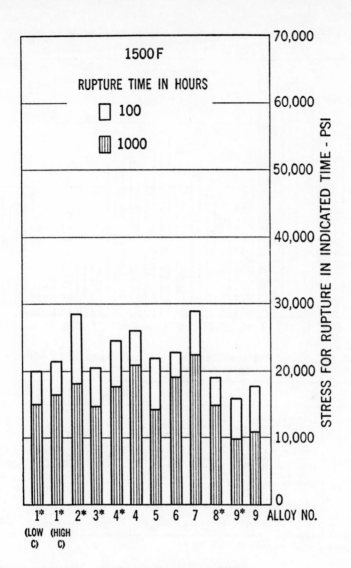

1500 F of Some Nonferrous High Temperature Alloys

No.*	Condition	Reference
5...............	(1350 F) precision cast; aged 50 hr at 1500 F........................	(40)
	(1500 F) precision cast; aged 50 hr at 1500 F........................	(42)
6...............	(1200 F) precision cast..	(44)
	(1350 F) precision cast; aged 50 hr at 1500 F......................	(40)
	(1500 F) precision cast; average of values for specimens aged 50 hr at 1350 F and 50 hr at 1500 F	(42)
7...............	(1350 F) precision cast; aged 50 hr at 1500 F....................	(40)
	(1500 F) precision cast; average of values for specimens aged 50 hr at 1350 F and 50 hr at 1500 F	(42)
8...............	2350 F oil quenched; aged 240 hr at 1500 F........................	(42)
9 (wrought)......	(1200 F) as-wrought..	(32)
	(1500 F) aged at 1700 to 1900 F...................................	(34)
9 (cast)..........	precision cast; 2125 F air cooled; aged 72 hr at 1700 F............	(44)

*for type composition, see Table 85

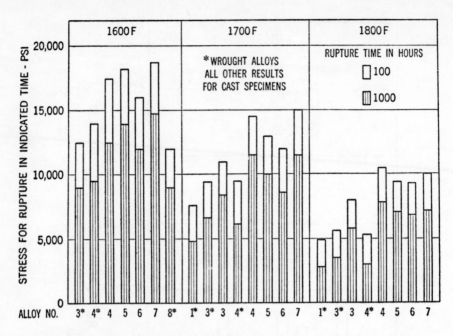

FIG 183 – Stress Rupture Strengths at 1600, 1700 and 1800 F of Some
Nonferrous High Temperature Alloys

No.*	Condition	Reference
1 (low C)........	2280 F air cooled..	(40)
3 (wrought)......	(1600 F) 2300 F water quenched; aged 50 hr at 1600 F.............	(42)
	(1700 and 1800 F) 2270 F water quenched; aged 16 hr at test temperature	(40)
3 (cast)..........	precision cast..	(40)
4 (wrought)......	(1600 F) 2300 F water quenched; aged 50 hr at 1600 F.............	(42)
	(1700 and 1800 F) 2300 F water quenched; aged 16 hr at test temperature	(40)
4 (cast)..........	precision cast..	(1600 F) (44) (1700 and 1800 F) (40)
5, 6, 7..........	(1600 F) precision cast; aged 50 hr at 1600 F......................	(42)
	(1700 and 1800 F) precision cast................................	(40)
8..............	2350 F oil quenched; aged 240 hr at 1500 F......................	(42)

*for type composition, see Table 85

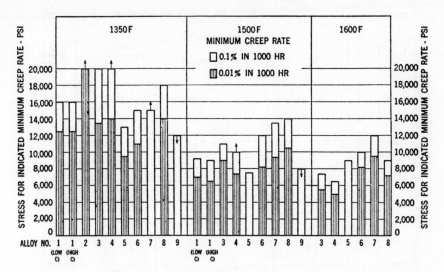

FIG 184 – Creep Strengths of Some Nonferrous High Temperature Alloys

No.*	Condition	Reference
1 (low C)........	2200 F water quenched; aged 50 hr at test temperature.............	(42)
1 (high C).......	(1350 F) 2200 F water quenched; aged 50 hr at 1350 F.............	(42)
	(1500 F) 2200 F oil quenched; aged 50 hr at 1500 F...............	(42)
2...............	2100 F oil quenched; aged 20 hr at 1500 F+20 hr at 1350 F........	(42)
3...............	(1350 and 1500 F) 2300 F water quenched; aged 50 hr at 1350 F....	(42)
	(1600 F) 2300 F water quenched; aged 50 hr at 1600 F.............	(42)
4...............	2300 F water quenched; aged 50 hr at test temperature.............	(42)
5...............	(1350 and 1500 F) precision cast; aged 50 hr at 1500 F............	(42)
	(1600 F) precision cast; aged 50 hr at 1600 F....................	(42)
6, 7............	precision cast; aged 50 hr at test temperature....................	(42)
8...............	(1350 F) 2350 F oil quenched; aged 50 hr at 1350 F...............	(42)
	(1500 and 1600 F) 2350 F oil quenched; aged 240 hr at 1500 F.....	(42)
9...............	aged 24 hr at 1900 F..	(45)

*for type composition, see Table 85

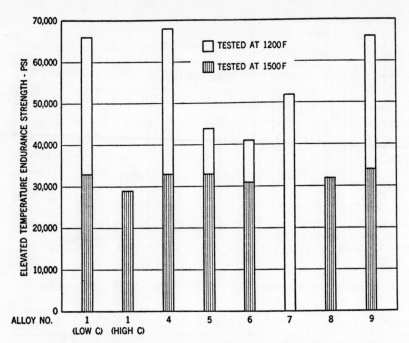

FIG 185 – Elevated Temperature Endurance Strengths of Some Nonferrous High Temperature Alloys (tested in alternate bending for 10^8 cycles)

No.*	Condition	Reference
1 (low C).......	hot worked; aged 50 hr at test temperature......................	(33)
1 (high C).......	2200 F water quenched; aged 50 hr at 1500 F....................	(33)
4..............	2300 F water quenched; aged at 1500 F.........................	(41)
5, 6.............	precision cast...	(33)
7..............	precision cast...	(44)
8..............	2350 F quenched; aged at 1500 F..............................	(35)
9..............	(1200 F) 2000 F water quenched; stress relieved four hours at 1200 F	(33)
	(1500 F) 2050 F air cooled; aged 24 hr at 1900 F	

*for type composition, see Table 85

TABLE 86

"Design Data" for Some Nonferrous High Temperature Alloys at 1500 F

No.*	Condition	Stress in 1000 psi for Indicated Percent Total Deformation in										Ref
		100 hr					1000 hr					
		0.1	0.2	0.5	1.0	(Transition)	0.1	0.2	0.5	1.0	(Transition)	
1 (low C).....	1	7.3	10.6	13.5	14.8	15.2	...	8.2	10.2	11.0	9.0	(42)
....	2	...	22	23.5	25	...	...	15	15.5	16	...	(36)
....	3	10.3	13.2	17.3	18.7	17.6	8.0	10.6	13.1	14.0	14.7	(42)
4 (wrought)...	4	10.0	15.0	19.7	22.1	20.0	...	9.0	14.0	16.7†	14.7	(42)
....	5	...	...	24.4	29.0	27.2	...	...	21.6	22.1	21.9	(42)
4 (cast)........	6	6.0	10.6	15.0	17.8	16.8	...	...	8.9	11.5†	...	(42)
....	7	...	10.3	14.4	19.6	25.2	...	...	11.5	...	19.7	(42)
....	8	...	12.5	15.0	16	16	...	12	13	14.5	14.5	(36)

* for type composition, see Table 85
† estimated

Conditions

1 2200 F water quenched; aged 50 hr at 1500 F
2 Forged bar stock; 2100 F oil quenched; aged 20 hr at 1500 F + 20 hr at 1350 F
3 2300 F water quenched; aged 50 hr at 1350 F
4 2300 F water quenched; some specimens aged 50 hr at 1350 F and some aged 50 hr at 1500 F
5 Precision cast; heat treated and aged
6 Precision cast; aged 50 hr at 1500 F
7 Precision cast (0.505 in. diameter specimens); aged 50 hr at 1500 F
8 Forged bar stock; 2350 F oil quenched; aged 240 hr at 1500 F

TABLE 87

"Design Data" for Some Nonferrous High Temperature Alloys at 1600 F

No.*	Condition	Stress in 1000 psi for Indicated Percent Total Deformation in										Ref
		100 hr					1000 hr					
		0.1	0.2	0.5	1.0	(Transition)	0.1	0.2	0.5	1.0	(Transition)	
3......	1	...	8.9	10.0	10.5	11.2	6.4	7.4	8.4	...	...	(42)
4......	1	5.8	8.7	11.2	11.8	10.0	...	5.7	...	...	...	(42)
7......	2	...	9.8	12.7	16.6	17.4	...	...	10.8†	13.2	14.1	(42)
8......	3	...	9.5	...	11.0	...	...	9.0	...	9.5	...	(36)

* for type composition, see Table 85
† estimated

Conditions
1 2300 F water quenched; aged 50 hr at 1600 F
2 Precision cast; aged 50 hr at 1600 F
3 Forged bar stock; 2350 F oil quenched; aged 240 hr at 1500 F

CONSTANT MODULUS ALLOYS

These alloys, which retain a substantially constant modulus of elasticity at ambient temperatures, have proved their worth for applications such as precision springs and tuning forks. An alloy with about 0.5% molybdenum has found wide use (Table 88). The proportional limit and therefore the working stresses are increased by a combination of a high degree of reduction by cold working and a low temperature stress relief (54).

TABLE 88
Properties of a Constant Modulus Alloy (53)

Analysis:	0.06% C, 0.60% Mn, 0.61% Si, 7.44% Cr, 0.43% Mo, 35.57% Ni, balance iron
Size:	0.0179 in. round
Treatment:	cold drawn 75%; stress relieved two hours at 650 F
Properties:	

Tensile Strength, psi	126,000
0.1% Offset Yield Strength, psi	111,000
Proportional Limit, psi	84,000
Torsional Modulus of Elasticity (Modulus of Rigidity), psi	9.4×10^6
Temperature Coefficient of Modulus of Rigidity per degree F	
0 to 100 F	$+ 1 \times 10^{-6}$
0 to 200 F	-14×10^{-6}

Good results have been reported (55) for watch springs made of a constant modulus iron-molybdenum-nickel alloy with 1% beryllium. A somewhat similar nickel base alloy with about 0.6% beryllium, 15% chromium, 15% iron, 2% manganese, 7% molybdenum and 0.5% silicon has also been used for watch springs (56). With the last two alloys the proportional limit is raised by precipitation hardening rather than cold work. Another watch spring composition (Table 89) is stated to contain 0.03% beryllium, 0.15% carbon, 20% chromium, 40% cobalt, 15% iron, 2% manganese, 7% molybdenum and 15.5% nickel (57).

TABLE 89
Comparison of Properties of Special Watch Spring Alloy and Carbon Spring Steel (57)

	0.03% Be, 0.15% C, 20% Cr, 40% Co, 15% Fe, 2% Mn, 7% Mo, 15.5% Ni	Carbon Spring Steel
Tensile Strength, psi	368,000	341,500
0.02% Offset Yield Strength, psi	280,000	248,000
Proportional Limit, psi	233,000	217,000
Modulus of Elasticity, psi	29.5×10^6	28.5×10^6
Vickers Hardness Number	702	695
Spring Properties (15/0)		
delivered torque (g-cm)	46.2	39.2
wind life (aver)	1036.0	565.0
set after wind life (turns)	3.8	6.0

CORROSION RESISTANT NONFERROUS ALLOYS

Table 90 gives the compositions of some nickel base corrosion resistant alloys.* Under strongly oxidizing conditions, such as in nitric acid, Alloys 1 to 7 with chromium are most satisfactory. In non-oxidizing acids, the higher molybdenum alloys generally have the highest corrosion resistance because the passivating effect of molybdenum on nickel becomes evident at about 15% molybdenum (Figure 186). Alloys 6 and 7, for example, are used in wet chlorine

TABLE 90
Nickel Base Corrosion Resistant Alloys

No.	Compositions *											Form
	%C	%Mn	%Si	%Be	%Co	%Cr	%Cu	%Fe	%Mo	%V	%W	
1	....	2	...	1	3	12	..	14	3	...	3	wrought
2	0.25	0.5	4	..	..	23	5	8	4	...	2	cast
3	....	1	1	..	..	24	8	3	4	...	2	cast
4	0.07	...	...	..	..	21	6	..	5	...	2	cast
5	....	2	...	1	..	15	..	15	7	...	..	wrought
6	0.10	1	1	..	..	18	..	2	18	...	..	cast
7	0.10	1	1	..	..	17	..	6	19	...	5	cast, wrought
8	0.10	1.5	0.3	..	..	..	..	20	21	0.4	..	cast, wrought
9	0.10	2	1	..	..	..	..	22	22	...	..	cast, wrought
10	0.10	1	0.3	..	..	..	..	10	27.5	0.4	..	cast, wrought
11**	0.10	1	1	..	..	..	..	6	32	...	..	cast, wrought

* balance nickel
** for high temperature properties of a similar alloy, see pp 320, 322-325, 327, 328

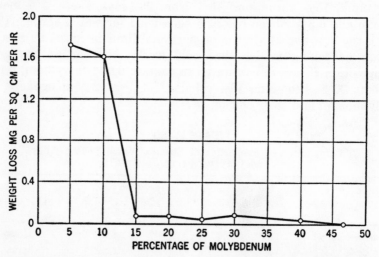

FIG 186 – Effect of Molybdenum on the Corrosion Resistance of Molybdenum-Nickel Alloys (10% hydrochloric acid at 158 F) (20)

* There are a few very high alloy, corrosion resistant alloys with iron as the largest constituent although under 50% (for example, cast alloys with about 25% chromium, 5% molybdenum, 35% nickel and balance iron and with 20% chromium, 2 to 4% copper, 2 to 4% molybdenum, 29% nickel and balance iron). These alloys are generally used where the higher iron alloys (see pp 141-143 and 245-247) are not adequate to resist severe corrosive influences. Likewise, the chromium-cobalt-molybdenum alloy mentioned under prosthetic alloys (p 334) is sometimes used for other corrosion resisting purposes.

gas and in hydrochloric acid at temperatures close to room temperature. Alloys 8 and 9 with higher molybdenum withstand hydrochloric acid at all temperatures up to about 160 F, while the highest molybdenum alloys (No. 10 and No. 11) are outstanding for their resistance to all concentrations of hydrochloric acid at all temperatures (Figure 187).

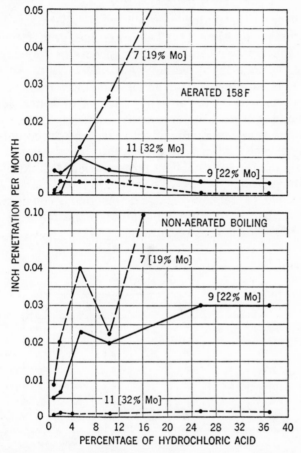

FIG 187 – Corrosion Resistance of Alloys 7, 9 and 11 in Hydrochloric Acid (for type composition, see Table 90) (20)

The field of application of some of these alloys can be extended by suitable hardening treatments. The alloys containing beryllium can be hardened to 320 to 450 Brinell by a precipitation hardening treatment of one to four hours at about 950 F (56). Alloy 7 can be hardened to Rockwell C 35 to 40 by air cooling from about 2200 F and holding for 8 to 16 hours at about 1600 F. Two treatments have been given for hardening Alloy 11 to Rockwell C 40 to 50: 1) rapid cooling from about 2125 F and holding a week at about 1400 F (58) and 2) water quenching from 2050 F and holding about ten hours at 1300 F (59). The loss in corrosion resistance as the result of the hardening treatments depends on the corroding conditions and may range from nil to considerable (58, 59).

PROSTHETIC ALLOYS

Non-toxicity is the major requirement of alloys for dental and surgical prostheses. Alloy 1* (Table 91) has been found to have much less tendency to pit during long exposure in the body than the same alloy without molybdenum (60). Because of this relative inertness, it is satisfactory for small appliances such as wire and screws (60) as well as for internal fixation of bones (61). Alloy 2** has found a wide use for dentures and all types of surgical appliances and prostheses (61, 62, 63). It is produced only as castings and apparently cannot be drawn into wire. Alloy 3 has been used successfully for external dental restorations but shows evidence of toxicity in buried parts (64). The wrought modification, Alloy 4**, has been stated to be non-toxic and has found consideration for applications where a certain amount of malleability is desirable (64). Alloy 5 is for dental restorations (65).

TABLE 91
Prosthetic Alloys

| No. | Compositions | | | | | | | | Condition in which used for Prosthetic Appliances |
	%Be	%C	%Co	%Cr	%Fe	%Mo	%Ni	%W	
1	...	0.09	..	18	bal	2.5	13	..	mainly wrought
2	...	....	65	30	...	5	....	..	precision cast
3	1.5	....	29	28	...	6	35.5	..	precision cast
4	...	....	30	28	...	6	36	..	wrought
5	...	....	..	15	bal	18.5	56	4	precision cast

* See Section V for a discussion of this alloy for general-purpose corrosion resistance and Section VI for its use at elevated temperatures.
** See pp 320, 321, 328-329 for the use of similar alloys at high temperatures.

Section X — Bibliography

(1) G. W. Elmen "Magnetic Alloys of Iron, Nickel and Cobalt" Bell System Technical Journal, Vol 15 (1936)

(2) O. L. Boothby and R. M. Bozorth "A New Magnetic Material of High Permeability" Journal of Applied Physics, Vol 18 (1947)

(3) H. Neumann "New Magnetic Alloy '1040' " Archiv für Technisches Messen Z 913-5 (1934)

(4) T. D. Yensen "Magnetically Soft Materials" Transactions, ASM, Vol 27 (1939)

(5) E. E. Schumacher "Magnetic Powders and Production of Cores for Inductance Coils" Powder Metallurgy, published by the ASM (1942)

(6) S. E. Buckley "Nickel-Iron Alloy Dust Cores" Section C-8 of Symposium on Powder Metallurgy, Iron and Steel Institute Special Report No. 38, published by the Iron and Steel Institute, London, England (1947)

(7) A. G. Ganz "Application of Thin Permalloy Tape for Wide-Band Telephone and Pulse Transformers" Transactions, AIEE, Vol 65 (Electrical Engineering) (1946)

(8) R. M. C. Greenidge "Loading Coils with Cores of Molybdenum Permalloy" Bell Laboratories Record, Vol 20 (1942)

(9) V. E. Legg and F. J. Given "Compressed Powdered Molybdenum Permalloy for High Quality Inductance Coils" Bell System Technical Journal, Vol 19 (1940)

(10) L. C. Hicks "Nickel-Iron Alloys for Magnetic Circuits" Electrical Manufacturing, Vol 37 (1946)

(11) R. L. Sanford "Permanent Magnets" Circular C 448, published by the National Bureau of Standards (1944)

(12) Metals Handbook, published by the ASM (1948)

(13) Special Alloy and Tool Steels, published by Wm. Jessop and Sons, Limited and the J. J. Saville and Company, Limited, Sheffield, England (1945)

(14) N. F. Bolkhovitinov, Metallovedenie i Termicheskaya Obrabotka Stali, published by Gosudarstvennoe Nauchno-Tekhnicheskoe Izdatel'stvo Literatury po chernoi i tsvetnoi Metallurgii, Moscow, U.S.S.R. (1946)

(15) K. S. Seljesater and B. A. Rogers "Magnetic and Mechanical Hardness of Dispersion Hardened Iron Alloys" Transactions, ASST, Vol 19 (1932)

(16) W. E. Ruder "Permanent Magnet Steels" Iron Age, Vol 157 (1946)

(17) E. I. Shobert II "Calculation of Electrical Contacts under Ideal Conditions" ASTM Standards on Electrical-Heating and Resistance Alloys with Related Information, published by the ASTM (1946)

(18) Contacts and Contact Materials, published by the P. R. Mallory & Company Inc., Indianapolis, Indiana (1946)

(19) E. M. Wise "Nickel in the Radio Industry" Proceedings of the Institute of Radio Engineers, Vol 25 (1937)

(20) F. T. McCurdy "Nickel-Molybdenum-Iron and Related Alloys – Their Physical and Corrosion-Resistant Properties" Proceedings, ASTM, Vol 39 (1939)

(21) Tungsten, Molybdenum and Wire Products, published by the North American Philips Company, Inc., Dobbs Ferry, New York

(22) J. H. Partridge "Glass-to-Metal Joints" Sheet Metal Industries, Vol 24 (1947)

(23) J. Kurtz "Molybdenum-Iron Alloys" Powder Metallurgy, published by the ASM (1942)

(24) F. R. Hensel and J. W. Wiggs "Special Metals in the Electrical Industry" Electrical Engineering, Vol 62 (1943)

(25) Anonymous "Bi-Metallic Strip" Metal Industry, Vol 68 (1946)

(26) J. G. Bennett and M. Pirani "Report on the Institute of Fuel Symposium on Gas Temperature Measurement" Temperature, Its Measurement and Control in Science and Industry, published by the Reinhold Publishing Corporation (1941)

(27) H. Cornelius "Effect of Composition on the Properties of Hard Surfacing Alloys" Archiv für das Eisenhüttenwesen, Vol 15 (1941)

(28) M. Schmidt, W. Lamarche and E. Kauhausen "Lowering of the Cobalt Content in Hard Surfacing Alloys" Archiv für das Eisenhüttenwesen, Vol 14 (1941)

(29) J. A. Cunningham "How to Select Wear-Resisting Alloys for Welding" Welding Journal, Vol 25 (1946)

(30) M. Riddihough "Hard Surfacing by Welding" Transactions of the Institute of Welding, Vol 8 (1945)

(31) G. E. Wilson "Protecting Mill Equipment with Hard Facing" Iron and Steel Engineer, Vol 23 (1946)

(32) F. S. Badger, Jr. and F. C. Kroft, Jr. "Cobalt-Base and Nickel-Base Alloys for Ultrahigh Temperature" Metal Progress, Vol 52 (1947)

(33) W. O. Sweeny "Haynes Alloys for High-Temperature Service" Transactions, ASME, Vol 69 (1947)

(34) W. L. Badger "Metallurgical Development of Materials for Turbosuperchargers and Aircraft Gas Turbines" Iron Age, Vol 158 (1946)

(35) R. B. Gordon "Precipitation Hardened Super Heat Resistant Alloys" Steel Processing, Vol 32 (1946)

(36) H. Scott and R. B. Gordon "Precipitation-Hardened Alloys for Gas-Turbine Service" Transactions, ASME, Vol 69 (1947)

(37) F. S. Badger, Jr. and W. O. Sweeny, Jr. "Metallurgy of High-Temperature Alloys used on Current Gas Turbine Designs" Symposium on Materials for Gas Turbines, published by the ASTM (1946)

(38) J. B. Henry, Jr. "Characteristics of Three High Temperature Alloys" Iron Age, Vol 159 (1947)
(39) T. Y. Wilson "High Strength, High Temperature Alloy S-816" Materials and Methods, Vol 24 (1946)
(40) J. W. Freeman, E. E. Reynolds and A. E. White "High-Temperature Alloys Developed for Aircraft Turbosuperchargers and Gas Turbines" Symposium on Materials for Gas Turbines, published by the ASTM (1946)
(41) Anonymous "Heat and Corrosion Resistant High Temperature Alloys" Product Engineering, Vol 17 (1946)
(42) H. C. Cross and W. F. Simmons "Heat-Resisting Metals for Gas-Turbine Parts" Symposium on Materials for Gas Turbines, published by the ASTM (1946)
(43) B. E. Field "Nickel-Molybdenum-Iron and Nickel-Molybdenum-Chromium-Iron Alloys" Metals Handbook, published by the ASM (1939)
(44) "Heat Resistant Castings" Metals Handbook, published by the ASM (1948)
(45) "Wrought Heat Resisting Alloys" Metals Handbook, published by the ASM (1948)
(46) N. J. Grant "High Temperature Alloys" Iron Age, Vol 157 (1946)
(47) N. J. Grant "Structural Variations in Gas Turbine Alloys Revealed by the Stress Rupture Test" Transactions, ASM, Vol 39 (1947)
(48) N. J. Grant "The Effect of Composition and Structural Changes on the Rupture Properties of Certain Heat Resistant Alloys at 1500 F" Transactions, ASM, Vol 39 (1947)
(49) F. S. Badger, H. C. Cross, C. T. Evans, Jr., R. Franks, R. B. Johnson, N. L. Mochel and G. Mohling "Superalloys for High Temperature Service in Gas Turbines and Jet Engines" Metal Progress, Vol 50 (1946)
(50) W. O. Binder "Alloys for High Temperature Service" Iron Age, Vol 158 (1946)
(51) N. J. Grant "The Stress Rupture and Creep Properties of Heat Resistant Gas Turbine Alloys" Transactions, ASM, Vol 39 (1947)
(52) W. O. Sweeny "Precision-Cast Parts of High Temperature Alloys" Product Engineering, Vol 17 (1946)
(53) N. B. Pilling and A. M. Talbot "Dispersion Hardening Alloys of Nickel and Iron-Nickel-Titanium" Age Hardening of Metals, published by the ASM (1940)
(54) M. F. Sayre and A. V. de Forest "New Spring Formulas and New Materials for Precision Spring Scales" Transactions, ASME, Vol 58 (1936)
(55) W. Rohn "Use of Beryllium Alloys in Clocks" Zeitschrift des Vereines Deutscher Ingenieure, Vol 79 (1935)
(56) G. T. Motock "Vacuum Melting in Germany" Iron Age, Vol 158 (1946)
(57) Anonymous "New Strong, Nonmagnetic Spring Material Has High Corrosion Resistance" Materials and Methods, Vol 25 (1947)
(58) Hastelloy High-Strength, Nickel-Base, Corrosion-Resistant Alloys, published by the Haynes Stellite Company, Kokomo, Indiana (1940)
(59) M. G. Fontana "New Alloys for Severe Corrosion Services" Chemical Engineering, Vol 53 (1946)
(60) C. S. Venable and W. G. Stuck "A General Consideration of Metals for Buried Appliances in Surgery" International Abstract of Surgery (Surgery, Gynecology and Obstetrics), Vol 76 (1943)
(61) J. A. Key "Stainless Steel and Vitallium in Internal Fixation of Bone" Archives of Surgery, Vol 43 (1941)
(62) C. S. Venable and W. G. Stuck "Three Years' Experience with Vitallium in Bone Surgery" Annals of Surgery, Vol 114 (1941)
(63) C. S. Venable and W. G. Stuck "Clinical Uses of Vitallium" Annals of Surgery, Vol 117 (1943)
(64) E. Campbell, A. Meirowsky and V. Tompkins "Studies on the Use of Metals in Surgery. Experiments on the Use of Ticonium in Cranial Repair" Annals of Surgery, Vol 116 (1942)
(65) G. C. Paffenbarger, H. J. Caul and G. Dickson "Base Metal Alloys for Oral Restorations" Journal of the American Dental Association, Vol 30 (1943)

APPENDIX A

CHEMICAL COMPOSITION RANGES FOR ALLOY ENGINEERING STEELS IN THE U. S. A.

Regular AISI-SAE Steels (Standard Steels, issued by the AISI (October 30, 1947))

AISI	%C	%Mn	%Si	%P†	%S†	%Cr	%Mo	%Ni	%Other	SAE
1320	0.18/0.23	1.60/1.90	0.20/0.35	0.040	0.040	....	....	....	......	1320
1321	0.17/0.22	1.80/2.10	0.20/0.35	0.050	0.050	....	....	....	......	....
1330	0.28/0.33	1.60/1.90	0.20/0.35	0.040	0.040	....	....	....	......	1330
1335	0.33/0.38	1.60/1.90	0.20/0.35	0.040	0.040	....	....	....	......	1335
1340	0.38/0.43	1.60/1.90	0.20/0.35	0.040	0.040	....	....	....	......	1340
2317	0.15/0.20	0.40/0.60	0.20/0.35	0.040	0.040	....	....	3.25/3.75	.....	2317
2330	0.28/0.33	0.60/0.80	0.20/0.35	0.040	0.040	....	....	3.25/3.75	.....	2330
2335	0.33/0.38	0.60/0.80	0.20/0.35	0.040	0.040	....	....	3.25/3.75	.....	....
2340	0.38/0.43	0.70/0.90	0.20/0.35	0.040	0.040	....	....	3.25/3.75	.....	2340
2345	0.43/0.48	0.70/0.90	0.20/0.35	0.040	0.040	....	....	3.25/3.75	......	2345
E 2512	0.09/0.14	0.45/0.60*	0.20/0.35	0.025	0.025	....	....	4.75/5.25	......	2512
2515	0.12/0.17	0.40/0.60	0.20/0.35	0.040	0.040	....	....	4.75/5.25	......	2515
E 2517	0.15/0.20	0.45/0.60*	0.20/0.35	0.025	0.025	....	....	4.75/5.25	......	2517
3115	0.13/0.18	0.40/0.60	0.20/0.35	0.040	0.040	0.55/0.75	....	1.10/1.40	......	3115
3120	0.17/0.22	0.60/0.80	0.20/0.35	0.040	0.040	0.55/0.75	....	1.10/1.40	......	3120
3130	0.28/0.33	0.60/0.80	0.20/0.35	0.040	0.040	0.55/0.75	....	1.10/1.40	......	3130
3135	0.33/0.38	0.60/0.80	0.20/0.35	0.040	0.040	0.55/0.75	....	1.10/1.40	......	3135
3140	0.38/0.43	0.70/0.90	0.20/0.35	0.040	0.040	0.55/0.75	....	1.10/1.40	......	3140
3141	0.38/0.43	0.70/0.90	0.20/0.35	0.040	0.040	0.70/0.90	....	1.10/1.40	......	3141
3145	0.43/0.48	0.70/0.90	0.20/0.35	0.040	0.040	0.70/0.90	....	1.10/1.40	......	3145
3150	0.48/0.53	0.70/0.90	0.20/0.35	0.040	0.040	0.70/0.90	....	1.10/1.40	......	3150
E 3310	0.08/0.13	0.45/0.60*	0.20/0.35	0.025	0.025	1.40/1.75	....	3.25/3.75	......	3310
E 3316	0.14/0.19	0.45/0.60*	0.20/0.35	0.025	0.025	1.40/1.75	....	3.25/3.75	......	3316
4017	0.15/0.20	0.70/0.90	0.20/0.35	0.040	0.040	....	0.20/0.30	....	......	4017
4023	0.20/0.25	0.70/0.90	0.20/0.35	0.040	0.040	....	0.20/0.30	....	......	4023
4024	0.20/0.25	0.70/0.90	0.20/0.35	0.040	0.035/0.050	....	0.20/0.30	....	......	4024
4027	0.25/0.30	0.70/0.90	0.20/0.35	0.040	0.040	....	0.20/0.30	....	......	4027
4028	0.25/0.30	0.70/0.90	0.20/0.35	0.040	0.035/0.050	....	0.20/0.30	....	......	4028
4032	0.30/0.35	0.70/0.90	0.20/0.35	0.040	0.040	....	0.20/0.30	....	....•..	4032
4037	0.35/0.40	0.70/0.90	0.20/0.35	0.040	0.040	....	0.20/0.30	....	......	4037
4042	0.40/0.45	0.70/0.90	0.20/0.35	0.040	0.040	....	0.20/0.30	....	......	4042
4047	0.45/0.50	0.70/0.90	0.20/0.35	0.040	0.040	....	0.20/0.30	....	......	4047
4053	0.50/0.56	0.75/1.00	0.20/0.35	0.040	0.040	....	0.20/0.30	....	......	4053
4063	0.60/0.67	0.75/1.00	0.20/0.35	0.040	0.040	....	0.20/0.30	....	......	4063
4068	0.63/0.70	0.75/1.00	0.20/0.35	0.040	0.040	....	0.20/0.30	....	......	4068
4130	0.28/0.33	0.40/0.60	0.20/0.35	0.040	0.040	0.80/1.10	0.15/0.25	....	....	4130
E 4132	0.30/0.35	0.40/0.60	0.20/0.35	0.025	0.025	0.80/1.10	0.18/0.25**	....	....	....
E 4135	0.33/0.38	0.70/0.90	0.20/0.35	0.025	0.025	0.80/1.10	0.18/0.25**	....	....	....
4137	0.35/0.40	0.70/0.90	0.20/0.35	0.040	0.040	0.80/1.10	0.15/0.25	....	....	4137
E 4137	0.35/0.40	0.70/0.90	0.20/0.35	0.025	0.025	0.80/1.10	0.18/0.25	....	....	....
4140	0.38/0.43	0.75/1.00	0.20/0.35	0.040	0.040	0.80/1.10	0.15/0.25	....	....	4140
4142	0.40/0.45	0.75/1.00	0.20/0.35	0.040	0.040	0.80/1.10	0.15/0.25	....	....	....
4145	0.43/0.48	0.75/1.00	0.20/0.35	0.040	0.040	0.80/1.10	0.15/0.25	....	....	4145
4147	0.45/0.50	0.75/1.00	0.20/0.35	0.040	0.040	0.80/1.10	0.15/0.25	....	....	....
4150	0.48/0.53	0.75/1.00	0.20/0.35	0.040	0.040	0.80/1.10	0.15/0.25	....	....	4150
4317	0.15/0.20	0.45/0.65	0.20/0.35	0.040	0.040	0.40/0.60	0.20/0.30	1.65/2.00	......	4317
4320	0.17/0.22	0.45/0.65	0.20/0.35	0.040	0.040	0.40/0.60	0.20/0.30	1.65/2.00	......	4320
4337	0.35/0.40	0.60/0.80	0.20/0.35	0.040	0.040	0.70/0.90	0.20/0.30	1.65/2.00	......	....
4340	0.38/0.43	0.60/0.80	0.20/0.35	0.040	0.040	0.70/0.90	0.20/0.30	1.65/2.00	......	4340
4608	0.06/0.11	0.25/0.45	0.25 max	0.040	0.040	....	0.15/0.25	1.40/1.75	......	4608
4615	0.13/0.18	0.45/0.65	0.20/0.35	0.040	0.040	....	0.20/0.30	1.65/1.75	......	4615
E 4617	0.15/0.20	0.45/0.65	0.20/0.35	0.025	0.025	....	0.20/0.27***	1.65/2.00	......	4617
4620	0.17/0.22	0.45/0.65	0.20/0.35	0.040	0.040	....	0.20/0.30	1.65/2.00	......	4620
X 4620	0.18/0.23	0.50/0.70	0.20/0.35	0.040	0.040	....	0.20/0.30	1.65/2.00	......	X 4620
E 4620	0.17/0.22	0.45/0.65	0.20/0.35	0.025	0.025	....	0.20/0.27	1.65/2.00	......	....
4621	0.18/0.23	0.70/0.90	0.20/0.35	0.040	0.040	....	0.20/0.30	1.65/2.00	......	4621
4640	0.38/0.43	0.60/0.80	0.20/0.35	0.040	0.040	....	0.20/0.30	1.65/2.00	......	4640
E 4640	0.38/0.43	0.60/0.80	0.20/0.35	0.025	0.025	....	0.20/0.27	1.65/2.00	......	....
4812	0.10/0.15	0.40/0.60	0.20/0.35	0.040	0.040	....	0.20/0.30	3.25/3.75	......	4812
4815	0.13/0.18	0.40/0.60	0.20/0.35	0.040	0.040	....	0.20/0.30	3.25/3.75	......	4815
4817	0.15/0.20	0.40/0.60	0.20/0.35	0.040	0.040	....	0.20/0.30	3.25/3.75	......	4817
4820	0.18/0.23	0.50/0.70	0.20/0.35	0.040	0.040	....	0.20/0.30	3.25/3.75	......	4820

APPENDIX A – (Continued)

AISI	%C	%Mn	%Si	%P†	%S†	%Cr	%Mo	%Ni	%Other	SAE
5045	0.43/0.48	0.70/0.90	0.20/0.35	0.040	0.040	0.55/0.75	....	....	......	5045
5046	0.43/0.50	0.75/1.00	0.20/0.35	0.040	0.040	0.20/0.35	....	....	......	5046
5120	0.17/0.22	0.70/0.90	0.20/0.35	0.040	0.040	0.70/0.90	....	....	......	5120
5130	0.28/0.33	0.70/0.90	0.20/0.35	0.040	0.040	0.80/1.10	....	....	......	5130
5132	0.30/0.35	0.60/0.80	0.20/0.35	0.040	0.040	0.80/1.05	....	....	......	5132
5135	0.33/0.38	0.60/0.80	0.20/0.35	0.040	0.040	0.80/1.05	....	....	......	5135
5140	0.38/0.43	0.70/0.90	0.20/0.35	0.040	0.040	0.70/0.90	....	....	......	5140
5145	0.43/0.48	0.70/0.90	0.20/0.35	0.040	0.040	0.70/0.90	....	....	......	5145
5147	0.45/0.52	0.75/1.00	0.20/0.35	0.040	0.040	0.90/1.20	....	....	......	5147
5150	0.48/0.53	0.70/0.90	0.20/0.35	0.040	0.040	0.70/0.90	....	....	......	5150
5152	0.48/0.55	0.70/0.90	0.20/0.35	0.040	0.040	0.90/1.20	....	....	......	5152
E 50100	0.95/1.10	0.25/0.45	0.20/0.35	0.025	0.025	0.40/0.60	....	....	......	50100
E 51100	0.95/1.10	0.25/0.45	0.20/0.35	0.025	0.025	0.90/1.15	....	....	......	51100
E 52100	0.95/1.10	0.25/0.45	0.20/0.35	0.025	0.025	1.30/1.60	....	....	..v..	52100
6120	0.17/0.22	0.70/0.90	0.20/0.35	0.040	0.040	0.70/0.90	....	....	0.10 min	....
6145	0.43/0.48	0.70/0.90	0.20/0.35	0.040	0.040	0.80/1.10	....	....	0.15 min	....
6150	0.48/0.53	0.70/0.90	0.20/0.35	0.040	0.040	0.80/1.10	....	....	0.15 min	6150
6152	0.48/0.55	0.70/0.90	0.20/0.35	0.040	0.040	0.80/1.10	....	....	0.10 min	....
8615	0.13/0.18	0.70/0.90	0.20/0.35	0.040	0.040	0.40/0.60	0.15/0.25	0.40/0.70	......	8615
8617	0.15/0.20	0.70/0.90	0.20/0.35	0.040	0.040	0.40/0.60	0.15/0.25	0.40/0.70	......	8617
8620	0.18/0.23	0.70/0.90	0.20/0.35	0.040	0.040	0.40/0.60	0.15/0.25	0.40/0.70	......	8620
8622	0.20/0.25	0.70/0.90	0.20/0.35	0.040	0.040	0.40/0.60	0.15/0.25	0.40/0.70	......	8622
8625	0.23/0.28	0.70/0.90	0.20/0.35	0.040	0.040	0.40/0.60	0.15/0.25	0.40/0.70	......	8625
8627	0.25/0.30	0.70/0.90	0.20/0.35	0.040	0.040	0.40/0.60	0.15/0.25	0.40/0.70	......	8627
8630	0.28/0.33	0.70/0.90	0.20/0.35	0.040	0.040	0.40/0.60	0.15/0.25	0.40/0.70	......	8630
8632	0.30/0.35	0.70/0.90	0.20/0.35	0.040	0.040	0.40/0.60	0.15/0.25	0.40/0.70	......	8632
8635	0.33/0.38	0.75/1.00	0.20/0.35	0.040	0.040	0.40/0.60	0.15/0.25	0.40/0.70	......	8635
8637	0.35/0.40	0.75/1.00	0.20/0.35	0.040	0.040	0.40/0.60	0.15/0.25	0.40/0.70	......	8637
8640	0.38/0.43	0.75/1.00	0.20/0.35	0.040	0.040	0.40/0.60	0.15/0.25	0.40/0.70	......	8640
8641	0.38/0.43	0.75/1.00	0.20/0.35	0.040	0.040/0.060	0.40/0.60	0.15/0.25	0.40/0.70	......	8641
8642	0.40/0.45	0.75/1.00	0.20/0.35	0.040	0.040	0.40/0.60	0.15/0.25	0.40/0.70	......	8642
8645	0.43/0.48	0.75/1.00	0.20/0.35	0.040	0.040	0.40/0.60	0.15/0.25	0.40/0.70	......	8645
8647	0.45/0.50	0.75/1.00	0.20/0.35	0.040	0.040	0.40/0.60	0.15/0.25	0.40/0.70	......	8647
8650	0.48/0.53	0.75/1.00	0.20/0.35	0.040	0.040	0.40/0.60	0.15/0.25	0.40/0.70	......	8650
8653	0.50/0.56	0.75/1.00	0.20/0.35	0.040	0.040	0.50/0.80	0.15/0.25	0.40/0.70	......	8653
8655	0.50/0.60	0.75/1.00	0.20/0.35	0.040	0.040	0.40/0.60	0.15/0.25	0.40/0.70	......	8655
8660	0.55/0.60	0.75/1.00	0.20/0.35	0.040	0.040	0.40/0.60	0.15/0.25	0.40/0.70	......	8660
8719	0.18/0.23	0.60/0.80	0.20/0.35	0.040	0.040	0.40/0.60	0.20/0.30	0.40/0.70	......	....
8720	0.18/0.23	0.70/0.90	0.20/0.35	0.040	0.040	0.40/0.60	0.20/0.30	0.40/0.70	......	8720
8735	0.33/0.38	0.75/1.00	0.20/0.35	0.040	0.040	0.40/0.60	0.20/0.30	0.40/0.70	......	8735
8740	0.38/0.43	0.75/1.00	0.20/0.35	0.040	0.040	0.40/0.60	0.20/0.30	0.40/0.70	......	8740
8742	0.40/0.45	0.75/1.00	0.20/0.35	0.040	0.040	0.40/0.60	0.20/0.30	0.40/0.70	......	....
8745	0.43/0.48	0.75/1.00	0.20/0.35	0.040	0.040	0.40/0.60	0.20/0.30	0.40/0.70	......	8745
8747	0.45/0.50	0.75/1.00	0.20/0.35	0.040	0.040	0.40/0.60	0.20/0.30	0.40/0.70	......	....
8750	0.48/0.53	0.75/1.00	0.20/0.35	0.040	0.040	0.40/0.60	0.20/0.30	0.40/0.70	......	8750
9255	0.50/0.60	0.70/0.95	1.80/2.20	0.040	0.040	....	....	....	......	9255
9260	0.55/0.65	0.70/1.00	1.80/2.20	0.040	0.040	....	....	....	......	9260
9261	0.55/0.65	0.75/1.00	1.80/2.20	0.040	0.040	0.10/0.25	....	....	......	9261
9262	0.55/0.65	0.75/1.00	1.80/2.20	0.040	0.040	0.25/0.40	....	....	......	9262
E 9310	0.08/0.13	0.45/0.65	0.20/0.35	0.025	0.025	1.00/1.40	0.08/0.15	3.00/3.50	......	9310
E 9315	0.13/0.18	0.45/0.65	0.20/0.35	0.025	0.025	1.00/1.40	0.08/0.15	3.00/3.50	......	9315
E 9317	0.15/0.20	0.45/0.65	0.20/0.35	0.025	0.025	1.00/1.40	0.08/0.15	3.00/3.50	......	9317
9437	0.35/0.40	0.90/1.20	0.20/0.35	0.040	0.040	0.30/0.50	0.08/0.15	0.30/0.60	......	9437
9440	0.38/0.43	0.90/1.20	0.20/0.35	0.040	0.040	0.30/0.50	0.08/0.15	0.30/0.60	......	9440
9442	0.40/0.45	1.00/1.30	0.20/0.35	0.040	0.040	0.30/0.50	0.08/0.15	0.30/0.60	......	9442
9445	0.43/0.48	1.00/1.30	0.20/0.35	0.040	0.040	0.30/0.50	0.08/0.15	0.30/0.60	......	9445
9747	0.45/0.50	0.50/0.80	0.20/0.35	0.040	0.040	0.10/0.25	0.15/0.25	0.40/0.70	......	9747
9763	0.60/0.67	0.50/0.80	0.20/0.35	0.040	0.040	0.10/0.25	0.15/0.25	0.40/0.70	......	9763
9840	0.38/0.43	0.70/0.90	0.20/0.35	0.040	0.040	0.70/0.90	0.20/0.30	0.85/1.15	......	9840
9845	0.43/0.48	0.70/0.90	0.20/0.35	0.040	0.040	0.70/0.90	0.20/0.30	0.85/1.15	......	9845
9850	0.48/0.53	0.70/0.90	0.20/0.35	0.040	0.040	0.70/0.90	0.20/0.30	0.85/1.15	......	9850

* %Mn =0.40/0.60 for open hearth steel
** %Mo =0.15/0.25 for open hearth steel
*** %Mo =0.20/0.30 for open hearth steel
† maximum except where a range is indicated
Note 1—The ranges and limits in this table apply only to material not exceeding 200 sq in. in cross-sectional area, or 18 in. in width, or 10,000 lb in weight, per piece.
Note 2—Grades shown in the above list with prefix letter E are manufactured by the basic electric furnace process. All others are normally manufactured by the basic open hearth process but may be manufactured by the basic electric furnace process with adjustments in phosphorus and sulphur.
Note 3—The chemical ranges and limits shown are subject to the standard permissible variations for check analysis.

APPENDIX A – (Continued)

"H" STEELS (Contributions to the Metallurgy of Steel — No. 11, Hardenability of Alloy Steels, issued by the AISI (June, 1947) and supplement of September 20, 1947)

AISI or SAE	%C	%Mn	%Si	%Cr	%Mo	%Ni	%Other
1320H	0.17/0.24	1.50/2.00	0.20/0.35	....	....	....	....
1330H	0.27/0.34	1.50/2.00	0.20/0.35	....	....	....	....
1335H	0.32/0.39	1.50/2.00	0.20/0.35	....	....	....	....
1340H	0.37/0.45	1.50/2.00	0.20/0.35	....	....	....	....
2512H	0.08/0.15	0.35/0.65	0.20/0.35	....	....	4.70/5.30	....
2515H	0.11/0.18	0.35/0.65	0.20/0.35	....	....	4.70/5.30	....
2517H	0.14/0.21	0.35/0.65	0.20/0.35	....	....	4.70/5.30	....
3140H	0.37/0.45	0.60/0.95	0.20/0.35	0.50/0.80	....	1.00/1.50	....
3310H	0.07/0.14	0.35/0.65	0.20/0.35	1.35/1.75	....	3.20/3.80	....
3316H	0.13/0.20	0.35/0.65	0.20/0.35	1.35/1.75	....	3.20/3.80	....
4130H	0.27/0.34	0.35/0.65	0.20/0.35	0.80/1.15	0.15/0.25	....	....
4132H	0.30/0.37	0.35/0.65	0.20/0.35	0.80/1.15	0.15/0.25	....	....
4135H	0.32/0.39	0.60/0.95	0.20/0.35	0.80/1.15	0.15/0.25	....	....
4137H	0.35/0.43	0.60/0.95	0.20/0.35	0.80/1.15	0.15/0.25	....	....
4140H	0.37/0.45	0.70/1.05	0.20/0.35	0.80/1.15	0.15/0.25	....	....
4142H	0.40/0.48	0.70/1.05	0.20/0.35	0.80/1.15	0.15/0.25	....	....
4145H	0.42/0.50	0.70/1.05	0.20/0.35	0.80/1.15	0.15/0.25	....	....
4147H	0.44/0.52	0.70/1.05	0.20/0.35	0.80/1.15	0.15/0.25	....	....
4150H	0.46/0.54	0.70/1.05	0.20/0.35	0.80/1.15	0.15/0.25	....	....
4317H	0.14/0.21	0.40/0.70	0.20/0.35	0.35/0.65	0.20/0.30	1.50/2.00	....
4320H	0.16/0.23	0.40/0.70	0.20/0.35	0.35/0.65	0.20/0.30	1.50/2.00	....
4340H	0.37/0.45	0.60/0.95	0.20/0.35	0.65/0.95	0.20/0.30	1.50/2.00	....
4620H	0.17/0.24	0.40/0.70	0.20/0.35	....	0.20/0.30	1.50/2.00	....
4640H	0.37/0.45	0.55/0.85	0.20/0.35	....	0.20/0.30	1.50/2.00	....
4812H	0.10/0.17	0.30/0.60	0.20/0.35	....	0.20/0.30	3.20/3.80	....
4815H	0.12/0.19	0.35/0.65	0.20/0.35	....	0.20/0.30	3.20/3.80	....
4817H	0.14/0.21	0.35/0.65	0.20/0.35	....	0.20/0.30	3.20/3.80	....
4820H	0.17/0.24	0.45/0.75	0.20/0.35	....	0.20/0.30	3.20/3.80	....
5140H	0.37/0.45	0.60/0.95	0.20/0.35	0.65/0.95	....	....	....
5145H	0.42/0.50	0.60/0.95	0.20/0.35	0.65/0.95	....	....	....
5150H	0.46/0.54	0.60/0.95	0.20/0.35	0.65/0.95	....	....	....
6150H	0.46/0.54	0.60/0.95	0.20/0.35	0.80/1.15	....	....	0.15 V min
8617H	0.14/0.21	0.60/0.95	0.20/0.35	0.35/0.65	0.15/0.25	0.35/0.75	....
8620H	0.17/0.24	0.60/0.95	0.20/0.35	0.35/0.65	0.15/0.25	0.35/0.75	....
8622H	0.20/0.27	0.60/0.95	0.20/0.35	0.35/0.65	0.15/0.25	0.35/0.75	....
8625H	0.22/0.29	0.60/0.95	0.20/0.35	0.35/0.65	0.15/0.25	0.35/0.75	....
8627H	0.25/0.32	0.60/0.95	0.20/0.35	0.35/0.65	0.15/0.25	0.35/0.75	....
8630H	0.27/0.34	0.60/0.95	0.20/0.35	0.35/0.65	0.15/0.25	0.35/0.75	....
8632H	0.30/0.37	0.60/0.95	0.20/0.35	0.35/0.65	0.15/0.25	0.35/0.75	....
8635H	0.32/0.39	0.70/1.05	0.20/0.35	0.35/0.65	0.15/0.25	0.35/0.75	....
8637H	0.35/0.43	0.70/1.05	0.20/0.35	0.35/0.65	0.15/0.25	0.35/0.75	....
8640H	0.37/0.45	0.70/1.05	0.20/0.35	0.35/0.65	0.15/0.25	0.35/0.75	....
8641H*	0.37/0.45	0.70/1.05	0.20/0.35	0.35/0.65	0.15/0.25	0.35/0.75	....
8642H	0.40/0.48	0.70/1.05	0.20/0.35	0.35/0.65	0.15/0.25	0.35/0.75	....
8645H	0.42/0.50	0.70/1.05	0.20/0.35	0.35/0.65	0.15/0.25	0.35/0.75	....
8647H	0.44/0.52	0.70/1.05	0.20/0.35	0.35/0.65	0.15/0.25	0.35/0.75	....
8650H	0.46/0.54	0.70/1.05	0.20/0.35	0.35/0.65	0.15/0.25	0.35/0.75	....
8655H	0.50/0.60	0.70/1.05	0.20/0.35	0.35/0.65	0.15/0.25	0.35/0.75	....
8660H	0.55/0.65	0.70/1.05	0.20/0.35	0.35/0.65	0.15/0.25	0.35/0.75	....
8720H	0.17/0.24	0.60/0.95	0.20/0.35	0.35/0.65	0.20/0.30	0.35/0.75	....
8735H	0.32/0.39	0.70/1.05	0.20/0.35	0.35/0.65	0.20/0.30	0.35/0.75	....
8740H	0.37/0.45	0.70/1.05	0.20/0.35	0.35/0.65	0.20/0.30	0.35/0.75	....
8742H	0.40/0.48	0.70/1.05	0.20/0.35	0.35/0.65	0.20/0.30	0.35/0.75	....
8745H	0.42/0.50	0.70/1.05	0.20/0.35	0.35/0.65	0.20/0.30	0.35/0.75	....
8747H	0.44/0.52	0.70/1.05	0.20/0.35	0.85/0.65	0.20/0.30	0.35/0.75	....
8750H	0.46/0.54	0.70/1.05	0.20/0.35	0.35/0.65	0.20/0.30	0.35/0.75	....
9260H	0.55/0.65	0.70/1.05	1.80/2.20	....	....	....	....
9261H	0.55/0.65	0.70/1.05	1.80/2.20	0.05/0.35	....	....	....
9262H	0.55/0.65	0.70/1.05	1.80/2.20	0.20/0.50	....	....	....
9437H	0.35/0.43	0.85/1.25	0.20/0.35	0.25/0.55	0.08/0.15	0.25/0.65	....
9440H	0.37/0.45	0.85/1.25	0.20/0.35	0.25/0.55	0.08/0.15	0.25/0.65	....
9442H	0.40/0.48	0.95/1.35	0.20/0.35	0.25/0.55	0.08/0.15	0.25/0.65	....
9445H	0.42/0.50	0.95/1.35	0.20/0.35	0.25/0.55	0.08/0.15	0.25/0.65	....

* %S = 0.040/0.060

Note 1—The ranges and limits in this table apply only to material not exceeding 200 sq in. in cross-sectional area, or 18 in. in width, or 10,000 lb in weight, per piece.

Note 2—Phosphorus and sulphur on open hearth steel to be 0.040% max each except where noted (*). Phosphorus and sulphur on electric furnace steel to be 0.025% max each except where noted (*). *

Note 3—The chemical ranges and limits shown are subject to the standard permissible variations for check analysis.

[339]

APPENDIX B

CHEMICAL COMPOSITION RANGES FOR EN ALLOY ENGINEERING STEELS

Wrought Steels, British Standard 970: 1947, issued by the British Standards Institution, London, England (1947)

En	%C	%Mn	%Si	%P*	%S*	%Cr	%Mo	%Ni	% Other
10	0.50/0.60	0.50/0.80	0.05/0.35	0.06	0.06	.....	.....	0.50/0.80	.....
11	0.50/0.70	0.50/0.80	0.10/0.35	0.05	0.05	0.50/0.80	.....	.....	.....
12	0.30/0.45	1.50 max	0.10/0.35	0.05	0.05	.....	.....	0.60/1.00	.....
13	0.15/0.25	1.40/1.80	0.10/0.35	0.05	0.05	.....	0.15/0.35	0.40/0.70	.....
14A	0.15/0.25	1.30/1.70	0.10/0.35	0.06	0.06	0.25 max	.....	0.40 max	.....
14B	0.20/0.30	1.30/1.70	0.10/0.35	0.06	0.06	.....	.....	0.40 max	.....
15	0.30/0.40	1.30/1.70	0.10/0.35	0.05	0.05	.....	.....	.....	.....
15A	0.30/0.40	1.30/1.70	0.05/0.35	0.06	0.06	.....	.....	.....	.....
15B	0.35/0.40	1.10/1.30	0.05/0.35	0.06	0.06	.....	.....	.....	.....
16	0.25/0.40	1.30/1.80	0.10/0.35	0.05	0.05	.....	0.20/0.35	.....	.....
16A	0.25/0.30	1.30/1.80	0.10/0.35	....	....	.....	0.20/0.35	.....	.....
16B	0.30/0.35	1.30/1.80	0.10/0.35	....	.....	.....	0.20/0.35	.....	.....
16C	0.35/0.40	1.30/1.80	0.10/0.35	....	.....	.....	0.20/0.35	.....	.....
17	0.30/0.40	1.30/1.80	0.10/0.35	0.05	0.05	.....	0.35/0.55	.....	.....
18	0.35/0.45	0.60/0.95	0.10/0.35	0.05	0.05	0.80/1.10	.....	.....	.....
18A	0.27/0.32	0.65/0.80	0.10/0.35	....	.....	0.80/1.10	.....	.....	.....
18B	0.30/0.35	0.65/0.80	0.10/0.35	....	.....	0.80/1.10	.....	.....	.....
18C	0.35/0.38	0.65/0.80	0.10/0.35	....	.....	0.80/1.10	.....	.....	.....
18D	0.38/0.43	0.65/0.80	0.10/0.35	....	.....	0.80/1.10	.....	.....	.....
19	0.35/0.45	0.50/0.80	0.10/0.35	0.05	0.05	0.90/1.50	0.20/0.40	.....	.....
19A	0.35/0.45	0.50/0.80	0.10/0.35	0.05	0.05	0.90/1.20	0.20/0.35	.....	.....
19B	0.35/0.40	0.50/0.80	0.10/0.35	....	.....	0.90/1.20	0.20/0.35	.....	.....
19C	0.40/0.45	0.50/0.80	0.10/0.35	....	.....	0.90/1.20	0.20/0.35	.....	.....
20	0.22/0.50	0.40/0.70	0.10/0.35	0.05	0.05	0.50/1.50	0.40/1.00	0.30 max	.....
21	0.25/0.35	0.35/0.75	0.10/0.35	0.05	0.05	0.30 max	.....	2.75/3.50	.....
22	0.35/0.45	0.50/0.80	0.10/0.35	0.05	0.05	0.30 max	.....	3.25/3.75	.....
23	0.25/0.35	0.45/0.70	0.10/0.35	0.05	0.05	0.50/1.00	0.65 max†	2.75/3.50	.....
24	0.35/0.45	0.45/0.70	0.10/0.35	0.05	0.05	0.90/1.40	0.20/0.35	1.30/1.80	.....
25	0.27/0.35	0.50/0.70	0.10/0.35	0.05	0.05	0.50/0.80	0.40/0.70	2.30/2.80	.....
26	0.36/0.44	0.50/0.70	0.10/0.35	0.05	0.05	0.50/0.80	0.40/0.70	2.30/2.80	.....
27	0.25/0.35	0.70 max	0.10/0.35	0.05	0.05	0.50/1.30	0.20/0.65	3.00/3.75	.....
28	0.25/0.40	0.70 max	0.10/0.35	0.05	0.05	0.75/1.50	0.20/0.65	3.00/4.50	.....
29	0.15/0.35	0.65 max	0.10/0.35	0.05	0.05	2.50/3.50	0.30/0.70	0.40 max	.....
30A	0.26/0.34	0.40/0.60	0.10/0.35	0.05	0.05	1.10/1.40	.....	3.90/4.30	.....
30B	0.26/0.34	0.40/0.60	0.10/0.35	0.05	0.05	1.10/1.40	0.20/0.40	3.90/4.30	.....
31	0.90/1.20	0.30/0.75	0.10/0.35	0.05	0.05	1.00/1.60	.....	.....	.....
33	0.10/0.15	0.30/0.60	0.10/0.35	0.05	0.05	0.30 max	.....	2.75/3.50	.....
34	0.14/0.20	0.30/0.60	0.10/0.35	0.05	0.05	.....	0.20/0.30	1.50/2.00	.....
35	0.20/0.28	0.30/0.60	0.10/0.35	0.05	0.05	.....	0.20/0.30	1.50/2.00	.....
35A	0.20/0.25	0.30/0.60	0.10/0.35	....	.....	.....	0.20/0.30	1.50/2.00	.....
35B	0.23/0.28	0.30/0.60	0.10/0.35	....	.....	.....	0.20/0.30	1.50/2.00	.....
36	0.18 max	0.30/0.60	0.10/0.35	0.05	0.05	0.60/1.10	.....	3.00/3.75	.....
37	0.16 max	0.45 max	0.10/0.35	0.05	0.05	0.30 max	.....	4.50/5.20	.....
38	0.16 max	0.60 max	0.10/0.35	0.05	0.05	0.30 max	0.15/0.30†	4.50/5.50	.....
39A	0.12/0.18	0.50 max	0.10/0.35	0.05	0.05	1.00/1.40	.....	3.80/4.50	.....
39B	0.12/0.18	0.50 max	0.10/0.35	0.05	0.05	1.00/1.40	0.15/0.35	3.80/4.50	.....

APPENDIX B – (Continued)

En	%C	%Mn	%Si	%P*	%S*	%Cr	%Mo	%Ni	% Other
40A	0.10/0.20	0.40/0.65	0.10/0.35	0.05	0.05	2.90/3.50	0.40/0.70	0.40 max	.....
40B	0.20/0.30	0.40/0.65	0.10/0.35	0.05	0.05	2.90/3.50	0.40/0.70	0.40 max	.....
40C	0.30/0.50	0.40/0.80	0.10/0.35	0.05	0.05	2.50/3.50	0.70/1.20	0.40 max	0.10/0.30V
41	0.18/0.45	0.65 max	0.10/0.45	0.05	0.05	1.40/1.80	0.10/0.25	0.40 max	0.90/1.80 Al
45	0.50/0.65	0.70/1.00	1.50/2.00	0.05	0.05	.....	.....	.....	.....
45A	0.53/0.63	0.70/1.00	1.70/2.00	0.05	0.05	.....	.....	.....	.....
46	0.35/0.45	0.60/1.00	1.50/2.00	0.05	0.05	.....	.....	.....	.....
47	0.45/0.55	0.50/0.80	0.50 max	0.05	0.05	0.80/1.20	.....	.....	0.15 V min
48	0.45/0.55	0.50/0.80	0.10/0.50	0.05	0.05	1.00/1.40	.....	.....	.....
50	0.40/0.50	0.50/0.70	0.10/0.35	0.04	0.04	1.00/1.50	.....	.....	0.15 V min
51	0.25/0.35	0.35/0.75	0.10/0.35	0.05	0.05	0.30 max	.....	2.75/3.50	.....
100	0.35/0.45	1.20/1.50	0.50 max	0.05	0.05	0.80/0.60	0.15/0.25	0.50/1.00	.....
100A	0.25/0.30	1.20/1.50	0.10/0.35	....	.....	0.80/0.60	0.15/0.25	0.50/1.00	.....
100B	0.30/0.35	1.20/1.50	0.10/0.35	....	.....	0.30/0.60	0.15/0.25	0.50/1.00	.....
100C	0.35/0.40	1.20/1.50	0.10/0.35	....	.....	0.30/0.60	0.15/0.25	0.50/1.00	.....
100D	0.40/0.45	1.20/1.50	0.10/0.35	....	.....	0.30/0.60	0.15/0.25	0.50/1.00	.....
110	0.35/0.45	0.40/0.80	0.10/0.35	0.05	0.05	0.90/1.40	0.10/0.20	1.20/1.60	.....
111	0.30/0.40	0.60/0.90	0.10/0.35	0.05	0.05	0.45/0.75	.....	1.00/1.50	.....
111A	0.33/0.38	0.60/0.90	0.10/0.35	....	.....	0.45/0.75	.....	1.00/1.50	.....
160	0.35/0.45	0.30/0.60	0.10/0.35	0.05	0.05	.....	0.20/0.35	1.50/2.00	.....
160A	0.38/0.43	0.30/0.60	0.10/0.35	....	.....	.....	0.20/0.35	1.50/2.00	.....
201	0.18 max	1.10/1.50	0.05/0.35	0.05	0.05	.....	.....	.....	.....
202	0.18 max	1.10/1.50	0.05/0.35	0.05	0.10/0.18	.....	.....	.....	.....
206	0.12/0.17	0.30/0.50	0.10/0.35	0.05	0.05	0.30/0.50	.....	.....	.....
207	0.16/0.21	0.60/0.80	0.10/0.35	0.05	0.05	0.60/0.80	.....	.....	.....
320	0.14/0.20	0.40/0.70	0.10/0.35	0.05	0.05	1.80/2.20	0.15/0.25	1.80/2.20	.....
325	0.17/0.22	0.45/0.65	0.10/0.35	0.05	0.05	0.40/0.60	0.20/0.30	1.50/2.00	.....

* maximum except where a range is indicated
† optional; for use at the discretion of the steelmaker in order to secure the desired mechanical properties

APPENDIX C

CHEMICAL COMPOSITION RANGES FOR CETAC ALLOY ENGINEERING STEELS

Constructional Steels issued by the Centre d'Etudes Techniques
de l'Automobile et du Cycle (1946)

CETAC	%C	%Mn	%Si	%P†	%S†	%Cr	%Mo	%Ni	% Other
Class 1									
35 M 5	0.32/0.38	1.00/1.35	0.40 max	•	•	.....	.....	.....	.....
45 M 5	0.39/0.48	1.20/1.50	0.40 max	•	•	.....	.....	.....	.....
Class 2									
45 S 8 (a)	0.42/0.50	0.40/0.80	1.70/2.10	•	•	.....	.....	.....	.....
55 S 6 (a)	0.52/0.58	0.50/0.90	1.50/1.90	•	•	.....	.....	.....	.....
45 SCD 6	0.42/0.50	0.5 max	1.25/1.75	••	••	0.70/0.90	0.20/0.30	.....	.....
Class 3									
12 C 3	0.09/0.15	0.60/0.90	0.40 max	•	•	0.60/1.00	.....	.....	.....
18 C 3	0.15/0.21	0.60/0.90	0.40 max	•	•	0.60/1.00	.....	.....	.....
32 C 4 (b)	0.30/0.35	0.60/0.90	0.40 max	•••	•••	0.70/1.10	.....	.....	.....
38 C 4 (b)	0.35/0.40	0.60/0.90	0.40 max	•••	•••	0.80/1.10	.....	.....	.....
45 C 4	0.40/0.48	0.60/0.90	0.40 max	•	•	0.70/1.10	.....	.....	.....
45 C 6	0.42/0.48	0.60/0.80	0.40 max	•	•	1.40/1.70	.....	.....	.....
100 C 3	0.95/1.10	0.40 max	0.40 max	••	••	0.60/1.00	.....	0.20 max	.....
100 C 5	0.95/1.10	0.40 max	0.40 max	••	••	1.00/1.30	.....	0.20 max	.....
100 C 6	0.95/1.10	0.40 max	0.40 max	••	••	1.30/1.60	.....	0.20 max	.....
Class 4 (c)									
16 MC 5	0.12/0.19	1.00/1.40	0.40 max	•	•	0.70/1.10	.....	.....	.....
20 MC 5	0.17/0.23	1.20/1.50	0.40 max	•	•	1.20/1.50	.....	.....	.....
Class 5 (c)									
12 CV 4	0.09/0.15	0.40/0.70	0.35 max	•	•	0.70/1.10	.....	.....	0.05/0.12 V
18 CV 4	0.15/0.22	0.40/0.70	0.35 max	•	•	0.70/1.10	.....	.....	0.05/0.12 V
30 CV 4	0.27/0.33	0.60/1.00	0.40 max	•	•	0.80/1.20	.....	.....	0.10/0.20 V
40 CV 4	0.37/0.43	0.60/1.00	0.40 max	•	•	0.80/1.20	.....	.....	0.10/0.20 V
50 CV 4	0.47/0.53	0.60/1.00	0.40 max	•	•	0.80/1.20	.....	.....	0.10/0.20 V
Class 6									
12 CD 4	0.08/0.15	0.60/0.80	0.35 max	•	•	0.90/1.20	0.20/0.30	.....	.....
18 CD 4 (b)	0.15/0.22	0.60/0.80	0.35 max	•••	•••	0.85/1.15	0.20/0.30	.....	.....
25 CD 4	0.22/0.30	0.60/0.80	0.40 max	•	•	0.85/1.15	0.20/0.30	.....	.....
35 CD 4 (b,d)	0.32/0.38	0.60/0.80	0.40 max	•••	•••	0.85/1.15	0.20/0.30	0.40 max	.....
42 CD 4 (b)	0.39/0.45	0.60/0.80	0.40 max	•••	•••	0.85/1.15	0.20/0.30	0.40 max	.....
Class 7									
10 NC 6 (b)	0.07/0.11	0.60/0.90	0.40 max	•••	•••	0.90/1.25	.....	1.20/1.60	.....
16 NC 6 (b)	0.12/0.18	0.60/0.90	0.40 max	•••	•••	0.90/1.25	.....	1.20/1.60	.....
20 NC 6	0.16/0.22	0.60/0.90	0.40 max	•••	•••	0.90/1.25	.....	1.20/1.60	.....
25 NC 6	0.22/0.29	0.60/0.90	0.40 max	•	•	0.75/1.10	.....	1.20/1.60	.....
35 NC 6 (b)	0.30/0.38	0.60/0.90	0.40 max	•	•	0.75/1.10	.....	1.20/1.60	.....
Class 8 (e)									
10 CND 6	0.12 max	0.35/0.65	0.35 max	•	•	1.20/1.60	0.10/0.20	0.80/1.20	.....
18 CND 6	0.15/0.22	0.45/0.75	0.35 max	•	•	1.40/1.80	0.10/0.20	0.80/1.20	.....
30 CND 8	0.27/0.33	0.40/0.65	0.35 max	•	•	1.80/2.20	0.25/0.35	0.30/0.60	.....
Class 9 (e)									
10 ND 4	0.07/0.13	0.40 max	0.40 max	•	•	0.20 max	0.10/0.20	0.80/1.20	.....
10 NCD 4	0.07/0.13	0.50/0.90	0.40 max	•	•	0.40/0.70	0.10/0.20	1.00/1.30	.....
16 NCD 4	0.12/0.19	0.50/0.90	0.40 max	•	•	0.40/0.70	0.10/0.20	1.00/1.30	.....
25 NCD 4	0.22/0.28	0.50/0.90	0.40 max	•	•	0.40/0.70	0.10/0.20	1.00/1.30	.....
35 NCD 4	0.32/0.38	0.50/0.90	0.40 max	...	...	0.40/0.70	0.10/0.20	1.00/1.30	.....

APPENDIX C – (Continued)

CETAC	%C	%Mn	%Si	%P†	%S†	%Cr	%Mo	%Ni	% Other
				No class (f)					
10 NC 12	0.08/0.13	0.40/0.70	0.35 max	**	**	0.60/0.90	.....	2.75/3.25	.....
12 NC 12	0.11/0.16	0.40/0.70	0.35 max	**	**	0.60/0.90	.....	2.75/3.25	.....
30 NC 11	0.26/0.33	0.40/0.70	0.40 max	**	**	0.60/0.90	.....	2.50/3.00	.....
35 NC 15	0.32/0.38	0.20/0.50	0.40 max	**	**	1.10/1.40	.....	3.50/4.00	.....
40 NC 17	0.37/0.43	0.15/0.55	0.40 max	**	**	1.50/2.00	.....	4.00/4.50	.....
16 NCD 13	0.14/0.19	0.50 max	0.35 max	**	**	0.85/1.15	0.20/0.30	3.00/3.50	.....
32 NCD 8	0.28/0.35	0.50 max	0.40 max	**	**	1.90/2.40	0.60/0.80	1.90/2.40	.....
30 NCD 11	0.25/0.35	0.20/0.50	0.40 max	**	**	0.70/1.10	0.30/0.40	2.70/3.30	.....
30 NCD 16	0.25/0.35	0.15/0.55	0.10/0.40	**	**	1.20/1.50	0.40/0.60	3.70/4.30	.....
40 NCD 18	0.35/0.45	0.15/0.55	0.10/0.40	**	**	1.40/1.70	0.40/0.60	4.30/4.90	.....
25 NCD 15	0.20/0.30	0.45 max	0.35 max	**	**	1.10/1.80	0.40/0.60	3.70/4.00	.....
35 NCD 14	0.30/0.40	0.40 max	0.35 max	**	**	1.20/1.50	0.20/0.30	3.20/3.70	.....
40 NDC 19	0.35/0.43	0.40 max	0.35 max	**	**	0.30/0.60	1.00/1.30	4.50/5.00	.....
				Nitriding Steels					
28 CD 12	0.28 (g)	0.40/0.80	0.40 max	0.040	0.035	2.50/3.50	0.30/0.50	.....	.....
28 CVD 12	0.28 (g)	0.40/0.80	0.40 max	0.040	0.035	2.50/3.50	0.15/0.25	.....	0.20/0.40 V
28 CV 12	0.28 (g)	0.40/0.80	0.40 max	0.040	0.035	2.50/3.50	.....	.....	0.25/0.45 V
30 CAV 6-03	0.30 (g)	0.40/0.80	0.40 max	0.040	0.035	1.50/1.75	.....	.....	0.25/0.45 V / 0.20/0.40 Al
30 CAV 6-06	0.30 (g)	0.40/0.80	0.40 max	0.040	0.035	1.50/1.75	.....	.....	0.25/0.45 V / 0.45/0.75 Al
30 CAD 6-06	0.30 (g)	0.40/0.80	0.40 max	0.040	0.035	1.50/1.75	0.25/0.45	.....	0.45/0.75 Al
45 CAD 6-06	0.45 (g)	0.40/0.80	0.40 max	0.040	0.035	1.50/1.75	0.25/0.45	.....	0.45/0.75 Al
45 CAD 6-12	0.45 (g)	0.40/0.80	0.40 max	0.040	0.035	1.50/1.75	0.25/0.45	.....	1.00/1.30 Al
45 CAV 6-06	0.45 (g)	0.40/0.80	0.40 max	0.040	0.035	1.50/1.75	.....	.....	0.25/0.45 V / 0.45/0.75 Al
45 CAV 6-12	0.45 (g)	0.40/0.80	0.40 max	0.040	0.035	1.50/1.75	.....	.....	0.25/0.45 V / 1.00/1.30 Al

* %P = 0.040 max   %S = 0.035 max   %P + %S = 0.065 max
** %P = 0.030 max   %S = 0.025 max   %P + %S = 0.055 max
*** either %P = 0.040 max   %S = 0.035 max   %P + %S = 0.065 max
     or   %P = 0.030 max   %S = 0.025 max   %P + %S = 0.055 max
† maximum

Notes:
(a) For the manufacture of spring sheet over 0.16 in. thick, these two steels should contain small amounts of chromium, molybdenum or tungsten.
(b) These grades may be ordered by selection of heats, to narrower limits of carbon, alloying additions, phosphorus and sulphur to correspond to the particular applications.
(c) These grades are no longer used in the automobile industry. They are to be avoided in all new studies. Their analyses are listed for the sake of convenience until the stock already in existence is exhausted.
(d) In view of the diversity of uses of this grade, it may be ordered to closer composition limits, obtained by selection of heats, provided each of these is ordered in reasonable proportions. For example, the two variants, 34 CD 4 and 36 CD 4, which correspond to certain particular needs, are ordered with, in addition to the general limits corresponding to the grade 35 CD 4, the further requirement of a relationship between the alloying elements defined by the formula $X = 4\,C + 3\,Mo + 2\,Mn + 1.2\,Cr + Ni$. Certain values of X corresponding to specific sections are given in the original reference.
(e) These steels are little used in the automobile industry. They are listed provisionally pending their definite abandonment.
(f) These steels, with a higher alloy content than those in the preceding classes, have a particularly high hardenability. Except in certain cases and to answer exceptional safety requirements, generally their use is seldom justified for the manufacture of parts for automobile vehicles which have for the most part small dimensions and are made very satisfactorily with lower alloy steels. The good performance of a part actually depends more often on its shape and correct heat treatment than on a large amount of alloying elements in the steel used.
(g) Average

APPENDIX D

DETERMINATION OF "EQUIVALENT ROUNDS"

Although many parts at the time of heat treatment are not round in section, most correlations of the cooling rates of Jominy end-quenched specimens and bars are based on rounds. It is often convenient, therefore, to determine at least approximately the "equivalent round" of such a part.

One procedure is covered in B.S. 971 "Wrought Steels (Carbon and Alloy Steels) T.A.C. 1 to 33 Steels En 1 to 58" prepared by the Technical Advisory Committee of the Special and Alloy Steels Committee, issued for the T.A.C. by the British Standards Institution, London, England (1944). The following information is taken from this publication.

A mathematical method was adopted for finding the diameters of round bars, the centers of which would cool through a given range of temperature in the same time as the centers of rectangular or square bars of different sizes (Alloy Steels Research Committee, Iron and Steel Institute Special Report No. 14 (1936)).

Although the calculations were made for cooling from 1510 to 570 F in air or oil at 70 F, the results are equally applicable to any range of temperature where the drop in temperature at the center has the same ratio to the original temperature (relative to the surrounding medium) as for the conditions assumed; that is, where:—

$$\frac{\text{Temperature at Center of Piece} - \text{Temperature of Oil (Air)}}{\text{Initial Temperature of Piece} - \text{Temperature of Oil (Air)}} = 0.35$$

The results of these calculations are given here in the form of tables for converting plates and rectangular sections into equivalent rounds for oil quenching and air cooling respectively (Tables D1 and D2). As an example of how the tables should be used, a point at the center of an oil quenched square section of 1½ in. sides will cool over the range of temperature covered in the same time as a round section of 1.620 in. in diameter, while the equivalent round for a rectangular section, having sides 1½ in. and 3 in. respectively, will be 2.124 in. diameter for oil quenching.

The tables must be used only to compare sections of the same steel.

Sections other than rounds or rectangles are difficult to treat mathematically, but close approximations may usually be obtained. Of the simpler sections, octagonal and hexagonal parts are intermediate in cooling rate between round and square sections, the order of increasing time of cooling being as follows:—

Round, Octagonal, Hexagonal, Square

[344]

TABLE D1

Equivalent Rounds for Oil Quenched Plates and Rectangular Sections

B = Breadth of Section
T = Thickness of Section
$\frac{B}{T}$ = α for Plate

T in.	Diameter of Equivalent Round in Inches $\frac{B}{T}$					
	1	1½	2	2½	3	α
½	0.524	0.630	0.706	0.762	0.797	0.863
1	1.070	1.280	1.424	1.516	1.572	1.636
1½	1.620	1.922	2.124	2.250	2.322	2.382
2	2.160	2.560	2.824	2.970	3.052	3.104
2½	2.705	3.200	3.520	3.685	3.770	3.880
3	3.252	3.840	4.212	4.392	4.488	4.548
3½	3.794	4.480	4.900	5.096	5.194	5.264
4	4.336	5.120	5.584	5.784	5.904	5.976

TABLE D2

Equivalent Rounds for Air Cooled Plates and Rectangular Sections

B = Breadth of Section
T = Thickness of Section
$\frac{B}{T}$ = α for Plate

T in.	Diameter of Equivalent Round in Inches $\frac{B}{T}$							
	1	1½	2	2½	3	3½	4	α
½	0.503	0.603	0.672	0.720	0.758	0.787	0.810	0.990
1	1.008	1.212	1.350	1.448	1.528	1.585	1.682	1.962
1½	1.515	1.827	2.033	2.186	2.307	2.400	2.466	2.926
2	2.022	2.440	2.716	2.924	3.092	3.220	3.810	3.864
2½	2.535	3.055	3.405	3.663	3.870	4.035	4.153	4.800
3	3.048	3.672	4.098	4.404	4.644	4.842	4.992	5.718
3½	3.563	4.295	4.799	5.145	5.418	5.653	5.828	6.622
4	4.078	4.920	5.492	5.884	6.192	6.460	6.660	7.504

If the factor is estimated intelligently, based in this case upon the dimensions of the octagon or hexagon across the flats, no serious error can be introduced.

For oval sections with major axis "a" and minor axis "b", the center will cool more slowly than that of a round of diameter "b", but more quickly than that of a rectangle "a" x "b". More accurate results may be obtained by converting an oval section to its equivalent rectangular section having sides of dimensions "A" and "B", such that the area of the rectangle is equal to the area of the oval section and A:B as a:b.

Careful consideration must be given to those cases where the "section" varies along the length of a forging or other part, in order to decide which section is to be looked upon as the controlling section at the time of heat treatment. In the case of parallel shafts having flanges, collars or other enlarged portions, the length of such enlarged portions in relation to the diameter should be taken into account. If the ratio of length to diameter is great, then the "diameter" of such portion will naturally be the determining dimension; if the ratio is small the part may be viewed as a disk or plate in which thickness is the determining feature. For intermediate cases the distance from the center of the enlarged section to the nearest point of the external surface will in general decide the ruling dimension. At the same time the importance or otherwise of the properties necessary at the portion in question must be considered.

For maximum hardening, water quenching may be used for plate. The correlation between plate quenched in agitated water and Jominy end-quenched specimens has been determined experimentally, based on the cooling rate at 1300 F as well as the time required to cool from 1350 to 900 F (Figure D1 from A. L. Boegehold and E. W. Weinman "Cooling Rates of Plates and Rounds" Metal Progress, Vol 51 (1947)).

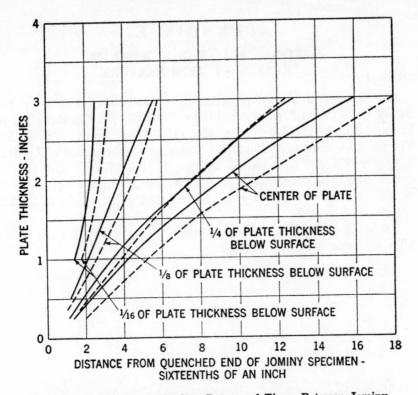

FIG D1 – Correlation of Cooling Rates and Times Between Jominy End-Quenched Specimens and Plates. The dotted lines indicate the correlation between the various distances below the surface of plates and the position on the Jominy end-quenched specimen that has the same cooling rate at 1300 F. The full lines correlate the time to cool various positions in the plates from 1350 to 900 F (which gives a better conception of hardenability in terms of hardness) with that position on the Jominy specimen that takes the same time to cool through the same temperature interval. All tests were made on 9445 or 9450 steel. The Jominy specimens were end-quenched from 1500 F in the standard fixture. The plate specimens were heated to 1525 F in a non-scaling atmosphere and quenched in a stream of water at 75 F flowing at 200 ft per min

APPENDIX E

MAXIMUM ALLOWABLE WORKING
STRESSES AT TEMPERATURE

The maximum allowable working stresses formulated by the Boiler Code Committee and published in Rules for Construction of Power Boilers, issued by the ASME (1946), are given in Table E1. The same stresses are included in Rules for Construction of Unfired Pressure Vessels, also issued by the ASME (1946). The specification numbers correspond to ASTM specification numbers with an added prefix of S; for example, SA-202 corresponds to ASTM specification A 202.

Table E2 shows the average chemical composition of each of the alloy steels covered in Table E1.

TABLE E1

Maximum Allowable Working Stresses in psi for Ferrous Materials

Specification Number	Grade	Spec. Minimum Tensile psi	Notes (See Last Page of Table)	20 to 650	700	750	800	850	900	950	1000	1050	1100	1150	1200 F
Plate Steels															
Carbon Steel															
SA-30	Flange	55000		11000	10400	9600	8000	6300							
SA-30	Firebox, Gr. A	52000		10400	9900	9200	7700	6100	4400	2600	1850				
SA-30	Firebox, Gr. B	48000	(1)	9600	9300	8750	7250	5900	4400	2600	1850				
SA-70		55000	(1)	11000	10400	9500	8000	6300	4400	2600	1850				
SA-89	A	45000		9000	8800	8400	6900	5700	4400	2600	1850				
SA-89	B	50000		10000	9600	9000	7500	6000	4400	2600	1350				
SA-129		44000		8800											
SA-201	A	55000		11000	10400	9600	8500	7200	5600	3800	2000				
SA-201	B	60000		12000	11400	10400	9100	7400	5600	3800	2000				
SA-212	A	65000		13000	12300	11100	9400	7600	5600	3800	2000				
SA-212	B	70000		14000	13300	11900	10000	7800	5600	3800	2000				
Low-Alloy Steel															
SA-202	A	75000		15000	14100	12400	10100	7800	5600	3800	2000				
SA-202	B	85000		15000	14100	12400	10100	7800	5600	3800	2000				
SA-203	A	66000		13000	12300	11100	9400	7600	5600	3800	2000				
SA-203	B	70000		14000	13300	11900	10000	7800	5600	3800	2000				
SA-203	C	75000		15000	14100	12400	10100	7800	5600	3800	2000				
SA-204	A	66000		13000	13000	13000	12500	11500	10000	8000	5000				
SA-204	B	70000		14000	14000	14000	13500	12000	10200	8000	5000				
SA-204	C	75000	(12)	15000	15000	15000	14400	12700	10400	8000	5000				
SA-225	A	70000	(12)	14000	14000	14000									
SA-225	B	75000		15000	15000	15000									
Medium and High-Alloy Steel															
SA-240	A	70000		14000	14000	14000	12800	9500	6750	4000	2400				
SA-240	B	70000		14000	14000	14000	12800	9500	6750	4000	2400				
SA-240	D	70000		14000	14000	14000	12800	9500	6750	4000	2400				
SA-240	S	75000	(2)	15000	15000	14600	14300	14000	13400	12800	10000	8000	6000	4600	3600
SA-240	M	75000	(2)	15000	15000	14600	14300	14000	13400	12600	11200	9000	7000	5000	3600
SA-240	T	75000		15000	15000	14600	14300	14000	13400	12300	10000	8000	6000	4600	3600
SA-240	C	75000		15000	15000	14600	14300	14000	13400	12300	10000	8000	6000	4600	3600
Pipe and Tubes															
Seamless Carbon Steel															
SA-53	A	48000		9600	9250	8700	8000	6850	5600	3800	2000				
SA-53	A	48000		9600	9100	8250	7250	5850	4400	2600	1850				
SA-53	B	60000	(3)	12000	11400	10400	9100	7400	5600	3800	2000				
SA-53	B	60000	(3)	12000	11400	9950	8800	6850	4400	2600	1350				

For Metal Temperatures Not Exceeding

TABLE E1—(Continued)

Specification Number	Grade	Spec. Minimum Tensile psi	Notes (See Last Page of Table)	—20 to 650	700	750	800	850	900	950	1000	1050	1100	1150	1200 F
Pipe and Tubes—(Continued)															
Seamless Carbon Steel—(Continued)															
SA-83	A		(3)	9400	9000	8600	7900	6800	5600	3800	2000				
SA-83	A			9400	9000	8160	7150	5850	4400	2600	1350				
SA-83	B		(3)	8000	7650	6900	8000	6850	5600	3800	2000				
SA-106	A	48000		9600	9250	8700	8250	5850	4400	2600	1850				
SA-106	A	48000		9600	11400	10400	9100	7250	5600	3800	2000				
SA-106	B	60000		12000	11400	8600	7900	6800	5600	3800	2000				
SA-192	A			9400	9000	8600	7900	7900	5600	3800	2000				
SA-210	:	60000		12000	11400	10400	9100	7400	5600	3800	2000				
Seamless Alloy Steel															
SA-158	P3a	60000		12000	12000	12000	11800	11200	10000	8000	5850	3850	2200	1400	900
SA-158	P3b	60000		12000	12000	12000	11800	11200	10000	8000	5850	3850	2200	1400	900
SA-158	P5a	60000		12000	11000	12000	11800	11200	10000	8000	5850	3850	2200	1400	900
SA-158	P5c	60000	(6)	11000	11000	11000	11000	10850	10000	8000	5850	3850	2200	1400	900
SA-158	P8a	75000		15000	15000	14600	14300	14000	13400	12300	10000	8000	6000	4600	3600
SA-158	P8b	60000	(2)	12000	12000	12000	11800	11200	13400	12300	5850	3850	2200	1400	900
SA-158	P11	55000		11000	11000	11000	10750	10600	10000	8000	5000				
SA-206	P1	55000		11000	11000	11000	10500	10500	10000	8000	5000				
SA-209	T1	60000		12000	12000	12000	11500	11000	10000	8000	5000				
SA-209	T1a	55000		10600	10600	10600	10400	10200	10000	8000	5000				
SA-209	T1b	60000		12000	12000	12000	11800	11000	10000	8000	5000				
SA-213	T3	53000		12000	12000	12000	11800	11200	10000	8000	5850	3860	2200	1400	900
SA-213	T5	60000		12000	12000	12000	11800	11200	10000	8000	5850	3850	2200	1400	900
SA-213	T11	60000		12000	12000	12000	11800	11200	10000	8000	5850	3850	2200	1400	900
SA-213	T12	60000		12000	12000	12000	11800	11200	8800	8000	5850	3850	2200	1400	900
SA-213	T13	60000		12000	12000	12000	11800	11200	10000	8000	5850	3850	2200	1400	900
SA-213	T14	60000		12000	12000	12000	11800	11200	10000	6000	4200	3000	2000	1400	900
SA-213	T16	60000	(2)	11000	11000	11000	11000	10850	10000	8000	5850	3850	2200	1400	900
SA-213	T8	60000		15000	15000	14600	14300	14000	13400	12300	10000	8000	6000	4600	3600
SA-213	T18	75000		15000	15000	14600	14300	14000	13400	12300	10000	8000	6000	4600	3600
SA-213	T19	75000		15000	15000	14600	14300	14000	13400	12300	10000	8000	6000	4600	3600
SA-213	T20	75000		15000	15000	14600	14300	14000	13400	12600	11200	9000	7000	5000	3600
SA-213	T17	75000	(2)	12000	12000	12000	11800	11200	10000	8250	6250	4800	3700	2700	1950
SA-213	T21	60000	(13)	12000	12000	12000	11800	11200	10000	8250	6250	4800	3700	2700	1950
SA-213	T22	60000		12000	12000	12000	11800	11200	10000	8000	5000				
SA-280	:	55000		11000	11000	11000	10750	10500	10000	8000	5000				
Electric-Resistance-Welded Carbon Steel															
SA-135	A	48000	(3), (4)	9600	9250	8700	8000	6850	5600	3800	2000				
SA-135	A	48000	(4)	9600	9100	8250	7250	5850	4400	2600	1850				

TABLE E1—(Continued)

Specification Number	Grade	Spec. Minimum Tensile psi	Notes (See Last Page of Table)	For Metal Temperatures Not Exceeding											
				−20 to 650	700	750	800	850	900	950	1000	1050	1100	1150	1200 F
Pipe and Tubes—(Continued)															
Electric-Resistance-Welded															
Carbon Steel—(Continued)															
SA-135	B	60000	(3), (4)	12000	11400	10400	9100	7400	5600	3800	2000	....	....	....	....
SA-135	B	60000	(4)	12000	11400	9950	8800	6350	4400	2600	1350	....	....	....	....
SA-178	A	.....	(3), (4)	9400	9000	8600	7900	6800	5600	3800	2000	....	....	....	....
SA-178	A	.....	(4)	9400	9000	8150	7150	5850	4400	2600	1350	....	....	....	....
SA-178	B	60000	(3), (4)	12000	11400	10400	9100	7400	5600	3800	2000	....	....	....	....
SA-178	C	60000	(4)	12000	11400	9950	8300	6350	4400	2600	1350	....	....	....	....
SA-226	..	None	(3), (4)	9400	9000	8600	7900	6800	5600	3800	2000	....	....	....	....
SA-226		None	(4)	9400	9000	8150	7150	5850	4400	2600	1350	....	....	....	....
Elec. Resis. and Atom. Hydrogen Welded															
Alloy Steel															
SA-249	T8	75000	(4)	15000	15000	14600	14300	14000	13400	12300	10000	8000	6000	4600	3600
SA-249	T18	75000	(4)	15000	15000	14600	14300	14000	13400	12300	10000	8000	6000	4600	3600
SA-249	T19	75000	(4)	15000	15000	14600	14300	14000	13400	12300	10000	8000	6000	4600	3600
SA-249	T20	75000	(4)	15000	15000	14600	14300	14000	13400	12600	11200	9000	7000	5000	3600
SA-249	T24	75000	(4)	15000	15000	14600	14300	14000	13400	12600	11200	9000	7000	5000	3600
SA-250	T1	55000	(4)	11000	12000	11000	10750	10500	10000	8000	5000	....	....	....	....
SA-250	T1a	60000	(4)	12000	12000	12000	11500	11000	10000	8000	5000	....	....	....	....
SA-250	T1b	53000	(4)	10600	10600	10600	10400	10200	10000	8000	5000	....	....	....	....
Lap-Welded															
SA-53	Steel	45000	(4)	9000	8500	7800	....	....	....	....	....	....	....	....	....
SA-72	Wrought Iron	40000	(4)	8000	7650	6900	....	....	....	....	....	....	....	....	....
SA-83	Steel	.....	(4)	9000	8500	7800	....	....	....	....	....	....	....	....	....
SA-106		45000	(4)	9000	8500	7800	....	....	....	....	....	....	....	....	....
Butt-Welded															
SA-53	Steel	45000	(4)	9000	8500	7800	....	....	....	....	....	....	....	....	....
SA-72	Wrought Iron	40000	(4)	8000	7650	6900	....	....	....	....	....	....	....	....	....
Forgings															
Carbon Steel															
SA-105	1	60000	(3)	12000	11400	10400	8300	6450	4400	2600	1350	....	....	....	....
SA-105	2	70000	(3)	14000	13300	11900	8950	6450	4400	2600	1350	....	....	....	....
SA-105	1	60000		12000	11400	10400	9100	7400	5600	3800	2000	....	....	....	....
SA-105	2	70000		14000	13300	11900	10000	7800	5800	3800	2000	....	....	....	....
SA-181	1	60000		12000	11400	10400	8800	6350	4400	2600	1350	....	....	....	....
SA-181	2	70000		14000	13300	11900	8950	6450	4400	2600	1350	....	....	....	....

TABLE E1—(Continued)

Specification Number	Grade	Spec. Minimum Tensile psi	Notes (See Last Page of Table)	For Metal Temperatures Not Exceeding											
				−20 to 650	700	750	800	850	900	950	1000	1050	1100	1150	1200 F
Forgings—(Continued)															
Carbon Steel—(Continued)															
SA-181	1	60000	(3)	12000	11400	10400	9100	7400	5600	3800	2000				
SA-181	2	70000	(3)	14000	13300	11900	10000	7800	5600	3800	2000				
SA-266	1	60000		12000	11400	10400	9100	7400	5600	3800	2000				
SA-266	2	70000		14000	13300	11900	10000	7800	5600	3800	2000				
SA-266	3	75000		15000	14100	12400	10100	7800	5600	3800	2000				
Alloy Steel															
SA-182	F1	70000		14000	14000	14000	13500	12000	10200	8000	5000				
SA-182	F3	70000		14000	14000	14000	14000	13400	11000	8250	5850	3850	2200	1400	900
SA-182	F4	90000		15000	15000	15000	14000	12500	10200	8000	5000				
SA-182	F5	90000	(6)	15000	15000	15000	14000	13400	11000	8250	5850	3350	2200		
SA-182	F6	85000		15000	14000	13000	11500	9500	6750	4000	2400				
SA-182	F7	100000		15000	15000	15000	14400	12700	10400	8000	5000				
SA-182	F8	75000	(2)	15000	15000	14600	14300	14000	13400	12300	10000	8000	6000	4600	3600
SA-182	F11	100000		15000	15000	15000	14400	12700	10400	8000	5000				
Castings															
Carbon Steel															
SA-27	B & B2	70000	(5), (7)	14000	13300	11900	8950	6450	4400	2600	1350				
SA-95	WCA	70000	(7)	14000	13300	11900	10000	7800	5600		2000				
SA-216	WCA	60000	(3), (7)	12000	11400	10400	9100	7400	5600	3800	2000				
SA-216	WCB	70000	(3), (7)	14000	13300	11900	10000	7800	5600	3800	2000				
Alloy Steel															
SA-157	C1	70000	(7)	14000	14000	14000	13500	12000	10200	8000	5000				
SA-157	C3	90000	(7)	15000	15000	15000	14000	13400	11000	8250	5850		2200	1400	900
SA-157	C4	100000		15000	15000	15000	14000	12500	10200	8000	5000				
SA-157	C5A	100000	(6), (7)	15000	15000	15000	14000	13400	11000	8250	5850	3850	2200	1400	900
SA-157	C5B	90000	(6), (7)	15000	15000	15000	14000	12500	8800	6000	4200	3000	2000	1400	900
SA-157	C6	90000	(7)	15000	15000	13000	11500	9500	6750	4000	2400				
SA-157	C9	85000	(7)	15000	14000	14000	13900	13700	13200	12300	10000	8000	6000	4600	3600
SA-157	C11	70000	(2), (7)	14000	15000	15000	14400	12700	10400	8000	5000				
SA-157	C12	100000	(6), (7)	15000	15000	15000	14000	13400	11000	8250	5850	3850	2200	1400	900
SA-217	WC1	90000	(7), (8)	14000	14000	14000	13600	12000	10200	8000	5000				
SA-217	WC1A	70000	(7)	14000	13650	12950	12000	9900	7800	5900	3500				
SA-217	WC2	65000	(7), (8)	13000	13000	13000	12500	11500	10000	8000	5000				
SA-217	WC4	80000	(7), (8)	15000	15000	15000	14000	12500	10200	8000	5000				
Bolting															
Carbon Steel															
SA-7	..	55000	(9)	13000	11950	10000	8000	5600							
SA-261	..	100000	(10), (11)												

TABLE E1—(Continued)

Specification Number	Grade	Spec. Minimum Tensile psi	Notes and Limitations	For Metal Temperatures Not Exceeding											
				−20 to 650	700	750	800	850	900	950	1000	1050	1100	1150	1200 F
Bolting—(Continued)															
Alloy Steel															
SA-96	A	....	(10), (11)	13000	11950	10900	....	....	....	....	....	....	....	....	....
SA-96	B	....	(10), (11)	15000	13750	12500	....	....	....	....	....	....	....	....	....
SA-96	C	....	(10), (11)	16000	14700	13400	....	....	....	....	....	....	....	....	....
SA-193	B4	....	(7),(10),(11)	16000	16000	16000	16000	13000	10000	8250	5850	3850	2200	....	....
SA-193	B5	....	(10), (11)	16000	16000	16000	16000	13800	11000	....	....	....	....	....	....
SA-193	B6	....	(10), (11)	16000	14700	13400	11500	9500	6750	....	....	....	....	....	....
SA-193	B7	....	(10), (11)	16000	16000	16000	16000	13000	10000	8250	5850	3850	2200	....	....
SA-193	B7a	....	(10), (11)	16000	16000	16000	16000	13800	11000	....	....	....	....	....	....
SA-193	B8	....	(2), (10)	15000	15000	14600	14300	14000	13400	12300	10000	8000	6000	4600	3600
SA-193	B11	....	(10), (11)	16000	16000	16000	16000	13800	11000	8250	5850	3850	2200	....	....
SA-193	B13	....	(10), (11)	16000	16000	16000	16000	13800	11000	8250	5850	3850	2200	....	....
SA-193	B14	....	(10), (11)	16000	16000	16000	16000	15000	13300	11400	8800	5000	2200	....	....
SA-193	B15	....	(10), (11)	16000	16000	16000	16000	13800	11000	8250	5850	3850	2200	....	....

Notes and Limitations:

(1) Flange quality not permitted above 850 F

(2) No allowance has been made for corrosive action in the allowable stresses given. Carbide precipitation in service is also to be expected at temperatures above 750 F

(3) These stresses permitted only if 0.10% Si min is expressly specified

(4) These are base stresses for the material; these stresses must be modified to take care of the type of longitudinal joint

(5) Sections over 2 in. thick not permitted for pressure parts

(6) These stresses permitted only with molybdenum

(7) To these stresses, a casting quality factor of 70% shall be applied. Consideration is being given to rules for inspection and radiographing castings with the view of establishing other quality factors in proportion to the degree of inspection

(8) These stresses apply to normalized material only

(9) Not permitted above 450 F; allowable stress 5500 psi

(10) These stresses are established from a consideration of strength only and will be satisfactory for average service. For bolted joints where freedom from leakage over a long period of time without retightening is required, lower stresses may be necessary as determined from the relative flexibility of the flange and bolts and corresponding relaxation properties

(11) Between temperatures of −20 to 400 F, stresses equal to the lower of the following will be permitted: 16% of tensile strength; 20% of yield point stress

(12) Between temperatures of 750 to 1000 F, the stresses given herein for killed carbon steel, Specification SA-212 Grade B, may be used until high temperature test data become available

(13) Between temperatures of 650 to 1000 F, inclusive, the stresses given herein for killed carbon steel, Specification SA-201 Grade B, may be used until high temperature test data become available

General:

Carbon steel materials covered by Code specifications which are not included in these tables are limited to use at temperatures of −20 to 650 F

The allowable stress in wrought materials is one fifth of the ultimate in cast materials, it is one fifth of the ultimate multiplied by the applicable quality factor for design purposes

TABLE E2

Average Chemical Compositions of Alloy Steels in Table E1

Specification Number	Grade	%C	%Mn	%Si	%Cr	%Mo	%Ni	%V	%W	Other
Plate Steels										
Low-Alloy Steel										
SA-202	A	0.17*	1.20	0.75	0.45					
SA-202	B	0.25*	1.20	0.75	0.45					
SA-203	A	0.23*	0.90*	0.20			2.40			
SA-203	B	0.25*	0.90*	0.20			2.40			
SA-203	C	0.27*	0.90*	0.20			2.40			
SA-204	A	0.25*	0.90*	0.20		0.50				
SA-204	B	0.27*	0.90*	0.20		0.50				
SA-204	C	0.28*	0.90*	0.20		0.50				
SA-225	A	0.18*	1.45*	0.20				0.11		
SA-225	B	0.20*	1.45*	0.20				0.11		
Medium and High-Alloy Steel										
SA-240	A	0.12*	0.60*	0.75*	18.00		0.60*			
SA-240	B	0.12*	1.00*	0.75*	15.00		0.60*			
SA-240	D	0.12*	1.00*	0.75*	17.00		0.60*			
SA-240	S	0.08*	2.50*	0.85*	18.00**		8.00**			
SA-240	M	0.08*	2.50*	0.85*	17.00**	2.0**	10.00**			
SA-240	T	0.08*	2.50*	0.85*	17.00**		9.00**			Ti (a)
SA-240	C	0.08*	2.50*	0.85*	17.00**		9.50**			Cb (b)
Pipe and Tubes										
Seamless Alloy Steel										
SA-158	P3a	0.15*	0.45	0.60*	1.75	0.70				
SA-158	P3b	0.15*	0.45	0.50*	2.00	0.55				
SA-158	P5a	0.15*	0.45	0.50*	5.00	0.55				
SA-158	P5c	0.12*	0.45	0.50*	5.00	0.55				
SA-158	P8a	0.08*	2.00*	0.75*	19.00		9.50			
SA-158	P8b	0.15*	0.45	0.75*	18.50		11.00			Cb (c) or Ti (d)
SA-158	P11	0.15	0.55	0.75	1.25	0.55				
SA-206	P1	0.15	0.55	0.30		0.55				
SA-209	T1	0.20	0.55	0.30		0.55				
SA-209	T1a	0.15*	0.55	0.30		0.55				
SA-209	T1b	0.11	0.45	0.60		0.55				
SA-213	T3	0.15*	0.45	0.60*	1.75	0.70				Ti (a)
SA-213	T5	0.15*	0.45	0.50*	5.00	0.55				
SA-213	T11	0.15*	0.45	0.75*	1.25	0.55				
SA-213	T12	0.15*	0.45	0.30*	0.95	0.55				
SA-213	T13	0.15*	0.45	1.50*	5.00	0.55				
SA-213	T14	0.15*	0.45	0.50*	2.00	0.55				
SA-213	T16	0.12*	0.45	0.50*	5.00	0.55				Ti (d)
SA-213	T8(e)	0.08*	2.00*	0.75*	19.00		9.50			

TABLE E2—(Continued)

Specification Number	Grade	%C	%Mn	%Si	%Cr	%Mo	%Ni	%V	%W	Other
Pipe and Tubes—(Continued)										
Seamless Alloy Steel—(Continued)										
SA-213	T18(f)	0.08*	2.00*	0.75*	18.50		11.00			Ti (a)
SA-213	T19(g)	0.08*	2.00*	0.75*	18.50		11.00			Cb (b)
SA-213	T20(h)	0.08*	2.00*	0.20	17.00	2.50	12.50			
SA-213	T17	0.20	0.45	0.50*	0.95	0.90		0.15**		
SA-213	T21	0.15*	0.45	0.50*	3.00	1.00				
SA-213	T22	0.15*	0.45	0.20	2.25					
SA-280		0.15			0.50	0.55				
Elec. Resis. and Atom. Hydrogen Welded Alloy Steel										
SA-249	T8(e)	0.08*	2.00*	0.75*	19.00		9.50			Ti (a)
SA-249	T18(f)	0.08*	2.00*	0.75*	18.50		11.00			Cb (b)
SA-249	T19(g)	0.08*	2.00*	0.75*	18.50		11.00			
SA-249	T20(h)	0.08*	2.00*	0.75*	17.00	2.50	12.50			
SA-249	T24(i)				19.00	3.50	12.50			
SA-250	T1	0.15	0.55	0.30		0.55				
SA-250	T1a	0.20	0.55	0.30		0.55				
SA-250	T1b	0.11	0.55	0.30		0.55				
Forgings										
Alloy Steel										
SA-182	F1	0.35*	0.55	0.35		0.50				
SA-182	F3	0.20	0.50	0.60	1.75	0.70	1.75			
SA-182	F4	0.40	0.65		0.65	0.35				
SA-182	F5	0.25*	0.40	0.50*	5.00	0.55	0.50*			
SA-182	F6	0.12*	0.50*	0.50*	12.5	0.20				
SA-182	F7	0.80*	0.50	0.30	0.95					
SA-182	F8	0.08*	2.50*	0.85*	18.00**		8.00**			Ti may be added (j)
SA-182	F11	0.30	1.35	0.50	0.75	0.35				
Castings										
Alloy Steel										
SA-157	C1	0.35*	1.00*	0.20**		0.40**				
SA-157	C3	0.30*	1.00*	***	1.85	0.55	1.15			
SA-157	C4	0.45*	1.00*	0.20*	0.75	0.45				
SA-157	C5A	0.30*	1.00*	0.75*	5.25	0.55				
SA-157	C5B	0.30*	1.00*	1.15	5.25	0.55				
SA-157	C6	0.15*	0.75*	1.00*	12.5	0.50*				
SA-157	C9	0.15*	1.00*	2.00**	18.00**	(k)	8.00**			
SA-157	C11	0.45*	1.00*	1.00*	0.75	0.80	0.80**			
SA-157	C12	0.30*	1.00*	1.00*	9.00	1.30	1.60			
SA-217	WC1	0.30*	0.70*	0.60*		0.50				(k)
SA-217	WC1A	0.50*	0.70*	0.60*		0.50				
SA-217	WC2	0.25*	0.70*	0.60*		0.50				
SA-217	WC4	0.30*	0.70*	0.60*	0.55	0.50	0.90			

TABLE E2—(Continued)

Specification Number	Grade	%C	%Mn	%Si	%Cr	%Mo	%Ni	%V	%W	Other
Bolting										
Alloy Steel										
SA-96	A	(m)	.....	.....	.....	.....	.....	.....	.....	.....
SA-96	B	(m)	.....	.....	.....	.....	.....	.....	.....	.....
SA-96	C	(m)	.....	.....	.....	.....	.....	.....	.....	.....
SA-193	B4	0.40	0.65	0.25	0.65	.....	.....	.....	.....	.....
SA-193	B5	0.20	0.45	0.45	5.00	0.35	1.75	.....	.....	.....
SA-193	B6	0.15*	1.25*	0.45	13.00	0.55	.....	.....	.....	.....
SA-193	B7	0.40	0.85	0.25	0.95	0.60*	.....	.....	.....	.....
SA-193	B7a	0.40	0.85	0.25	0.95	0.20	.....	.....	.....	.....
SA-193	B8	0.10*	2.00*	1.00*	18.00	0.60	10.00	.....	.....	.....
SA-193	B11	0.45	0.80	0.25	1.25	.....	.....	0.25	.....	Cb (n) or Ti (o)
SA-193	B13	0.45	0.85	0.25	0.60	0.55	.....	.....	2.00	.....
SA-193	B14	0.40	0.55	0.25	0.95	0.35	.....	0.25	1.10	.....
SA-193	B15	0.45	0.55	0.65	1.25	0.50	.....	.....	.....	.....

* maximum. In some of the plate specifications the maximum carbon and manganese vary with the thickness; in such cases the maximum for the thickest plate is given. In some of the casting specifications the maximum manganese may be increased if the carbon is below the maximum

** minimum

*** either 0.75% maximum or 0.75 to 1.25%

(a) Ti = five times the carbon content minimum, and not more than 0.60%
(b) Cb = ten times the carbon content minimum, and not more than 1.00%
(c) Cb = eight to ten times the carbon content
(d) Ti = four times the carbon content minimum, and not more than 0.70%
(e) now identified in ASTM specification as Grade TP 304
(f) now identified in ASTM specification as Grade TP 321
(g) now identified in ASTM specification as Grade TP 347
(h) now identified in ASTM specification as Grade TP 316
(i) now identified in ASTM specification as Grade TP 317
(j) if added Ti = not more than 1.00%
(k) the addition of such elements as Cb, Mo, Ti, V, and W shall be a matter of agreement between the manufacturer and the purchaser
(m) only the phosphorus and sulphur contents are specified. These compositions are now included in SA-193 and ASTM Specification A 193
(n) Cb = ten times the carbon content minimum
(o) Ti = five times the carbon content minimum

Note: This table is based on 1946 ASTM standards. In some of the specifications, either molybdenum or tungsten is permitted. However, since the working stresses apply only to the molybdenum modification, the optional tungsten is not indicated.

APPENDIX F

TABLE F1

TEMPERATURE CONVERSION TABLE

−459.4 to 0

C		F
−273	**−459.4**	
−268	**−450**	
−262	**−440**	
−257	**−430**	
−251	**−420**	
−246	**−410**	
−240	**−400**	
−234	**−390**	
−229	**−380**	
−223	**−370**	
−218	**−360**	
−212	**−350**	
−207	**−340**	
−201	**−330**	
−196	**−320**	
−190	**−310**	
−184	**−300**	
−179	**−290**	
−173	**−280**	
−169	**−273**	−459.4
−168	**−270**	−454
−162	**−260**	−436
−157	**−250**	−418
−151	**−240**	−400
−146	**−230**	−382
−140	**−220**	−364
−134	**−210**	−346
−129	**−200**	−328
−123	**−190**	−310
−118	**−180**	−292
−112	**−170**	−274
−107	**−160**	−256
−101	**−150**	−238
−96	**−140**	−220
−90	**−130**	−202
−84	**−120**	−184
−79	**−110**	−166
−73	**−100**	−148
−68	**−90**	−130
−62	**−80**	−112
−57	**−70**	−94
−51	**−60**	−76
−46	**−50**	−58
−40	**−40**	−40
−34	**−30**	−22
−29	**−20**	−4
−23	**−10**	14
−17.8	**0**	32

0 to 100

C		F	C		F
−17.8	**0**	32	10.0	**50**	122.0
−17.2	**1**	33.8	10.6	**51**	123.8
−16.7	**2**	35.6	11.1	**52**	125.6
−16.1	**3**	37.4	11.7	**53**	127.4
−15.6	**4**	39.2	12.2	**54**	129.2
−15.0	**5**	41.0	12.8	**55**	131.0
−14.4	**6**	42.8	13.3	**56**	132.8
−13.9	**7**	44.6	13.9	**57**	134.6
−13.3	**8**	46.4	14.4	**58**	136.4
−12.8	**9**	48.2	15.0	**59**	138.2
−12.2	**10**	50.0	15.6	**60**	140.0
−11.7	**11**	51.8	16.1	**61**	141.8
−11.1	**12**	53.6	16.7	**62**	143.6
−10.6	**13**	55.4	17.2	**63**	145.4
−10.0	**14**	57.2	17.8	**64**	147.2
−9.4	**15**	59.0	18.3	**65**	149.0
−8.9	**16**	60.8	18.9	**66**	150.8
−8.3	**17**	62.6	19.4	**67**	152.6
−7.8	**18**	64.4	20.0	**68**	154.4
−7.2	**19**	66.2	20.6	**69**	156.2
−6.7	**20**	68.0	21.1	**70**	158.0
−6.1	**21**	69.8	21.7	**71**	159.8
−5.6	**22**	71.6	22.2	**72**	161.6
−5.0	**23**	73.4	22.8	**73**	163.4
−4.4	**24**	75.2	23.3	**74**	165.2
−3.9	**25**	77.0	23.9	**75**	167.0
−3.3	**26**	78.8	24.4	**76**	168.8
−2.8	**27**	80.6	25.0	**77**	170.6
−2.2	**28**	82.4	25.6	**78**	172.4
−1.7	**29**	84.2	26.1	**79**	174.2
−1.1	**30**	86.0	26.7	**80**	176.0
−0.6	**31**	87.8	27.2	**81**	177.8
0	**32**	89.6	27.8	**82**	179.6
0.6	**33**	91.4	28.3	**83**	181.4
1.1	**34**	93.2	28.9	**84**	183.2
1.7	**35**	95.0	29.4	**85**	185.0
2.2	**36**	96.8	30.0	**86**	186.8
2.8	**37**	98.6	30.6	**87**	188.6
3.3	**38**	100.4	31.1	**88**	190.4
3.9	**39**	102.2	31.7	**89**	192.2
4.4	**40**	104.0	32.2	**90**	194.0
5.0	**41**	105.8	32.8	**91**	195.8
5.6	**42**	107.6	33.3	**92**	197.6
6.1	**43**	109.4	33.9	**93**	199.4
6.7	**44**	111.2	34.4	**94**	201.2
7.2	**45**	113.0	35.0	**95**	203.0
7.8	**46**	114.8	35.6	**96**	204.8
8.3	**47**	116.6	36.1	**97**	206.6
8.9	**48**	118.4	36.7	**98**	208.4
9.4	**49**	120.2	37.2	**99**	210.2
			37.8	**100**	212.0

100 to 1000

C		F	C		F
38	**100**	212	260	**500**	932
43	**110**	230	266	**510**	950
49	**120**	248	271	**520**	968
54	**130**	266	277	**530**	986
60	**140**	284	282	**540**	1004
66	**150**	302	288	**550**	1022
71	**160**	320	293	**560**	1040
77	**170**	338	299	**570**	1058
82	**180**	356	304	**580**	1076
88	**190**	374	310	**590**	1094
93	**200**	392	316	**600**	1112
99	**210**	410	321	**610**	1130
100	**212**	413.6	327	**620**	1148
104	**220**	428	332	**630**	1166
110	**230**	446	338	**640**	1184
116	**240**	464	343	**650**	1202
121	**250**	482	349	**660**	1220
127	**260**	500	354	**670**	1238
132	**270**	518	360	**680**	1256
138	**280**	536	366	**690**	1274
143	**290**	554	371	**700**	1292
149	**300**	572	377	**710**	1310
154	**310**	590	382	**720**	1328
160	**320**	608	388	**730**	1346
166	**330**	626	393	**740**	1364
171	**340**	644	399	**750**	1382
177	**350**	662	404	**760**	1400
182	**360**	680	410	**770**	1418
188	**370**	698	416	**780**	1436
193	**380**	716	421	**790**	1454
199	**390**	734	427	**800**	1472
204	**400**	752	432	**810**	1490
210	**410**	770	438	**820**	1508
216	**420**	788	443	**830**	1526
221	**430**	806	449	**840**	1544
227	**440**	824	454	**850**	1562
232	**450**	842	460	**860**	1580
238	**460**	860	466	**870**	1598
243	**470**	878	471	**880**	1616
249	**480**	896	477	**890**	1634
254	**490**	914	482	**900**	1652
			488	**910**	1670
			493	**920**	1688
			499	**930**	1706
			504	**940**	1724
			510	**950**	1742
			516	**960**	1760
			521	**970**	1778
			527	**980**	1796
			532	**990**	1814
			538	**1000**	1832

The middle column in bold face gives the value to be converted. If this value is degrees Centigrade, the equivalent degrees Fahrenheit will be found in the right hand column. If this value is degrees Fahrenheit, the equivalent degrees Centigrade will be found in the left hand column

TABLE F1—(Continued)

	1000 to 2000					2000 to 3000			
C	F	C	F	C	F	C	F

C		F	C		F	C		F	C		F
538	**1000**	1832	816	**1500**	2732	1093	**2000**	3632	1371	**2500**	4532
543	**1010**	1850	821	**1510**	2750	1099	**2010**	3650	1377	**2510**	4550
549	**1020**	1868	827	**1520**	2768	1104	**2020**	3668	1382	**2520**	4568
554	**1030**	1886	832	**1530**	2786	1110	**2030**	3686	1388	**2530**	4586
560	**1040**	1904	838	**1540**	2804	1116	**2040**	3704	1393	**2540**	4604
566	**1050**	1922	843	**1550**	2822	1121	**2050**	3722	1399	**2550**	4622
571	**1060**	1940	849	**1560**	2840	1127	**2060**	3740	1404	**2560**	4640
577	**1070**	1958	854	**1570**	2858	1132	**2070**	3758	1410	**2570**	4658
582	**1080**	1976	860	**1580**	2876	1138	**2080**	3776	1416	**2580**	4676
588	**1090**	1994	866	**1590**	2894	1143	**2090**	3794	1421	**2590**	4694
593	**1100**	2012	871	**1600**	2912	1149	**2100**	3812	1427	**2600**	4712
599	**1110**	2030	877	**1610**	2930	1154	**2110**	3830	1432	**2610**	4730
604	**1120**	2048	882	**1620**	2948	1160	**2120**	3848	1438	**2620**	4748
610	**1130**	2066	888	**1630**	2966	1166	**2130**	3866	1443	**2630**	4766
616	**1140**	2084	893	**1640**	2984	1171	**2140**	3884	1449	**2640**	4784
621	**1150**	2102	899	**1650**	3002	1177	**2150**	3902	1454	**2650**	4802
627	**1160**	2120	904	**1660**	3020	1182	**2160**	3920	1460	**2660**	4820
632	**1170**	2138	910	**1670**	3038	1188	**2170**	3938	1466	**2670**	4838
638	**1180**	2156	916	**1680**	3056	1193	**2180**	3956	1471	**2680**	4856
643	**1190**	2174	921	**1690**	3074	1199	**2190**	3974	1477	**2690**	4874
649	**1200**	2192	927	**1700**	3092	1204	**2200**	3992	1482	**2700**	4892
654	**1210**	2210	932	**1710**	3110	1210	**2210**	4010	1488	**2710**	4910
660	**1220**	2228	938	**1720**	3128	1216	**2220**	4028	1493	**2720**	4928
666	**1230**	2246	943	**1730**	3146	1221	**2230**	4046	1499	**2730**	4946
671	**1240**	2264	949	**1740**	3164	1227	**2240**	4064	1504	**2740**	4964
677	**1250**	2282	954	**1750**	3182	1232	**2250**	4082	1510	**2750**	4982
682	**1260**	2300	960	**1760**	3200	1238	**2260**	4100	1516	**2760**	5000
688	**1270**	2318	966	**1770**	3218	1243	**2270**	4118	1521	**2770**	5018
693	**1280**	2336	971	**1780**	3236	1249	**2280**	4136	1527	**2780**	5036
699	**1290**	2354	977	**1790**	3254	1254	**2290**	4154	1532	**2790**	5054
704	**1300**	2372	982	**1800**	3272	1260	**2300**	4172	1538	**2800**	5072
710	**1310**	2390	988	**1810**	3290	1266	**2310**	4190	1543	**2810**	5090
716	**1320**	2408	993	**1820**	3308	1271	**2320**	4208	1549	**2820**	5108
721	**1330**	2426	999	**1830**	3326	1277	**2330**	4226	1554	**2830**	5126
727	**1340**	2444	1004	**1840**	3344	1282	**2340**	4244	1560	**2840**	5144
732	**1350**	2462	1010	**1850**	3362	1288	**2350**	4262	1566	**2850**	5162
738	**1360**	2480	1016	**1860**	3380	1293	**2360**	4280	1571	**2860**	5180
743	**1370**	2498	1021	**1870**	3398	1299	**2370**	4298	1577	**2870**	5198
749	**1380**	2516	1027	**1880**	3416	1304	**2380**	4316	1582	**2880**	5216
754	**1390**	2534	1032	**1890**	3434	1310	**2390**	4334	1588	**2890**	5234
760	**1400**	2552	1038	**1900**	3452	1316	**2400**	4352	1593	**2900**	5252
766	**1410**	2570	1043	**1910**	3470	1321	**2410**	4370	1599	**2910**	5270
771	**1420**	2588	1049	**1920**	3488	1327	**2420**	4388	1604	**2920**	5288
777	**1430**	2606	1054	**1930**	3506	1332	**2430**	4406	1610	**2930**	5306
782	**1440**	2624	1060	**1940**	3524	1338	**2440**	4424	1616	**2940**	5324
788	**1450**	2642	1066	**1950**	3542	1343	**2450**	4442	1621	**2950**	5342
793	**1460**	2660	1071	**1960**	3560	1349	**2460**	4460	1627	**2960**	5360
799	**1470**	2678	1077	**1970**	3578	1354	**2470**	4478	1632	**2970**	5378
804	**1480**	2696	1082	**1980**	3596	1360	**2480**	4496	1638	**2980**	5396
810	**1490**	2714	1088	**1990**	3614	1366	**2490**	4514	1643	**2990**	5414
			1093	**2000**	3632				1649	**3000**	5432

| C | | F | C | | F | C | | F | C | | F |

The middle column in bold face gives the value to be converted. If this value is degrees Centigrade, the equivalent degrees Fahrenheit will be found in the right hand column. If this value is degrees Fahrenheit, the equivalent degrees Centigrade will be found in the left hand column.

TABLE F2

LOAD CONVERSION TABLE

Tons per Square Inch to Pounds per Square Inch						Kilograms per Square Millimeter to Pounds per Square Inch					
tons per sq in.	psi	tons per sq in.	psi	tons per sq in.	psi	kg per sq mm	psi	kg per sq mm	psi	kg per sq mm	psi
10.0	22,400	35.0	78,400	70	156,800	10	14,223	60	85,340	110	156,457
10.5	23,520	35.5	79,520	71	159,040	11	15,646	61	86,763	111	157,880
11.0	24,640	36.0	80,640	72	161,280	12	17,068	62	88,185	112	159,302
11.5	25,760	36.5	81,760	73	163,520	13	18,490	63	89,607	113	160,724
12.0	26,880	37.0	82,880	74	165,760	14	19,913	64	91,030	114	162,147
12.5	28,000	37.5	84,000	75	168,000	15	21,335	65	92,452	115	163,569
13.0	29,120	38.0	85,120	76	170,240	16	22,757	66	93,874	116	164,991
13.5	30,240	38.5	86,240	77	172,480	17	24,180	67	95,297	117	166,414
14.0	31,360	39.0	87,360	78	174,720	18	25,602	68	96,719	118	167,836
14.5	32,480	39.5	88,480	79	176,960	19	27,024	69	98,141	119	169,258
15.0	33,600	40.0	89,600	80	179,200	20	28,447	70	99,564	120	170,681
15.5	34,720	40.5	90,720	81	181,440	21	29,869	71	100,986	121	172,103
16.0	35,840	41.0	91,840	82	183,680	22	31,291	72	102,408	122	173,525
16.5	36,960	41.5	92,960	83	185,920	23	32,714	73	103,831	123	174,948
17.0	38,080	42.0	94,080	84	188,160	24	34,136	74	105,253	124	176,370
17.5	39,200	42.5	95,200	85	190,400	25	35,558	75	106,675	125	177,792
18.0	40,320	43.0	96,320	86	192,640	26	36,981	76	108,098	126	179,215
18.5	41,440	43.5	97,440	87	194,880	27	38,403	77	109,520	127	180,637
19.0	42,560	44.0	98,560	88	197,120	28	39,826	78	110,943	128	182,059
19.5	43,680	44.5	99,680	89	199,360	29	41,248	79	112,365	129	183,482
20.0	44,800	45.0	100,800	90	201,600	30	42,670	80	113,787	130	184,904
20.5	45,920	45.5	101,920	91	203,840	31	44,093	81	115,210	131	186,327
21.0	47,040	46.0	103,040	92	206,080	32	45,515	82	116,632	132	187,749
21.5	48,160	46.5	104,160	93	208,320	33	46,937	83	118,054	133	189,171
22.0	49,280	47.0	105,280	94	210,560	34	48,360	84	119,477	134	190,594
22.5	50,400	47.5	106,400	95	212,800	35	49,782	85	120,899	135	192,016
23.0	51,520	48.0	107,520	96	215,040	36	51,204	86	122,321	136	193,438
23.5	52,640	48.5	108,640	97	217,280	37	52,627	87	123,744	137	194,861
24.0	53,760	49.0	109,760	98	219,520	38	54,049	88	125,166	138	196,283
24.5	54,880	49.5	110,880	99	221,760	39	55,471	89	126,588	139	197,705
25.0	56,000	50	112,000	100	224,000	40	56,894	90	128,011	140	199,128
25.5	57,120	51	114,240	101	226,240	41	58,316	91	129,433	141	200,550
26.0	58,240	52	116,480	102	228,480	42	59,738	92	130,855	142	201,972
26.5	59,360	53	118,720	103	230,720	43	61,161	93	132,278	143	203,395
27.0	60,480	54	120,960	104	232,960	44	62,583	94	133,700	144	204,817
27.5	61,600	55	123,200	105	235,200	45	64,005	95	135,122	145	206,239
28.0	62,720	56	125,440	106	237,440	46	65,428	96	136,545	146	207,662
28.5	63,840	57	127,680	107	239,680	47	66,850	97	137,967	147	209,084
29.0	64,960	58	129,920	108	241,920	48	68,272	98	139,389	148	210,506
29.5	66,080	59	132,160	109	244,160	49	69,695	99	140,812	149	211,929
30.0	67,200	60	134,400	110	246,400	50	71,117	100	142,234	150	213,351
30.5	68,320	61	136,640	111	248,640	51	72,539	101	143,656	151	214,778
31.0	69,440	62	138,880	112	250,880	52	73,962	102	145,079	152	216,196
31.5	70,560	63	141,120	113	253,120	53	75,384	103	146,501	153	217,618
32.0	71,680	64	143,360	114	255,360	54	76,806	104	147,923	154	219,040
32.5	72,800	65	145,600	115	257,600	55	78,229	105	149,346	155	220,463
33.0	73,920	66	147,840	116	259,840	56	79,651	106	150,768	156	221,885
33.5	75,040	67	150,080	117	262,080	57	81,073	107	152,190	157	223,307
34.0	76,160	68	152,320	118	264,320	58	82,496	108	153,613	158	224,730
34.5	77,280	69	154,560	119	266,560	59	83,918	109	155,035	159	226,152

TABLE F3
HARDNESS CONVERSION TABLE FOR STEEL

The following conversion table was prepared jointly by the SAE, ASM and ASTM.

As stated in ASTM E 48-43T, these conversions "are based on extensive tests on carbon and alloy steels, mostly in the heat-treated condition, but have been found to be reliable on practically all constructional alloy steels and tool steels in the as-forged, annealed, normalized and quenched and tempered conditions, provided they are homogeneous. Such special cases as high-manganese steel, 18 per cent chromium, 8 per cent nickel steel, and other austenitic steels, nickel-base alloys as well as constructional alloy steels and tool steels in the cold-worked condition, may not conform to these relationships with the same degree of accuracy as the steels for which they are intended."

Brinell Indentation Diameter, mm	Brinell Hardness Number			Diamond Pyramid Hardness Number	Rockwell Hardness Number			Rockwell Superficial Hardness Number			Brinell Indentation Diameter, mm
	10 mm Standard Ball, 3000kg Load	10 mm Hultgren Ball, 3000kg Load(a)	10 mm Carbide Ball, 3000kg Load		C Scale, 150 kg Load, Brale Penetrator	A Scale, 60 kg Load, Brale Penetrator	D Scale, 100 kg Load, Brale Penetrator	15 N Scale, 15 kg Load, Superficial Brale Penetrator	30 N Scale, 30 kg Load, Superficial Brale Penetrator	45 N Scale, 45 kg Load, Superficial Brale Penetrator	
2.35		...	682	737	61.7	82.2	72.0	91.0	79.0	68.5	2.35
2.40	•	...	653	697	60.0	81.2	70.7	90.2	77.5	66.5	2.40
2.45	•	...	627	667	58.7	80.5	69.7	89.6	76.3	65.1	2.45
2.50	•	601	...	677	59.1	80.7	70.0	89.8	76.8	65.7	2.50
	...	...	601	640	57.3	79.8	68.7	89.0	75.1	63.5	
2.55	•	578	...	640	57.3	79.8	68.7	89.0	75.1	63.5	2.55
	...	...	578	615	56.0	79.1	67.7	88.4	73.9	62.1	
2.60	•	555	...	607	55.6	78.8	67.4	88.1	73.5	61.6	2.60
	...	...	555	591	54.7	78.4	66.7	87.8	72.7	60.6	
2.65	•	534	...	579	54.0	78.0	66.1	87.5	72.0	59.8	2.65
	...	...	534	569	53.5	77.8	65.8	87.2	71.6	59.2	
2.70	•	514	...	553	52.5	77.1	65.0	86.7	70.7	58.0	2.70
	...	...	514	547	52.1	76.9	64.7	86.5	70.3	57.6	
2.75	495	...	...	539	51.6	76.7	64.3	86.3	69.9	56.9	2.75
	...	495	...	530	51.1	76.4	63.9	86.0	69.5	56.2	
	...	...	495	528	51.0	76.3	63.8	85.9	69.4	56.1	
2.80	477	...	...	516	50.3	75.9	63.2	85.6	68.7	55.2	2.80
	...	477	...	508	49.6	75.6	62.7	85.3	68.2	54.5	
	...	...	477	508	49.6	75.6	62.7	85.3	68.2	54.5	
2.85	461	...	...	495	48.8	75.1	61.9	84.9	67.4	53.5	2.85
	...	461	...	491	48.5	74.9	61.7	84.7	67.2	53.2	
	...	...	461	491	48.5	74.9	61.7	84.7	67.2	53.2	
2.90	444	...	...	474	47.2	74.3	61.0	84.1	66.0	51.7	2.90
	...	444	...	472	47.1	74.2	60.8	84.0	65.8	51.5	
	...	...	444	472	47.1	74.2	60.8	84.0	65.8	51.5	

Brinell Indentation Diameter, mm	Brinell Hardness Number			Diamond Pyramid Hardness Number	Rockwell Hardness Number			Rockwell Superficial Hardness Number			Brinell Indentation Diameter, mm
	10 mm Standard Ball, 3000 kg Load	10 mm Hultgren Ball, 3000 kg Load(a)	10 mm Carbide Ball, 3000 kg Load		C Scale, 150 kg Load, Brale Penetrator	A Scale, 60 kg Load, Brale Penetrator	D Scale, 100 kg Load, Brale Penetrator	15 N Scale, 15 kg Load, Superficial Brale Penetrator	30 N Scale, 30 kg Load, Superficial Brale Penetrator	45 N Scale, 45 kg Load, Superficial Brale Penetrator	
2.95	429	429	429	455	45.7	73.4	59.7	83.4	64.6	49.9	2.95
3.00	415	415	415	440	44.5	72.8	58.8	82.8	63.5	48.4	3.00
3.05	401	401	401	425	43.1	72.0	57.8	82.0	62.3	46.9	3.05
3.10	388	388	388	410	41.8	71.4	56.8	81.4	61.1	45.3	3.10
3.15	375	375	375	396	40.4	70.6	55.7	80.6	59.9	43.6	3.15
3.20	363	363	363	383	39.1	70.0	54.6	80.0	58.7	42.0	3.20
3.25	352	352	352	372	37.9	69.3	53.8	79.3	57.6	40.5	3.25
3.30	341	341	341	360	36.6	68.7	52.8	78.6	56.4	39.1	3.30
3.35	331	331	331	350	35.5	68.1	51.9	78.0	55.4	37.8	3.35
3.40	321	321	321	339	34.3	67.5	51.0	77.3	54.3	36.1	3.40
3.45	311	311	311	328	33.1	66.9	50.0	76.7	53.3	34.4	3.45
3.50	302	302	302	319	32.1	66.3	49.3	76.1	52.2	33.8	3.50
3.55	293	293	293	309	30.9	65.7	48.3	75.5	51.2	32.4	3.55
3.60	285	285	285	301	29.9	65.3	47.6	75.0	50.3	31.2	3.60
3.65	277	277	277	292	28.8	64.6	46.7	74.4	49.3	29.9	3.65
3.70	269	269	269	284	27.6	64.1	45.9	73.7	48.3	28.5	3.70
3.75	262	262	262	276	26.6	63.6	45.0	73.1	47.3	27.3	3.75
3.80	255	255	255	269	25.4	63.0	44.2	72.5	46.2	26.0	3.80
3.85	248	248	248	261	24.2	62.5	43.2	71.7	45.1	24.5	3.85
3.90	241	241	241	253	22.8	61.8	42.0	70.9	43.9	22.8	3.90
3.95	235	235	235	247	21.7	61.4	41.4	70.3	42.9	21.5	3.95
4.00	229	229	229	241	20.5	60.8	40.5	69.7	41.9	20.1	4.00

*No Brinell hardness values are given above 500 Brinell hardness number for the 10 mm standard steel ball in conformance with limitations established by the Standard Method of Test for Brinell Hardness of Metallic Materials (ASTM E 10-27)

(a) Brinell hardness values are given for the Hultgren ball to 601 Brinell hardness; however, flattening of the ball at the higher hardnesses gives lower Brinell hardness values than obtained with the carbide ball. For example, material having a DPH value of 667 has a carbide ball Brinell hardness of 627, while material having a DPH value of 677 has a Hultgren ball Brinell hardness of only 601.

APPENDIX G

PHYSICAL PROPERTIES OF METALLIC MOLYBDENUM

Metallic molybdenum is a refractory metal regularly produced in the form of wire, small bars, tube and sheet. New developments in powder metallurgy techniques are meeting the demand for larger sections. The Climax Molybdenum Company has recently adapted a vacuum arc method of melting to the production of forgeable molybdenum ingots (1). It is believed that even larger sizes may be possible with this method than with the previous processes.

Atomic Number	42	
Atomic Weight	95.95	(2)
Crystal Structure	Body-centered cubic	
	a_0 = 3.1399 kX	(3)
	3.1403 kX	(4)
Melting Point	2622 ± 40 C	(5)
Boiling Point	4804 C	(5)

Vapor Pressure

Atmospheres	Temperature C	
0.0001	2727	
0.001	3057	
0.01	3477	
0.1	4027	
0.25	4307	
0.5	4537	
1.0	4804	(5)

Specific Heat	0.058 cal per g per degree C at 25 C	(6)

Thermal Conductivity

Cal-cm-sec-degree C	Temperature C	
0.346	17	(7)
0.259	927	(8)
0.159	1627	(8)

Electrical Resistivity

Microhm-cm	Temperature C	
5.2	0	(9)
5.78	27	(10)
23.9	727	(10)
29.2	927	(11)
35.2	1127	(10)
41.2	1327	(11)
47.2	1527	(10, 11)
53.5	1727	(11)

Electrical Resistivity —	59.5	1927	(10, 11)
(Continued)	66.0	2127	(11)
	69.2	2227	(11)
	71.8	2327	(10)
	78.2	2527	(10)
	81.4	2622	(10)

Coefficient of Linear Expansion	5.35×10^{-6} per degree C	0 to 20 C	(12)
	5.7×10^{-6} per degree C	0 to 500 C	(13)

Density	Calculated*	10.23 g per cc	(3)
	Powder	10.28	(14)
	Cast two inch section	10.2	(3)
	Sintered one inch section	9.6	(15)
	Sintered, swaged, drawn	10.2	(15)

* using kX $= 3.1399$

Avogadro number $= 6.0228 \times 10^{23}$

Young's Modulus of Elasticity	47.7×10^6 psi	(16)
	49.4×10^6 psi	(3)

Lowest Temperature of Recrystallization	870 ± 25 C	(3)

Bibliography

(1) R. M. Parke and J. L. Ham "The Melting of Molybdenum in the Vacuum Arc" AIME TP 2052; Metals Technology, Vol 13 (1946)

(2) G. P. Baxter "Report of the Committee on Atomic Weights of the American Chemical Society" Journal, ACS, Vol 65 (1943)

(3) Climax Molybdenum Company

(4) Private communication to the ASM from Dr. C. S. Barrett, University of Chicago, and H. C. Vacher, National Bureau of Standards (1946)

(5) K. K. Kelley, Contributions to the Data on Theoretical Metallurgy, III. Free Energies of Vaporization and Vapor Pressures of Inorganic Substances, Bureau of Mines Bulletin No 383 (1935)

(6) K. K. Kelley, Contributions to the Data on Theoretical Metallurgy, IX. The Entropies of Inorganic Substances. Revision (1940) of Data and Methods of Calculation. Bureau of Mines Bulletin No 434 (1941)

(7) T. Barratt and R. M. Winter "Thermal Conductivity of Wires and Rods" Annalen der Physik, Vol 77 (1925)

(8) R. H. Osborn "Thermal Conductivities of Tungsten and Molybdenum at Incandescent Temperatures" Journal of the Optical Society of America, Vol 31 (1941)

(9) W. G. Kannuluik "The Thermal and Electrical Conductivities of Several Metals between $-188°$ C and 100° C" Proceedings of the Royal Society of London, Series A, Vol 141 (1933)

(10) A. G. Worthing "Physical Properties of Well Seasoned Molybdenum and Tantalum as a Function of Temperature" Physical Review, Vol 28 (1926)

(11) C. Zwikker "Physical Properties of Molybdenum at High Temperatures" Physica, Vol 7 (1927)

(12) F. C. Nix and D. MacNair "The Thermal Expansion of Pure Metals, II. Molybdenum, Palladium, Silver, Tantalum, Tungsten, Platinum and Lead" Physical Review, Vol 61 (1942)

(13) Tungsten, Molybdenum and Wire Products, published by the North American Philips Company, Inc., Dobbs Ferry, New York

(14) J. H. Müller "Atomic Weight of Molybdenum" Journal, ACS, Vol 37 (1915)

(15) J. W. Marden and D. M. Wroughton "The Effect of Working on the Physical Properties of Molybdenum" Transactions of the Electrochemical Society, Vol 89 (1946)

(16) M. J. Druyvesteyn "Elastic Anisotropy of Molybdenum" Physica, Vol 8 (1941)

INDEX

Note: Some special applications of molybdenum steels, as well as a few general ones which are mainly illustrative, are listed in the book and indexed below. The selection of the best steel is controlled by many local considerations in addition to the basic metallurgical requirements. A list of molybdenum steels used for crankshafts, for example, would actually include practically all the standard medium carbon grades, and thus would be useless to engineers and designers. Therefore, no attempt has been made to present such general lists.

A

---

* See Note above.

─────────

* See Note on p 365.

Cast Iron—(Continued)

gray iron—(continued)

Chromium-Molybdenum Steels (Wrought)

Chromium-Nickel Steels (Wrought)

Chromium Plating, high speed steel
Chromium-Silicon Steels (Wrought)

---

* See Note on p 365.

* See Note on p 365.

---

* See Note on p 365.

Dies—(Continued)

---

* See Note on p 365.

* See Note on p 365.

* See Note on p 365.

[377]

* See Note on p 365.

---

* See Note on p 365.

---

* See Note on p 365.

---

* See Note on p 365.

O

* See Note on p 365.

Pistons—(Continued)

Q

R

---

* See Note on p 365.

* See Note on p 365.

* See Note on p 365.

* See Note on p 365.

Tempering (General)—(Continued)

[389]

* See Note on p 365.

---

* See Note on p 365.